ADVANCES IN
ELECTRON TRANSFER
CHEMISTRY

Volume 2 • 1992

ADVANCES IN ELECTRON TRANSFER CHEMISTRY

A Research Annual

Editor: PATRICK S. MARIANO

Department of Chemistry and Biochemistry
University of Maryland-College Park

VOLUME 2 • 1992

 JAI PRESS INC.

Greenwich, Connecticut   London, England

CONTENTS

LIST OF CONTRIBUTORS

Nathan L. Bauld

Department of Chemistry
University of Texas at Austin
Austin, Texas

Shunichi Fukuzumi

Department of Applied Chemistry
Faculty of Engineering
Osaka University
Osaka, Japan

Aziz Sancar

Deparment of Biochemistry
and Biophysics
University of North Carolina
School of Medicine
Chapel Hill, North Carolina

Richard B. Silverman

Department of Chemistry
Northwestern University
Evanston, Illinois

INTRODUCTION TO THE SERIES: AN EDITOR'S FOREWORD

The JAI series in chemistry has come of age over the past several years. Each of the volumes already published contain timely chapters by leading exponents in the field who have placed their own contributions in a perspective that provides insight to their long-term research goals. Each contribution focuses on the individual author's own work as well as the studies of others that address related problems. The series is intended to provide the reader with in-depth accounts of important principles as well as insight into the nuances and subtleties of a given area of chemistry. The wide coverage of material should be of interest to graduate students, postdoctoral fellows, industrial chemists and those teaching specialized topics to graduate students. We hope that we will continue to provide you with a sense of stimulation and enjoyment of the various sub-disciplines of chemistry.

Department of Chemistry
Emory University
Atlanta, Georgia

Albert Padwa
Consulting Editor

PREFACE

The consideration of reaction mechanisms involving the movement of single electrons is relatively new in the fields of chemistry and biochemistry. Despite this, studies conducted in recent years have uncovered a large number of chemical and enzymatic process which proceed via single electron transfer pathways. At the current time numerous investigations are underway probing the operation of electron transfer reactions in organic, organometallic, biochemical and excited state systems. In addition, theoretical and experimental studies are being conducted to gain information about the factors that govern the rates of single electron transfer. It is clear from the current level of activity that electron transfer chemistry has now become one of the most active areas of chemical study.

The series, *Advances in Electron Transfer Chemistry*, has been designed to allow scientists who are developing new knowledge in this rapidly expanding area to describe their most recent research findings. Each contribution will be in a mini-review format focusing on the individual author's own work as well as the studies of others which address related problems. Volume 1 in this series contained reviews by distinguished researchers whose studies cover a variety of aspects of electron transfer chemistry. Marye Anne Fox summarized the results of her investigations of photoinduced reactions of organic substances occurring on irradiated semiconductor surfaces. Key findings from their investigations of electron transfer induced reactions of aromatic donors promoted by both thermal and photochemical methods were reviewed by Christian Amatore and Jay Kochi. A chapter by George McLendon and Anna Helms covered their research work on

xi

distance and angle dependencies of the rates of electron transfer in both chemical and biological systems. Finally, two areas involving rapid bond cleavage reactions of intermediates generated in electron transfer processes and the details of electron transfer exchange mechanisms for luminescence were described in a chapter by Gary Schuster.

Following this tradition, Volume 2 in this series again contains contributions from distinguished scientists whose research work is at the frontier of studies of electron transfer chemistry and biochemistry. Hopefully, by following this protocol, *Advances in Electron Transfer Chemistry* will serve as useful series for those interested in learning about current breakthroughs in this rapidly expanding area of chemical research.

Patrick S. Mariano
Series Editor

HOLE AND ELECTRON TRANSFER CATALYZED PERICYCLIC REACTIONS

Nathan L. Bauld

Advances in Electron Transfer Chemistry,
Volume 2, pages 1–66
Copyright © 1992 by JAI Press Inc.
All rights of reproduction in any form reserved.
ISBN: 1-55938-168-X

1. INTRODUCTION

Electron transfer (ET) catalysis, the newest of the major catalytic concepts to emerge, is currently undergoing vigorous exploration and expansion. In the most formal sense, this type of catalysis is characterized minimally by a classic catalytic cycle which involves one or more electron transfer steps. Entry into the catalytic cycle may also be *via* electron transfer, but can involve a pre-formed catalyst. In organic systems especially, it is more commonly the case that ET initiates a chain reaction, one propagation step of which also involves ET. Alder has proposed the term electron transfer chain (ETC) catalysis for this closely related phenomenon.[1] Chanon has further emphasized that both the classic and chain catalytic mechanisms are readily embraced within the sphere of a generalized electron transfer catalytic concept.[2]

The catalytic cycle or chain of an ET or ETC catalyzed reaction can be entered by either oxidation or reduction. For organic systems, where typically both the reactants and products are neutral singlet molecules, oxidative ET (or ETC) catalysis involves cation radical intermediates ($R^{\ddot{+}}$), whereas reductive ET catalysis involves anion radicals ($R^{\dot{-}}$). In oxidative ET catalysis, electron transfer is typically from a neutral molecule to a cation radical, a variant of electron transfer conventionally referred to as hole transfer (HT). In view of this latter terminology and of the unification of ET and ETC catalysis within the classification of generalized electron transfer catalysis, the generalized catalytic concept involved in both oxidative ET (i.e., HT) and ETC (i.e., HTC) catalysis has been called hole catalysis (Scheme 1; $H^{\ddot{+}}$ is the hole catalyst).1).[3] In

Hole Transfer (HT) Catalysis

$$H^{+\cdot} + R \xrightarrow{k_i} H + R^{+\cdot}$$

$$R^{+\cdot} \xrightarrow{k_p} P^{+\cdot}$$

$$P^{+\cdot} + H \xrightarrow{k_{HT}} P + H^{+\cdot}$$

Hole Transfer Chain (HTC) Catalysis

$$H^{+\cdot} + R \xrightarrow{k_i} H + R^{+\cdot} \qquad \text{Initiation}$$

$$R^{+\cdot} \xrightarrow{k_p} P^{+\cdot}$$

$$\qquad\qquad\qquad\qquad \text{Propagation}$$

$$P^{+\cdot} + R \xrightarrow{k_{HT}} P + R^{+\cdot}$$

Scheme 1. Hole catalysis.

analogous fashion, reductive ET and ETC catalysis can be designated electron catalysis. These terms, in our view, felicitously stress the nature of the actual catalytic entities in the relevant catalytic processes, and they direct attention to the status of the hole and the electron as catalytic entities comparable, e.g., to the proton and hydroxide ion.

The 1980s vividly brought to light the extraordinary power of hole catalysis, especially in the realm of pericyclic reactions, and the implications of the catalytic concept for organic, bioorganic, and organometallic chemistry will undoubtedly be explored intensively during the present decade. This chapter reviews key aspects of the development of hole catalysis of pericyclic reactions during the previous decade and augments this with a brief review of the seminal field of electron catalyzed pericyclic reactions.

2. HOLE CATALYZED CYCLOADDITIONS

The initial discovery of hole catalysis occurred in the realm of cycloaddition (*vide infra*). From the present perspective it is clear that this association of hole catalysis and cycloaddition was by no means coincidental. Indeed, subsequent research has so far overwhelmingly supported the perception that cycloaddition in particular, and pericyclic reactions more generally, constitute the inherently preferred reaction domain for hole catalysis in organic chemistry. Conversely, where applicable, hole catalysis arguably represents the most powerful catalytic form for pericyclic reactions. The ability of hole catalysis to expunge essentially the entire activation barrier to either formally allowed (e.g. the Diels-Alder) or formally forbidden (e.g., cyclobutanation) cycloadditions while retaining a selectivity profile more excellent than that of typical uncatalyzed cycloadditions qualifies it as a formidable synthetic tool, as well as a mechanistically novel catalytic concept.

2.1. Discovery of Hole Catalysis

A thorough mechanistic study of the cyclodimerization of N-vinylcarbazole (1) induced by ferric, ceric, and cupric salts in methanol brought the first documented instance of a hole catalyzed reaction to light only 20 years ago (Scheme 2).[4] The original cyclodimerization of 1 had actually been carried out five years earlier (albeit without true mechanistic insight) by the method now known as photosensitized electron transfer (PET).[5] Additional mechanistic studies then established an analogous hole catalytic mechanism for the cyclodimerization of 1 as carried out under the original PET conditions. Extensions of the new reaction during the 1970s were few and exclusively involved the PET procedure for initiation (*vide infra*).[6-8] Synthetic utility appeared highly improbable as a consequence of the narrow reaction scope and the circumstance that the cyclobutane dimers were typically unstable under the PET conditions, so that synthetically attractive conversions could usually not be achieved.

2.2. Hole Catalyzed Diels-Alder Cycloaddition

The pioneering observation that hole catalysis powerfully facilitates cyclobutanation, a pericyclic reaction which is formally symmetry forbidden in both

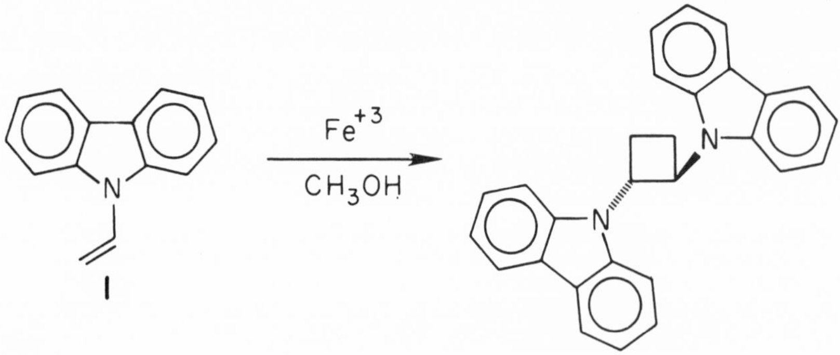

Scheme 2. Discovery of hole catalysis.

the neutral and cation radical states and which generates a product possessing major ring strain, suggested that hole catalyzed Diels-Alder cycloaddition, which is formally symmetry allowed in both the neutral and cation radical states and which yields a nearly strainless product, might be even more facile. To efficiently search for and develop this chemistry for synthetic applications, a chemical hole catalyst system was considered highly desirable. Such a catalyst should relieve many of the problems encountered in the PET procedure, including extended reaction times, scale up difficulties, powerful albeit unselective excited state hole catalysts, product instability (a consequence of the preceding unselectivity) and back electron transfer leading to reaction inefficiency and/or triplet state formation. Further, an organic hole catalyst which is soluble in aprotic and non-nucleophilic solvents (e.g., dichloromethane) should be far more hospitable to pericyclic cation radical reactivity of organic substrates than the inorganic oxidant/nucleophilic solvent system (Fe^{3+}/CH_3OH) developed earlier.

Triarylaminium salts ($Ar_3N^{+} X^{-}$), of historic importance in the recognition of cation radicals as a distinct species, appeared to be an ideal selection. Such salts had been isolated as early as 1905[9] but were not recognized as cation radicals until 1927.[10] At present, a variety of such salts having a range and multiplicity of substituents and thus a wide range of hole energies is synthetically accessible. One of the most conveniently accessible aminium salts is tris(4-bromophenyl)-aminium hexachloroantimonate, a dark purple, shelf stable salt now available commercially.[11] The efficiency and convenience of the reaction system Ar_3N^{+} $SbCl_6^{-}/CH_2Cl_2$ made possible a comprehensive study of the hole catalyzed Diels-Alder.[12] As a consequence of these studies the reaction was established as a generic reaction mode of cation radicals which is synthetically viable and which indeed fills an important niche in Diels-Alder synthetic methodology. Subsequent studies using the new hole catalytic system also extended the scope of the hole catalyzed cyclobutanation reaction and permitted the development of new types of hole catalyzed pericyclic reactions, including cyclopropanation, [1,3] sigmatropic shifts, and the Cope rearrangement.

Hole Catalyzed Diels-Alder Cyclodimerization of 1,3-Cyclohexadiene

The uncatalyzed thermal Diels-Alder cyclodimerization of 1,3-cyclohexadiene (**2**) requires at least 20 hr at 200 °C to afford the modest and optimum yield of 30% (*endo*:*exo* = 4:1).[13] In sharp contrast, when 5 mol% of the stable cation radical salt tris(4-bromophenyl)aminium hexachloroantimonate (**3^{+}**) is used to initiate a hole catalyzed reaction of **2** in dichloromethane at 0°C, the Diels-Alder cyclodimers are obtained in 70% yield in less than 5 min (*endo*:*exo* = 4.5:1; Scheme 3).[14] The only volatile byproducts (diene oligomers are also formed) of the reaction are the *syn* and *anti* cyclobutane dimers of **2** (1.5%; *anti* > 99%:*syn*, trace). The established facility of hole catalyzed cyclobutanation, taken in conjunction with the observation of small amounts of the cyclobutane dimers of

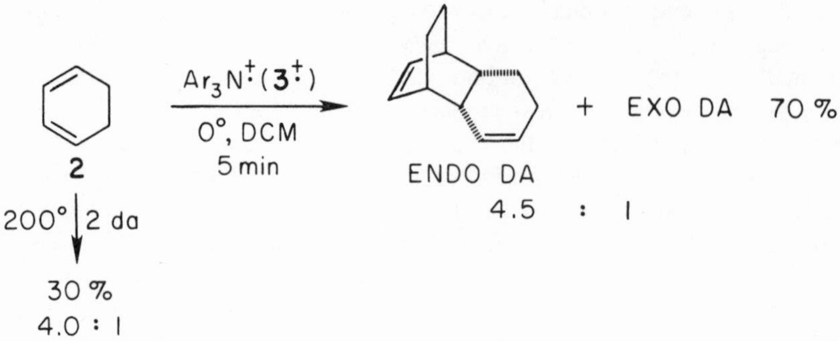

Scheme 3. The hole catalyzed Diels-Alder.

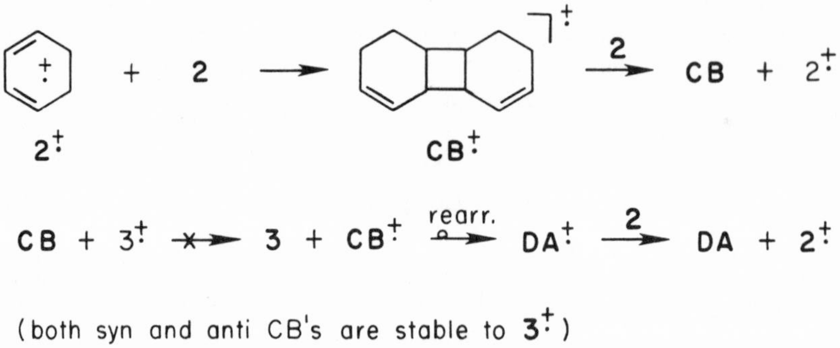

(both syn and anti CB's are stable to $3^{+\cdot}$)

Scheme 4. Hypothetical sequential cyclobutanation/vinylcyclobutane mechanism.

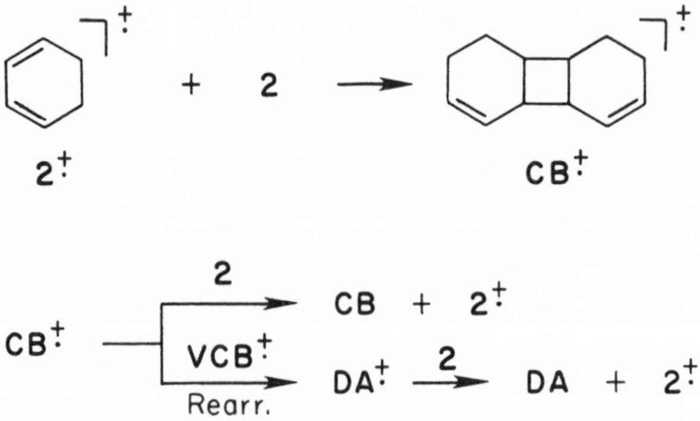

Scheme 5. Hypothetical rearrangement of a nascent cyclobutane dimer cation radical.

2, raises the interesting possibility of an indirect route to the Diels-Alder dimers of **2**, proceeding *via* initial cyclobutanation followed by a hole catalyzed vinylcyclobutane rearrangement (Scheme 4). The cyclobutane dimers, however, prove to be wholly stable under the reaction conditions and cannot themselves be intermediates in the formation of the Diels-Alder adducts. A more subtle possibility is an extremely rapid vinylcyclobutane rearrangement of intermediate cyclobutane dimer cation radicals in competition with quenching of these latter cation radicals (Scheme 5). This possibility is also ruled out by the observation that the cyclodimer composition is independent of the initial concentration of **2**, the most abundant quenching agent and presumably the only one present initially, over a 100-fold range of concentration and is also constant over the entire course of the reaction, even though the very efficient quencher **3** is generated by the progressive decomposition of **3**†.[15] The formation of Diels-Alder cyclodimers is therefore clearly not an event subsequent to cyclobutanation.

A hole catalyzed mechanism for this reaction is supported by the observation of the same cyclodimerization under PET conditions, although here substantial quantities (*ca.* 20%) of the cyclobutane dimers are formed *via* a mechanism involving triplet **2**, the product of back electron transfer in the radical ion pair **2**†//S^{-}.[16] The Diels-Alder cycloaddition is selectively quenched by efficient hole transfer agents and a cycloaddition rate (**2**†/2) of 3 × 10^8, only about a factor of 60 less than the diffusion controlled rate, was established.[17] A Bronsted acid catalyzed reaction mechanism for the aminium salt initiated reaction is specifically excluded by the observation that 2,6-bis(*tert*-butyl) pyridine does

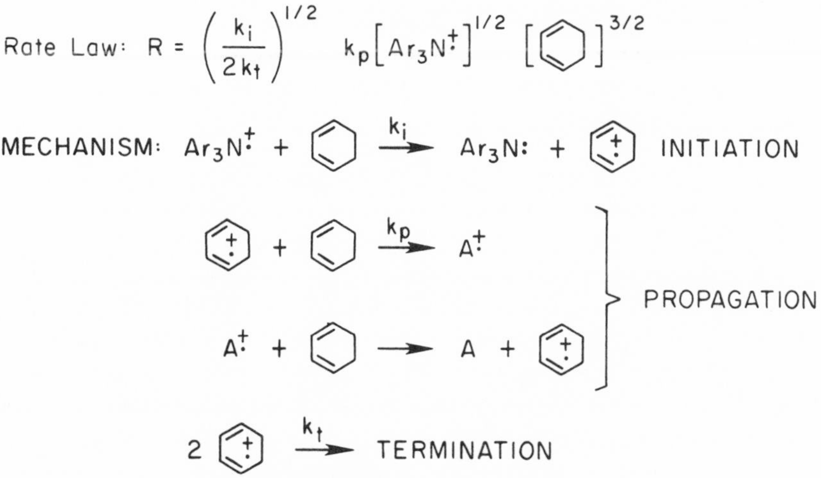

$$\text{Rate Law:} \quad R = \left(\frac{k_i}{2k_t}\right)^{1/2} k_p \left[Ar_3N^{\ddagger}\right]^{1/2} \left[\bigbox\right]^{3/2}$$

Scheme 6. Kinetics and mechanism.

not inhibit the reaction.[18] A detailed kinetic study provides a rate law $R = k_{app}[\text{Ar}_3\text{N}^{\overset{+}{\cdot}}]^{1/2}[\textbf{2}]^{3/2}$, consistent with the HTC mechanism of Scheme 6, with activation parameters $\Delta H^* = 7.95$ kcal/mol, $\Delta S^* = -26.9$ e.u., and $\Delta G^* = 15.6$ kcal/mol.[19] A comparison of the oxidation potentials of **2** and **3** indicates that most of the activation enthalpy is associated with the initiation step, and that the activation enthalpy of the cycloaddition step is at most 1.6 kcal/mol, corresponding to a rate constant of *ca.* 6×10^8. The involvement of full fledged cation radicals (**2**$^{\overset{+}{\cdot}}$) as opposed to an aminium salt/diene complex (Ar$_3$N$^{\overset{+}{\cdot}}$ ...**2**) is decisively attested by the kinetic rate law and by the observation of rate depression by added (neutral) **3**. A hole catalyzed (HTC) mechanism for the aminium salt initiated Diels-Alder is thus firmly established, and the powerful kinetic impetus is manifested in the catalytic factor of 10^{23}. The possibility of a classic hole catalytic mechanism is inconsistent with the results (rate law) of the detailed kinetic study and inherently appears unlikely because this mechanism requires the most inefficient reaction step (**3**$^{\overset{+}{\cdot}}$ + **2** → **3** + **2**$^{\overset{+}{\cdot}}$) to be repeated in each cycle, whereas the HTC mechanism employs this inefficient step only in the initiation phase.[20] The question ultimately reduces to whether the dimer cation radicals are quenched by **2** (giving more **2**$^{\overset{+}{\cdot}}$ to repeat the propagation cycle) or by **3** (giving **3**$^{\overset{+}{\cdot}}$ and requiring the slow generation of more **2**$^{\overset{+}{\cdot}}$). Since **3** is initially absent from the reaction mixture and is present in rather small amounts even up to 50% reaction under the conditions of the kinetic study, quenching of dimer cation radicals by **3** could prevail only if the quenching reaction with **2** is quite slow. Since the hole transfer (D$_2$$^{\overset{+}{\cdot}}$ + **2** → D$_2$ + **2**$^{\overset{+}{\cdot}}$) is more than 0.5 V (11.5 kcal/mol) exoergic, the assumption of a reasonable ΔG_o^* for this hole transfer (*vide infra*) permits the prediction that this hole transfer occurs at the diffusion controlled rate. Nevertheless, it appears likely that, in the latter stages of the reaction when the relative concentrations of **2** and **3** become comparable, the classic catalytic and HTC mechanisms are both operative.

The Hole Catalyzed Diels-Alder as a True Pericyclic Reaction

The mechanism originally proposed for the hole catalyzed cyclodimerization (cyclobutanation) of *N*-vinylcarbazole (Scheme 2) involved a stepwise cycloaddition proceeding *via* an acyclic cation/radical intermediate. Although a stereochemical test of this proposition failed as a consequence of the unreactivity of *cis*-propenylcarbazole, the mechanism nevertheless became the accepted prototype for hole catalyzed cycloaddition. Theoretical results were also construed to suggest that cation radical cycloadditions in general should occur in a stepwise fashion.[21] According to this mechanism, the hole catalyzed cyclodimerization of **2** would proceed *via* a bis(allylic) cation/radical which could cyclize to either cyclobutane or Diels-Alder adducts. The latter might well be favored by product development control. Such a mechanism, incidentally, would not be rigorously classified as pericyclic in the mechanistic sense, since the requirement of a concerted reaction would not be fulfilled.

In any case it was of importance to determine the reaction stereochemistry of the hole catalyzed Diels-Alder. The cross cycloadditions of the three geometric isomers of 2,4-hexadiene to **2** were examined and found to proceed with complete suprafacial stereospecificity with respect to the dienophile (Scheme 7).[3,22] These results are consistent with a concerted and thus mechanistically pericyclic Diels-Alder addition. They are inconsistent with the formation of an acyclic bis(allylic) cation radical intermediate unless such intermediate undergoes cyclization *ca.* 100 times more rapidly than torsion. An ab initio MC SCF MO reaction path calculation (MP2/6-31G*//3-21G) reaction path for the prototype Diels-Alder cycloaddition of the *s-cis*-1,3-butadiene cation radical to ethene provides additional support for a concerted path.[23] Apparently, Diels-Alder cycloaddition and cyclobutanation are independent reaction paths, at least in the present systems and solvent, and the former is rather strongly favored.

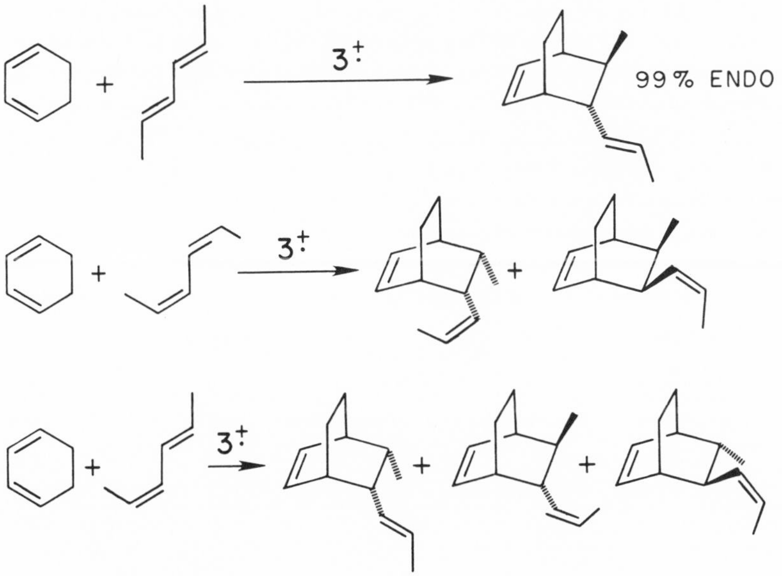

(MP2/6-31G*//3-21G reaction path calculations support a concerted path)

Scheme 7. Concerted vs. stepwise addition.

Endo Diastereoselection and the cis-*Propenyl Effect*

The unusually high degree of *endo* diastereoselection (>99%) observed in the hole catalyzed cycloaddition of **2** and *E,E*-2,4-hexadiene is especially noteworthy for a reaction which occurs at a rate within two orders of magnitude of diffusion control. Similarly high *endo* stereoselection is observed in other instances where the pendant double bond in the adduct is vinyl or *trans*-propenyl, but very modest selectivities are the contrary rule when the pendant double bond has a *cis* substituent (*cis*-propenyl, isobutenyl, etc.).[22] The uncatalyzed reaction of **2** and *E,E*-2,4-hexadiene is also unspectacular in the level of diastereoselection, but it is exceptional in that the *exo* isomer is favored (3:1). The conclusion appears justified that the hole catalyzed Diels-Alder inherently has an extremely high *endo* diastereoselectivity as a consequence of the low reaction temperature and the enhancement of secondary orbital interactions by the hole. Apparently *cis*-alkenyl substituents sharply attenuate these interactions, and the only satisfactory explanation appears to involve the *s-cis* conformation of the dienophilic diene, at least in the instances where *endo* stereoselection is high. The additional secondary orbital interactions which are possible in this disposition could account for the especially high *endo* diastereoselection, and a *cis* substituent could hinder the proximate approach of the two sites of unsaturation in the *endo* transition state and thus minimize secondary orbital interactions (Scheme 8). Alternatively, the *cis* substituent could hinder the formation of the *s-cis* diene conformation. However, since E,Z-2,4-hexadiene displays both high (addition to the Z-double bond) and low (addition to the E-double bond) *endo* diastereoselectivity, the latter explanation appears unlikely. Consequently either the *s-cis* cation radical of the acyclic diene is formed selectively in the endothermic aminium salt hole transfer reaction or else this diene undergoes *trans* → *cis*

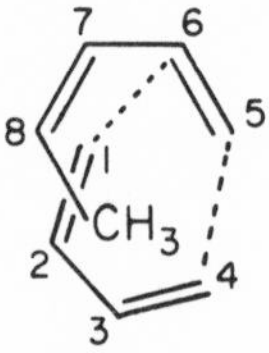

Secondary interactions (C_2-C_7 and C_3-C_8) between two s-cis dienes are attenuated by the steric effect of a Z-alkyl group.

Scheme 8. The *cis*-propenyl effect on endo diastereoselectivity.

conformational isomerization in a complex with $2^{\ddot{+}}$ prior to cycloaddition. This raises the fundamental question of mechanistic roles, i.e., which diene is the hole carrying species (i.e. the cation radical), and this question will be addressed in a subsequent section.

Regiospecificity

The experiments described previously show the hole catalyzed Diels-Alder to be direct and capable of impressively high levels of stereospecificity and *endo* selectivity. A third element of the selectivity profile, regiospecificity, is at least equally impressive. The combination of an unsymmetrical diene component with an unsymmetrical dienophile permits scrutiny of this selectivity element.[22] The cyclodimerization of 1-methyl-1,3-cyclohexadiene, e.g., under typical aminium salt conditions occurs efficiently (75%) to give a 2:1 (see *cis*-propenyl effect) *endo:exo* mixture of Diels-Alder adducts with 100% regiospecificity (Scheme 9). The sense of this specificity is in accord with a conventional non-synchronous transition state model (the more stable bis (allylic) cation/radicaloid transition state is favored). A variety of other examples confirm the reliability and predictability of this selectivity element.

Site Selectivity

The cyclodimerization of 1-methyl-1,3-cyclohexadiene also illustrates another element of the selectivity profile of the hole catalyzed Diels-Alder, viz. selection between two nonequivalent double bonds of an unsymmetrical diene (acting as the dienophilic component). The exclusive reaction site for the previously mentioned diene and for other dienes of the same substitution pattern (Scheme 9) is the less highly substituted double bond, in accord with both steric factors and the maximum stabilization of a transition state which has bis (allylic) cation/radical character.[22]

Although subject to steric effects, the hole catalyzed Diels-Alder is far less sensitive than the uncatalyzed reaction to such effects. The moderately hindered diene 2,5-dimethyl-2,4-hexadiene (Scheme 10) had never previously been ob-

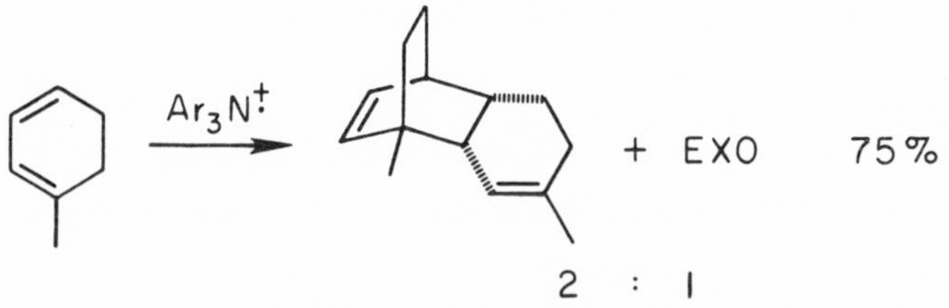

$Ar_3N^{\ddot{+}}$ + EXO 75%

2 : 1

Scheme 9. Regiospecificity.

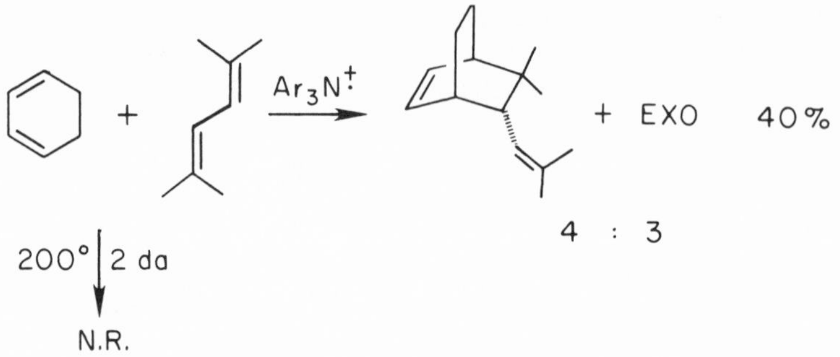

Scheme 10. Sterically hindered dienes.

served to participate in a Diels-Alder reaction as either diene or dienophile. Under the relatively forcing conditions used to thermally cyclodimerize 1,3-cyclohexadiene, the hindered diene fails to react at all with the latter diene. Under the aminium salt conditions (0 °C, 5 min), this cross addition occurs smoothly and installs a quaternary carbon with ease.

The previous examples illustrate that steric effects do indeed operate in the hole catalyzed Diels-Alder but that the kinetic impetus of the reaction is capable of overcoming them. Other examples reveal that steric effects are not necessarily dominant even in the context of site selection, and this circumstance confers a uniqueness upon the site selectivity of the hole catalyzed Diels-Alder. The cross addition of 4-methyl-1,3-pentadiene and 1,3-cyclohexadiene exemplifies predominant reactivity at the more highly substituted double bond (Scheme 11). Again one notes the high *endo* selectivity when the pendant double bond is vinyl. Control of site selectivity by charge density effects has been postulated to explain preferential reaction at the more highly substituted double bond. Molecular orbital calculations confirm the intuitive feeling that the more highly substituted terminus of the diene cation radical has the greater positive charge density. This effect is opposed to the steric and bis (allylic) stabilization effects discussed earlier and appears to be dominant only when the charge density difference between the relevant termini is relatively large (disubstituted vs. unsubstituted

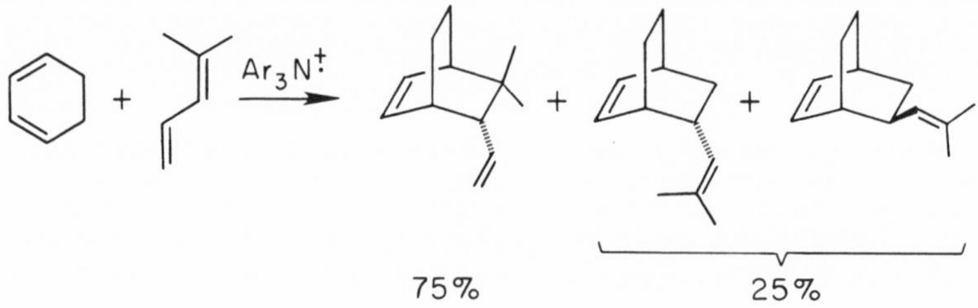

Scheme 11. Site selectivity.

termini) or when steric effects are small (monosubstituted vs. unsubstituted termini). It is important, moreover, to note that such charge density control may be effective only when the dienophilic diene is the hole carrier (the cation radical component).

Electron Rich Alkenes as Dienophiles

Another major constraint on the generality of the uncatalyzed Diels-Alder reaction is the inherent inefficiency of reactions involving approximately neutral or electron rich dienophiles. The hole catalyzed reactions of 1,3-cyclohexadiene with vinyl ethers, vinyl sulfides, and *trans*-anethole (Scheme 12) illustrate the efficacy of hole catalysis in removing this constraint.[24] This strategy has been applied to the formal total synthesis of the sesquiterpene natural product (−)-β-selenine (Scheme 13).[25] The hole catalyzed Diels-Alder addition of phenyl vinyl sulfide to the triene derived from perillaldehyde is regiospecific and site specific (the isopropenyl double bond is unreactive). This selectivity element is highlighted by an attempt to effect the thermal Diels-Alder cycloaddition of phenyl vinyl sulfone, an electron deficient dienophile, to the same triene. This latter reaction, in contrast to the mild conditions of the hole catalyzed Diels-Alder, requires extended heating in refluxing xylene and produces 11 isomers in comparable amounts, the predominant reaction mode involving the isopropenyl double bond, presumably in an ene type reaction. Thus, the kinetic impetus and the selectivity of the hole catalyzed Diels-Alder, which are its most fundamental distinctives, are capable of providing major synthetic advantages over thermal Diels-Alder reactions even where the latter involve electron-deficient dienophiles.

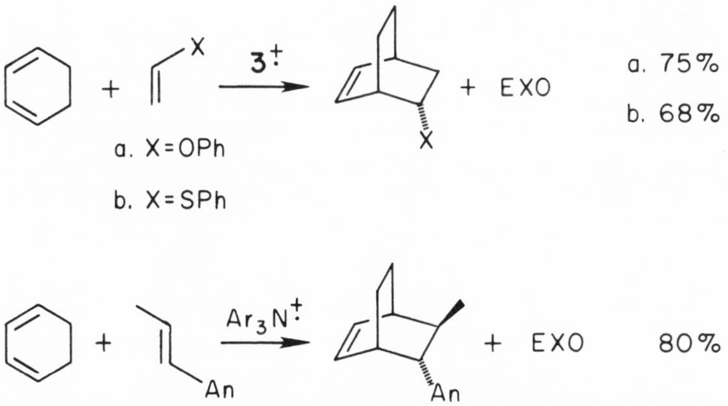

a. X = OPh

b. X = SPh

a. 75%

b. 68%

80%

Scheme 12. Electron rich alkenes.

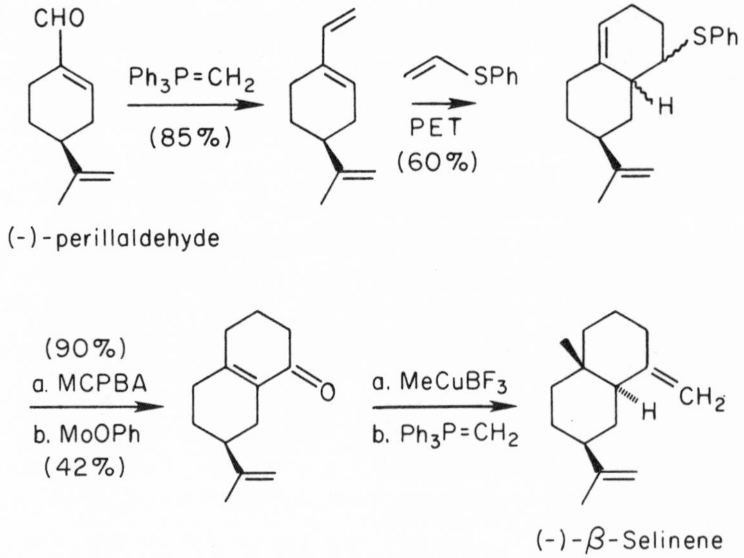

(-)-perillaldehyde

(-)-β-Selinene

Scheme 13. Formal total synthesis of (−)-β-Selinene.

The Intramolecular Hole Catalyzed Diels-Alder

The intramolecular Diels-Alder reaction is characterized by a special entropic driving force which makes feasible additions to neutral or electron rich dienophiles and by its unique capacity for the simultaneous construction of two fused rings. The stereochemistry of the resulting ring juncture is a feature of special urgency in a synthetic context and is controlled by the *endo/exo* stereoselection of the reaction. Unfortunately the modest *endo* selectivity inherent in the uncatalyzed Diels-Alder, which is further attenuated for neutral or electron rich dienophiles and at the elevated temperatures required with such dienophiles, has not proved sufficient to deliver the desired high degree of ring juncture stereoselectivity. In contrast, the hole catalyzed Diels-Alder is routinely capable of high *endo* stereoselection. As illustrated in Scheme 14, the superposition of the kinetic impetus and *endo* stereoselection of the hole catalyzed Diels-Alder upon the intramolecular Diels-Alder engenders an extraordinarily facile ring closure of 99–100% *endo* diastereoselectivity.[26] The dienophile moieties of the trienes were selected for their relative ease of ionization. As one colleague quipped, the reaction produces *two* rings in *one* minute!

Acyclic Dienes

The observation of direct hole catalyzed Diels-Alder cycloadditions to rigidly *s-cis*-dienes such as 1,3-cyclohexadiene establishes the inherent preference for the Diels-Alder reaction mode relative to cyclobutanation. Nevertheless, hole

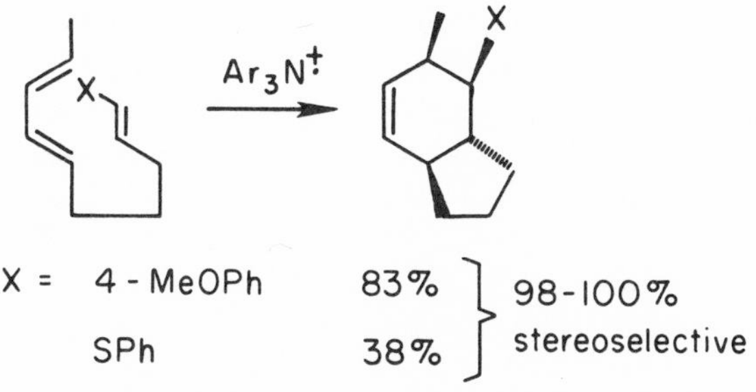

$$X = \quad 4\text{-}MeOPh \qquad 83\% \quad \left.\begin{array}{l} \\ \end{array}\right\} \begin{array}{l} 98\text{-}100\% \\ \text{stereoselective} \end{array}$$

$$SPh \qquad\qquad 38\%$$

Scheme 14. The intramolecular hole catalyzed Diels-Alder.

catalyzed cyclobutanation is an extremely facile reaction, and the preference for the Diels-Alder addition mode even in these systems, which are conformationally ideal for Diels-Alder addition, is not necessarily overwhelming (cf. 1.5% cyclobutanation in the dimerization of 1,3-cyclohexadiene). A question therefore remains concerning the dominance of the Diels-Alder mode in cycloadditions to conformationally flexible dienes. The cycloaddition of phenyl vinyl sulfide to the triene derived from perillaldehyde (Scheme 13) reveals that direct Diels-Alder addition *can* be the predominant reaction course even in such instances. Diels-Alder cycloadditions to both 2,3-dimethyl-1,3-butadene and 1,1'-dicyclopentenyl provide additional support for the proposition that direct Diels-Alder additions can be substantially favored with dienic components which have at least modest *s-cis*-conformational populations (Scheme 15). Simple

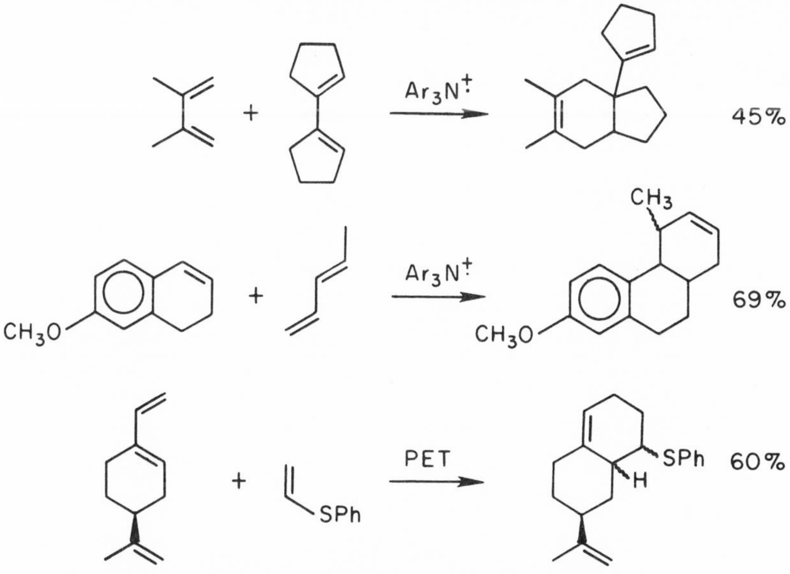

Scheme 15. Acyclic diene components.

acyclic dienes, with minimal *s-cis*-conformational populations, however, tend to undergo either competitive cyclobutanation/Diels-Alder addition or even predominant cyclobutanation (Scheme 16). Indeed, even dienes with moderate *s-cis* contents have been found to undergo competitive cyclobutanation and Diels-Alder addition (Scheme 17), although the divinylcyclobutane products of the reaction shown rapidly undergo hole catalyzed rearrangement to the Diels-Alder adducts.[27] This rearrangement along with additional factors which influence the cyclobutane/Diels-Alder competition will be discussed in subsequent sections.

Hole Catalyzed Cycloadditions to Cyclopentadiene

It may seem curious that relatively few hole catalyzed cycloadditions to this very common diene have been reported. Although efficient cross additions with highly ionizable dienophiles have indeed been observed (Scheme 18), neither the

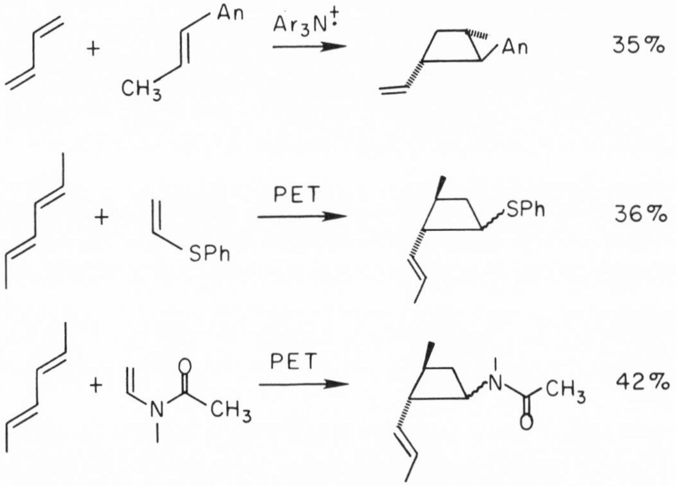

Scheme 16.   Selective cyclobutanation of simple acyclic dienes.

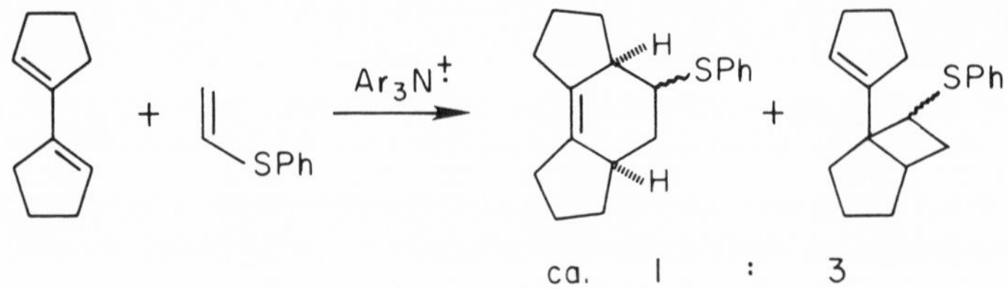

Scheme 17.   Competing CB/DA additions.

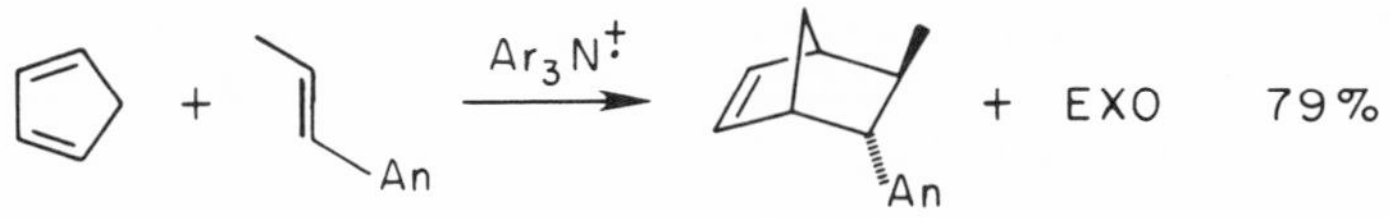

Scheme 18. Cyclopentadiene in hole catalyzed DA additions.

hole catalyzed dimerization of this diene nor any of its cross additions to simple dienes have been reported or observed. Although relatively little effort has yet been expended in this area, the problem related to these reactions appears to be the unique difficulty of ionizing cyclopentadiene, which has an oxidation potential 0.14 V (3.2 kcal/mol) greater than that of 1,3-cyclohexadiene. The uniquely high oxidation potential of 1,3-cyclopentadiene correlates directly with the presence, in the highest occupied molecular orbital (HOMO), of a nodal plane through the methylene group. Consequently, hyperconjugative delocalization of the hole is precluded in this diene, and the HOMO more closely resembles the HOMO of 1,3-butadiene than that of 1,3-cyclohexadiene. Hole catalyzed cyclodimerization of 1,3-butadiene and other simple, relatively difficult ionizable dienes is also unsuccessful under typical aminium salt or PET conditions.

The Photosensitized Electron Transfer (PET) Procedure for Hole Catalysis of Cycloadditions

Subsequent to the discovery of the aminium salt catalyzed Diels-Alder reaction, the hole catalyzed cyclodimerization of 1,3-cyclohexadiene (**2**) under PET conditions (9,10-dicyanoanthracene sensitizer $\equiv$ DCA, CH_2Cl_2, hν/pyrex) was reported.[16] The simultaneous formation of the cyclobutane dimers of **2** *via* triplet **2** arising from back electron transfer in the ion radical pair ($\mathbf{2}^{+}\mathbf{S}^{-}$) has previously been noted. In sharp contrast to the facility of the corresponding aminium salt catalyzed reaction, the cycloaddition of **2** to the hindered diene 2,5-dimethyl-2,4-hexadiene (**4**) is completely unsuccessful under PET conditions. Apparently the cycloaddition of $\mathbf{4}^{+}$/**2**, which is presumably slowed by steric hindrance, is completely overwhelmed by back electron transfer producing ground state **4**. Significantly, the cyclodimerization of **2** is also completely suppressed under these conditions. Since the quenching of the excited state sensitizer by electron transfer from either diene (giving $\mathbf{2}^{+}$ and $\mathbf{4}^{+}$) is thermodynamically highly favorable, both of these cation radicals should be generated at rates approaching diffusion control. The selective production of $\mathbf{4}^{+}$ to the exclusion of $\mathbf{2}^{+}$ is therefore highly unlikely. Further, since the cycloaddition reaction $\mathbf{2}^{+}$/**2** occurs at a rate only sixty fold less than the diffusion controlled rate, it appears that the hole transfer between $\mathbf{2}^{+}$ and **4** (giving **2** and $\mathbf{4}^{+}$) must occur at a rate very close to diffusion control and, additionally, this hole transfer must be much faster than the cycloaddition $\mathbf{2}^{+}$/**4**. The question of the relative rates of hole transfer and cycloaddition in cation radical/neutral complexes is of fundamental mechanistic importance and will be discussed more fully in a subsequent section.

An extensive study of hole catalyzed cycloadditions under PET conditions does, however, reveal significant advantages for this method in specific reaction systems.[28] The cyclodimerization of 1-methoxy-1,3-cyclohexadiene occurs smoothly under PET conditions (71%; Scheme 19), but only traces of the cyclodimers are detected under aminium salt conditions. These dimers have been shown to be unstable in the presence of the aminium salt, in part as a result of the strong acid generated in the latter procedure. The avoidance of acidic conditions in the PET procedure is also valuable in the dimerization of 2,4-dimethyl-1,3-pentadiene, which undergoes Bronsted acid catalyzed cyclodimerization under typical aminium salt conditions.[18] The latter is suppressed by 2,6-bis(*tert*-butyl) pyridine, restoring the hole catalyzed mechanism and leading to the same cyclodimer formed in the PET procedure (Scheme 20).

Heterogeneous Hole Catalysis

The adaptation of the kinetic power and selectivity of hole catalysis to an industrial context is a major goal of this laboratory. For these purposes, naturally, heterogeneous catalytic systems appeared most attractive. The first heterogeneous hole catalytic system targeted was a stable, hole-containing polymer.[29] The Friedel-Crafts alkylation of triphenylamine by 2% divinylbenzene cross-linked Merrifield resin smoothly afforded the corresponding triphenylaminated polymer (Scheme 21). In the typical manner for the conversion of triarylamines to the corresponding aminium salts ($SbCl_5/CH_2Cl_2/O^\circ$), the latter polymer was converted to a dark purple, air stable polymer containing aminium ion hole sites at 5% of the styrene residues. This hole catalytic polymer is indeed effective in promoting essentially the same range of hole catalytic reactions as the monomeric aminium salts. It is conveniently removed by filtration and can be recycled. In addition, no residue of neutral triarylamine is left in the solution to complicate purification. Although the loading of hole sites on the polymer is still

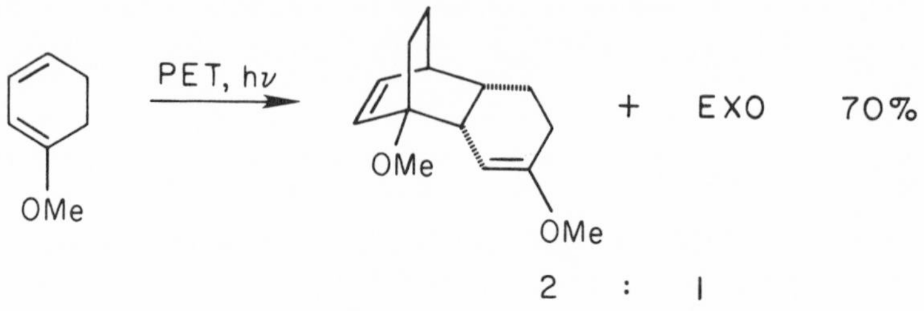

2 : 1

Scheme 19. Photosensitized electron transfer (PET).

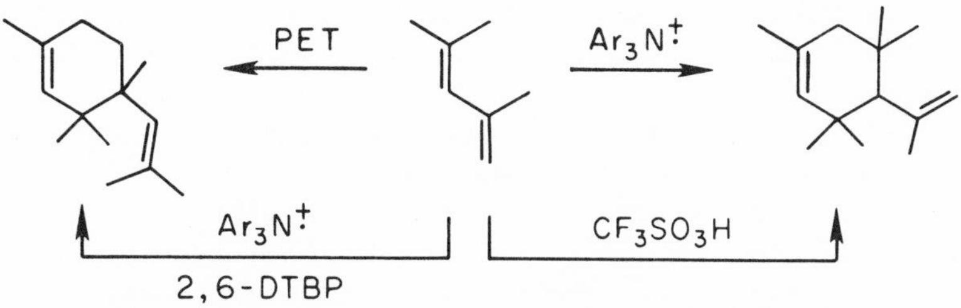
PET
Ar3N+•
Ar3N+•
CF3SO3H
2,6-DTBP

Scheme 20. Competing hole and acid catalyzed additions.

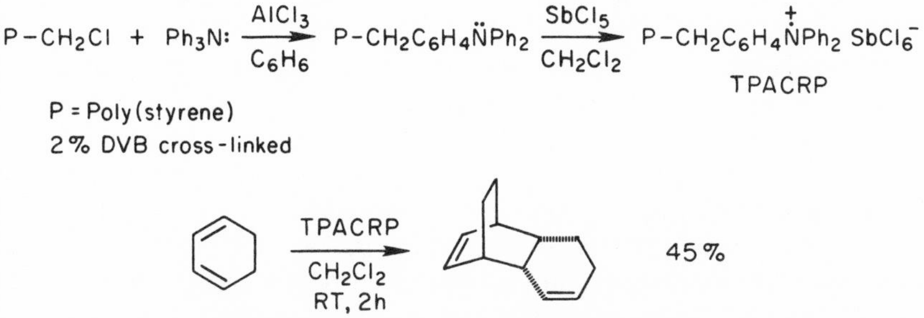
P–CH2Cl + Ph3N:
AlCl3
C6H6
P–CH2C6H4N̈Ph2
SbCl5
CH2Cl2
P–CH2C6H4N+•Ph2 SbCl6−
TPACRP
P = Poly(styrene)
2% DVB cross-linked
TPACRP
CH2Cl2
RT, 2h
45%

Scheme 21. Heterogeneous hole catalysis.

somewhat on the low side, the approach has merit and is receiving further attention.[30]

A second attractive category of heterogeneous hole catalytic systems is the zeolites. Widespread use of zeolite catalysis in the chemical industry is a major incentive for considering these natural catalysts for development as hole catalysts. Further, it is well known that aromatic cation radicals can be generated and often are quite long lived on zeolite surfaces. The hole catalyzed cyclodimerization of **2** on 13X and other zeolites has been confirmed, although this reaction is much slower than the aminium salt catalyzed reaction.[31] Elevated temperatures do not prove useful in accelerating the desired reaction, but photoassistance is observed. The range of hole catalyzed reactions observed on these zeolites thus far is not encouraging. In contrast, a much wider range of hole catalytic reactivity is observed on montmorillonite clays doped with *tert*-butylphenol/ferric ion.[32] Hole catalyzed cycloadditions have also been observed on UV irradiated semiconductor surfaces[33] and at anodes.[34]

Synthetic Profile and Limitations

The cation radical Diels-Alder reaction can be carried out in a synthetically convenient manner, on virtually any scale, using chemical or photochemical initiation procedures. The reactions are, of course, extremely rapid (in the case of chemical initiation) and often outstandingly stereoselective and stereospecific. The optimum chemical initiator system appears, at present, to be $Ar_3N^{+\cdot}$/DCM/ 0 °C/5 min. A particularly convenient PET initiator system is DCB/CH_3CN/ hν/pyrex/RT. The latter is a more powerfully ionizing system than the optimum chemical one and can produce higher yields, but is somewhat limited in scope by back electron transfer. In such cases, 2,4,6-triphenylpyrylium fluoroborate may be the PET sensitizer of choice.

Diene components should either be cyclic (i.e. rigidly s-cis) or, if acyclic, have at least moderate (say ≥ 10%) s-cis conformational populations. Neither the diene nor dienophile is permitted electron withdrawing groups, since these adversely affect both caticophilicity (reactivity toward a cation radical) and caticogenicity (ionizability).

The dienophile typically is of one of three basic structural types: conjugated diene, styrene, or electron rich alkene. Alkyl substituents placed anywhere in these systems typically enhance reaction efficiency, and multiple alkyl substitutions are especially advantageous. When unsubstituted vinyl groups are present as part of the conjugated system, polymerization is often predominant.

In general practice, the preferred synthetic strategy appears to be to utilize dienophiles which are more readily ionizable (caticogenic) than the diene component. When this condition is not met, cyclodimerization of the diene component may be prevalent. This latter reaction may or may not be susceptible of suppression by use of an excess of dienophile. The ideal preference, which normally results in excellent yields even when dienophile and diene are employed on an equimolar basis is for dichotomous addends, i.e, the circumstance in which the dienophile is much more caticogenic than the diene, and the latter is much more caticophilic than the dienophile. Caticogenicity can be quantitatively assessed on the basis of oxidation potentials or ionization potentials (Table 1). Caticophilicity, specifically in the case of the Diels-Alder reaction, is considered to be affected by ability to stabilize the bisallylic cation radicaloid transition state, steric hindrance toward bond formation, s-cis conformation content and other factors yet to be defined. Nevertheless, many reactions which are nondichotomous may proceed well, especially when appropriate reagent excesses are provided.

Orbital Symmetry Effects on Role Selectivity

Two potentially distinct mechanistic roles have been recognized for the hole catalyzed Diels-Alder reaction. The mechanism in which the hole carrying (i.e., cation radical) component reacts as the dienophile is classified as a [4 + 1] cycloaddition and is formally symmetry allowed.[35] The alternative reaction mode in which the hole carrying component reacts in the s-cis diene role is classified as a [3 + 2] cycloaddition and is formally symmetry forbidden. That these peri-

Table 1. Half Wave Oxidation Potentials (vs. S.C.E., CH_3CN, irreversible)

Compound	Potential
E-anethole	1.11
1,1'-dicyclopentenyl	1.36
4-methyl-1,3-pentadiene	1.42
phenyl vinyl sulfide	1.42
4-isopropenyl-1-vinylcyclohexene	1.52
1,3-cyclohexadiene	1.53
N-methyl-N-vinylacetamide	1.55
E,E-2,4-hexadiene	1.59
ethyl vinyl ether	1.60
phenyl vinyl ether	1.62
E-2-methyl-1,3-pentadiene	1.70
α-methylstyrene	1.72
E-1,3-pentadiene	1.73
2,3-dimethyl-1,3-butadiene	1.95
2-methyl-1,3-butadiene	1.98

cyclic classifications are not irrelevant *a priori* is supported by the previously discussed evidence for concert (i.e., true pericyclicity) in the hole catalyzed Diels-Alder. On the other hand, the reaction path for the hole catalyzed Diels-Alder does appear to be rather highly non-synchronous, so that low pericyclicity could greatly attenuate any effects correlated by orbital symmetry. Further, hole catalyzed cyclobutanation, a [2 + 1] cycloaddition where concerted, is symmetry forbidden, but is nevertheless incredibly facile. As will be discussed subsequently, evidence for concert in at least some hole catalyzed cyclobutanations has also been presented. Consequently it does appear highly likely that the formally forbidden [3 + 2] cycloaddition is at least as facile as cyclobutanation and could not possibly be strongly impeded by symmetry imposed barriers. The feasibility of [3 + 2] cycloadditions has indeed been demonstrated for systems where the less ionizable component, a styrene derivative, is unable to function effectively in the dienic role (Scheme 22),[36] but the fundamental question of

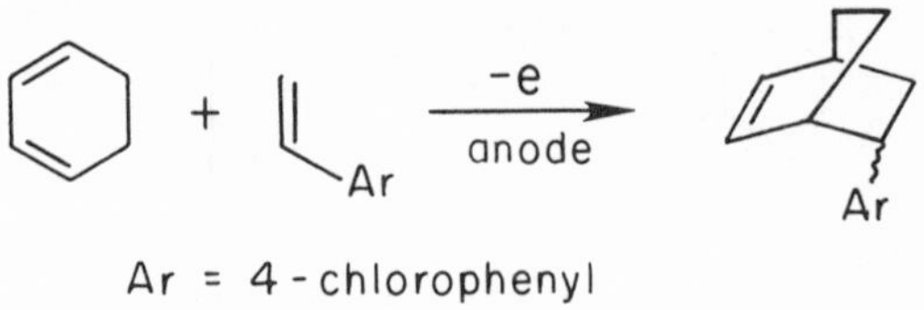

Ar = 4 - chlorophenyl

Scheme 22. "Role Reversed" DA additions.

whether orbital symmetry effects favor the [4 + 1] cycloaddition mode to any significant extent has only recently been rigorously addressed.

In uncatalyzed Diels-Alder additions, dienic aptitude is strongly correlated with the *s-cis* conformational population of the diene. The same should be true of the [4 + 1] reaction. However, the [3 + 2] addition is even more acutely affected by diene conformation since the barrier to conformational equilibration in a diene cation radical is much higher than the activation energy for the cycloaddition. Therefore, to the extent that dienes exist in the *s-trans* conformation and are ionized to the *s-trans* cation radical, [3 + 2] cycloaddition is precluded and either [4 + 1] or [2 + 1] cycloaddition must result (Scheme 23). It was therefore critical to eliminate differential conformational effects as a factor influencing the role selectivity ([3 + 2] vs. [4 + 1]) by involving only rigidly *s-cis* dienes. Further, mechanistic role assignments must be rendered unequivocal by the choice of diene pairs which differ in oxidation potential by a wide enough margin to assure that the more ionizable species is indeed the hole carrying species mechanistically. A diene pair which rather ideally conforms to these requirements is **5** (E_{ox} = 1.36 V) and **6** (E_{ox} = 1.85 V; ΔE_{ox} = 0.49V = 11.3 kcal/mol). The difficulty of ionization of **6** by **3**$\overset{+}{\cdot}$ (E_{ox} = 1.05 V for **3**) is

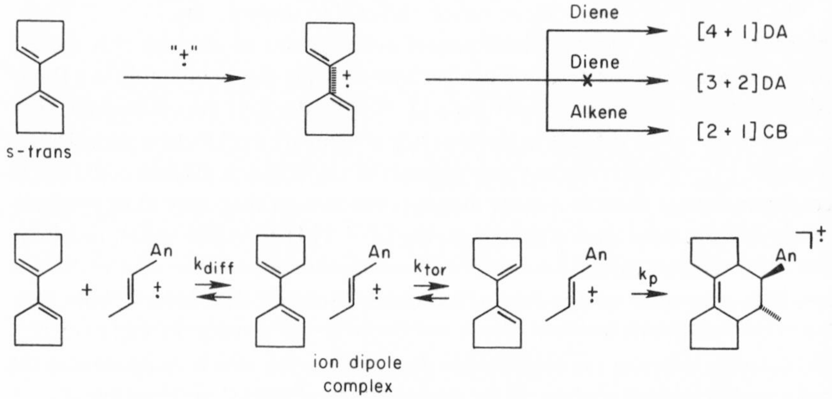

Scheme 23. Conformational effects on CB/DA periselectivity.

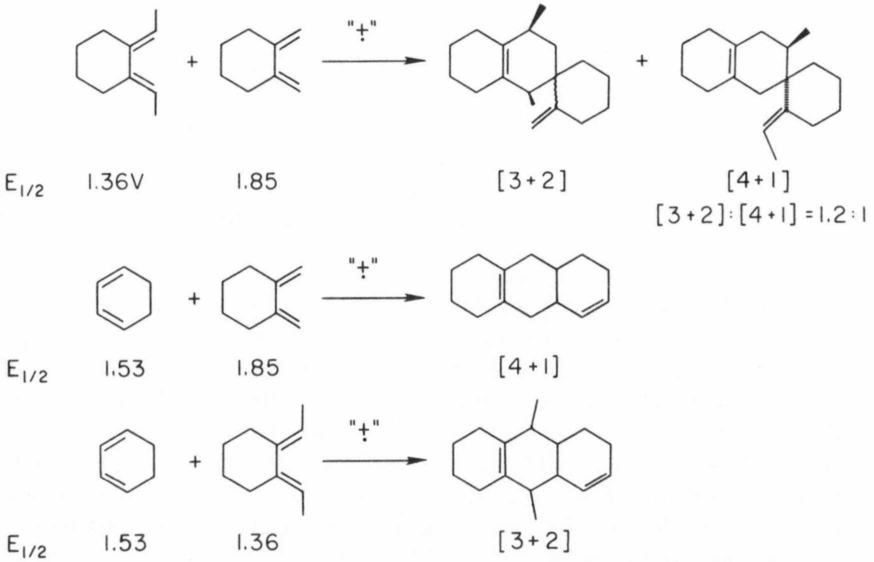

$E_{1/2}$	1.36V	1.85	[3+2]	[4+1]

$$[3+2]:[4+1] = 1.2:1$$

$E_{1/2}$	1.53	1.85	[4+1]

$E_{1/2}$	1.53	1.36	[3+2]

Scheme 24. Role selectivity.

confirmed by the stability of **6** under aminium salt conditions. The aminium salt catalyzed reaction of **5** and **6** (Scheme 24), as well as the corresponding PET induced reaction, reflect a [3 + 2]:[4 + 1] ratio of only 1.2:1. These and related results suggest that orbital symmetry allowedness/forbiddenness has little or no discernible effect on role selectivity in the hole catalyzed Diels-Alder.[37]

Role Effects on Periselectivity; Mechanistic Role Duality

The inability of *s-trans* diene cation radicals to undergo the [3 + 2] Diels-Alder requires that the cycloadditions of such species to electron rich alkenes (which lack a diene function and can perform only the dienophilic role in a Diels-Alder reaction) occur exclusively *via* a [2 + 1] mode, i.e., the cycloadditions of *s-trans* diene cation radicals to electron rich alkenes are cyclobutane periselective (Scheme 23). In contrast, the cation radicals of electron rich alkenes could add to conformationally flexible *s-trans* dienes (even though they may exist predominantly in the *s-trans* conformation) *via* the [4 + 1] Diels-Alder mode, providing that the activation energy for conformational equilibration in the neutral diene is less than activation energy for cycloaddition (Scheme 23). Indeed, hole catalyzed cycloadditions between dienes and electron rich alkenes do tend to display distinctively different periselectivities depending upon which component is the more readily ionized species. In the cycloaddition of phenyl vinyl sulfide ($E_{ox} = 1.42$ V) to the triene derived from perillaldehyde ($E_{ox} = 1.52$ V), $\geq 90\%$ Diels-

Alder periselectivity is observed, and it appears logical to assume that the reaction occurs *via* the [4 + 1] route involving the phenyl vinyl sulfide cation radical.[25] In vivid contrast, the cycloaddition of ethyl vinyl ether (E_{ox} = 1.59 V) to this same diene is 100% cyclobutane periselective.

The effect is even more dramatically illustrated in a series of cycloadditions to 1,1'-dicyclopentenyl (Scheme 25). Especially interesting in this series is the cycloaddition of phenyl vinyl sulfide (PVS) to 1,1'-dicyclopentenyl (DCP). Here the oxidation potentials of the two reaction partners are quite similar and, indeed, a mixture of CB and DA products is observed with, appropriately, the CB products dominating.[38] The possibility of a mechanistic dichotomy therefore arises, *viz.*, that cyclobutane adducts may be produced exclusively *via* the

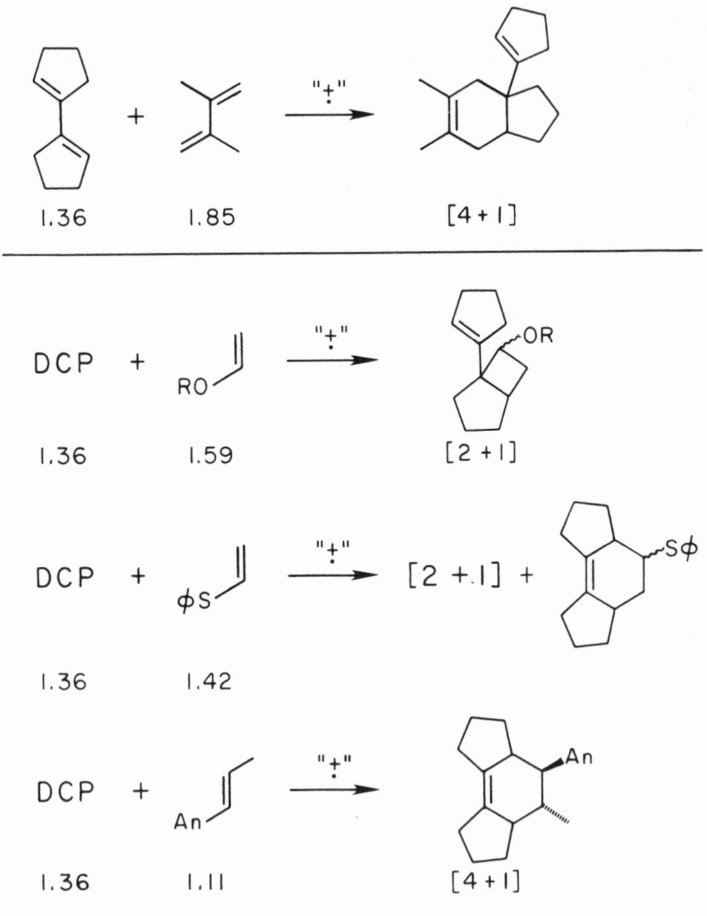

| 1.36 | 1.85 | [4 + 1] |

| DCP | 1.36 | 1.59 | [2 + 1] |

| DCP | 1.36 | 1.42 | [2 + 1] + |

| DCP | 1.36 | 1.11 | [4 + 1] |

Scheme 25. Periselectivity.

reaction $DCP^{\dot{+}}$/PVS; and Diels-Alder adducts may solely arise from the reaction $PVS^{\dot{+}}$/DCP (Scheme 26).

The system was therefore subjected to a detailed kinetic study, the results of which decisively confirm the existence of the proposed mechanistic dichotomy. Figure 1 reveals that the cycloaddition phase of the reaction is essentially complete within 100 sec. The four observed cycloadducts, obtained in 70% yield, are identified as the *syn* and *anti* cyclobutanes (CB1 and CB2, respectively) and the *exo* and *endo* Diels-Alder adducts (DA1 and DA2, respectively). The cyclobutanes clearly dominate in this phase of the reaction, but significant amounts of Diels-Alder adducts are formed. Since DCP is more readily ionized than PVS, and since the reaction $DCP^{\dot{+}}$/PVS should furnish CB adducts, primarily, the predominance of CB adducts is in qualitative accord with expectation. In the second phase of the reaction (100–200 sec), the initially preponderant *syn* cyclobutane (CB1) is converted to the *anti* cyclobutane (CB2) and the latter begins to rearrange to the *endo* DA adducts (DA2). In the third and final stage (200–300 sec), essentially the only reaction occurring is the stereoselective rearrangement of CB2 to DA2 (sr stereochemistry). Note that DA1 is not produced at all subsequent to the cycloaddition stage.

These results are confirmed by analogous studies at -30 °C, at which temperature the vinylcyclobutane (VCB) rearrangement is completely suppossessed. The most startling aspect of the reaction profile in Figure 1 is that the CB/DA periselectivity ratio *increases* from 2.99, initially, to a maximum value of 8.02, prior to decaying as a result of the ensuing $VCB^{\dot{+}}$ rearrangement. Further, the relatively larger amounts of Diels-Alder adducts produced initially are essentially completely attributable to DA1, which is not a product of the $VCB^{\dot{+}}$ rearrangement and which must therefore be engendered by a direct cycloaddition reaction (presumably $PVS^{\dot{+}}$/DCP). Studies of the rate of reactant

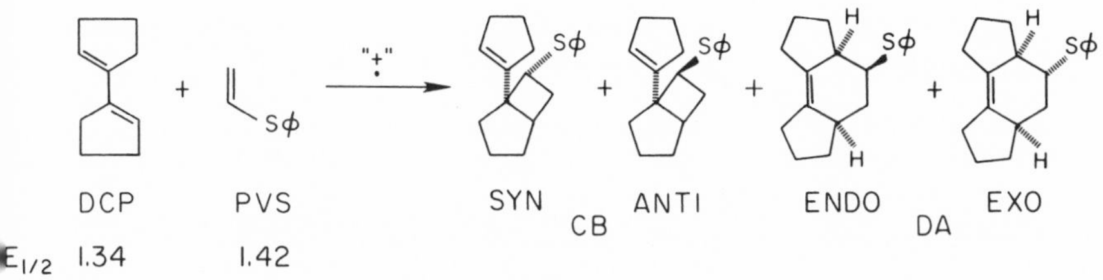

$E_{1/2}$ for DCP 1.34, PVS 1.42

$$DCP\dot{+} + PVS \xrightarrow{k_{CB}} CB?$$
$$DCP + PVS\dot{+} \xrightarrow{k_{DA}} DA?$$
$$k_{CB}, k_{DA} > k_{HT}?$$

Scheme 26. Mechanistic dichotomy/role duality.

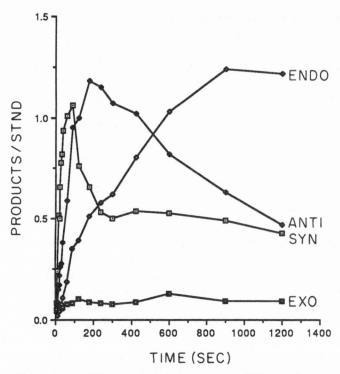

Figure 1.   Kinetic study of the reaction of phenyl vinyl sulfide and dicyclopentenyl.

consumption revealed that DCP is consumed more rapidly than PVS as a consequence of the competing cyclodimerization of the former. Consequently, it appeared possible that the dramatic rise in the periselectivity ratio might be correlated with a variation in the relative concentrations of DCP and PVS, as would be expected if dual role differentiated mechanisms having disparate CB/DA periselectivities are operative.

   An analogous kinetic study using an initial 2:1 ratio of PVS:DCP was thus carried out. Under these conditions, the periselectivity ratio is indeed found to be increased over the entire cycloaddition stage, commencing at 3.63 and increasing to a maximum of 8.93. Conversely, at a 1:2 initial ratio of PVS:DCP, the periselectivity ratio is diminished over the entire range (1.94 to 6.74). However, since the relative concentrations of PVS:DCP decrease in the relevant portion of the reaction (0–30 sec) to no more than 2:1 (from an initial 1:1 ratio), the very high CB/DA ratio observed during the latter part of this reaction phase cannot be *solely* attributed to a relative concentration effect.

   The progressive formation of neutral **3** has been demonstrated to be a concomitant of hole catalyzed cycloaddition. Accordingly, a kinetic study of the reaction

Table 2. The Effects of Relative and Absolute Substrate Concentrations and of Added Triarylamine of the Initial Periselectivity Ratio

[PVS]/[DCP]	$[Ar_3N]$	[PVS], M	$(CB/DA)_{t=0}$
1 : 1	0.	0.14	2.99
2 : 2	0.	0.14	3.63
1 : 2	0.	0.14	1.94
1 : 1	0.017	0.14	4.67
2 : 1	0.01	0.09	7.0

with added **3** (17 mol %) was also carried out. The initial periselectivity ratio was found to be enhanced to 4.64. Finally, under conditions which closely mimic those of high CB/DA periselectivity (i.e., at 30 sec reaction time), an initial periselectivity of 7.0 is attainable (Table 2). Thus, combination of the increasing [PVS]:[DCP] ratio, the generation of **3**, and the diminishing absolute concentrations of the substrates, i.e., [PVS] + [DCP], fully accounts for the dramatic increase in the CB/DA ratio with time. Studies using aryl vinyl sulfides with electron donating and electron withdrawing p-substituents (Scheme 27) further support the assertion that it is the PVS $^{\overset{+}{\cdot}}$/DCP reaction which generates the Diels-Alder adduct.

The effect of **3** and of the absolute concentration appear to be associated with a competition between HT and HTC catalysis (Scheme 28). The CB/DA periselec-

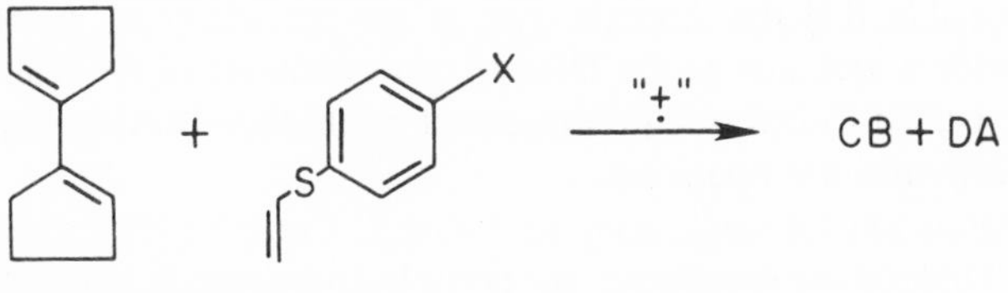

X	$E_{1/2}$	$(CB/DA)_{t=0}$
H	1.33	3.02
CH_3CH_2	1.23	0.85
Br	1.38	8.74
(DCP)	1.22	

Scheme 27. Which mechanism is CB periselective?

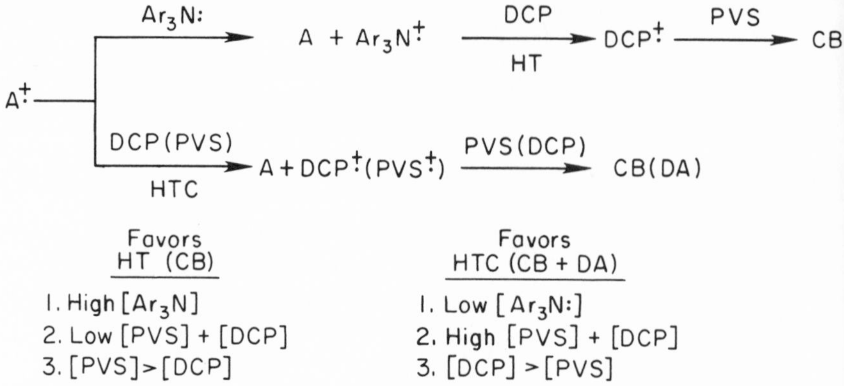

$$\text{A}^{\text{+}\centerdot}\begin{cases} \xrightarrow{\text{Ar}_3\text{N:}} \text{A} + \text{Ar}_3\text{N}^{\text{+}\centerdot} \xrightarrow[\text{HT}]{\text{DCP}} \text{DCP}^{\text{+}\centerdot} \xrightarrow{\text{PVS}} \text{CB} \\[2ex] \xrightarrow[\text{HTC}]{\text{DCP(PVS)}} \text{A} + \text{DCP}^{\text{+}\centerdot}(\text{PVS}^{\text{+}\centerdot}) \xrightarrow{\text{PVS(DCP)}} \text{CB(DA)} \end{cases}$$

Favors HT (CB)	Favors HTC (CB + DA)
I. High [Ar$_3$N]	I. Low [Ar$_3$N:]
2. Low [PVS] + [DCP]	2. High [PVS] + [DCP]
3. [PVS]>[DCP]	3. [DCP] >[PVS]

Scheme 28.   HT vs. HTC catalysis.

tivity depends, of course, on the relative rates of generation of DCP$^{+\centerdot}$ and PVS$^{+\centerdot}$ and is thus dependent upon the specific hole transfer agent which ionizes DCP and PVS. In the hole transfer chain (HTC) mechanism, exoergic hole transfer from an adduct cation radical (A$^{+\centerdot}$, of the simple olefinic type) should generate DCP$^{+\centerdot}$ and PVS$^{+\centerdot}$ relatively unselectively. In contrast, in a true hole transfer (HT) catalytic process, the hole transfer agent which ionizes DCP or PVS is 3$^{+\centerdot}$. This hole transfer is quite endoergic and should be far more selective in generating DCP$^{+\centerdot}$ and thus in favoring cyclobutanation. Higher concentrations of **3** favor the latter process, while higher total concentrations of DCP + PVS favor the HTC process. Consequently, the HTC mechanism of low CB/DA periselectivity dominates in the early stage where the **3** is low and the [PVS] + [DCP] is high, but a true catalytic process of high CB periselectivity begins to compete and then dominate as **3** increases and the [PVS] + [DCP] decreases. It should be noted that such effects could only be observed if there exist discrete, role differentiated mechanisms of disparate periselectivity.

The observation of distinct role differentiated mechanisms is of especial significance in that it establishes that hole catalyzed cycloaddition is capable of occurring at rates faster than hole transfer within the cation radical/neutral ion dipole complex (Scheme 29). The maximum rate for hole transfer within such a complex, which is 10^{13} M^{-1}sec^{-1}, is expected to prevail in an intramolecular context or within an encounter complex when the hole transfer exoergicity ($\Delta G_o'$) is just equal to the reorganization energy for hole transfer ($4\Delta G_0^* = \lambda$), where ΔG_0^* is the intrinsic activation free energy or the activation free energy for hole transfer having no thermodynamic driving force, i.e. $\Delta G_o' = 0$; see Eq. (1). The value of the intrinsic activation energy for the present systems has not

$$\Delta G^* = \Delta G_0^*(1 + \Delta G_o'/4\Delta G_0^*)^2 \tag{1}$$

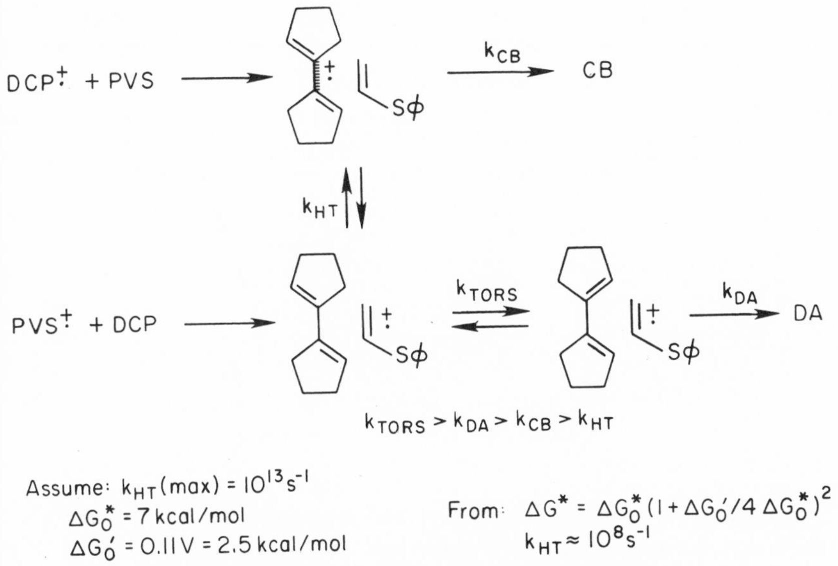
DCP⁺˙ + PVS
k_CB
CB
k_HT
PVS⁺˙ + DCP
k_TORS
k_DA
DA
k_TORS > k_DA > k_CB > k_HT
Assume: k_HT(max) = 10^13 s^-1
ΔG₀* = 7 kcal/mol
ΔG₀′ = 0.11 V = 2.5 kcal/mol
From: ΔG* = ΔG₀*(1 + ΔG₀′/4 ΔG₀*)²
k_HT ≈ 10^8 s^-1

Scheme 29. Hole transfer vs. cycloaddition.

yet been defined, but typical values for other organic systems appear to range from 6–12 kcal/mol, corresponding to hole transfer rates of from 10^8 to 10^3 M^{-1} sec^{-1}.[39,40] Thus, for hole transfer reactions of low exoergicity, such as the PVS$^{\dot{+}}$/DCP → PVS/DCP$^{\dot{+}}$ hole transfer, activation energies for hole transfer can remain rather high. The difference in the oxidation potentials of PVS and DCP (~.06 V) corresponds to an exoergicity ($\Delta G_o'$) of only 1.4 kcal/mol and thus to an activation energy $\Delta G^* = 5.3 - 11.3$ kcal/mol. The latter range corresponds to rate constants for hole transfer of from 5×10^8 to 10^4. Since hole catalyzed cycloadditions often have rate constants in excess of 10^8,[17] it is clear that the observation of dual role differentiated mechanisms is consistent with hole transfer theory.

Role Effects on Regiospecificity

The assignment of role sense, i.e. which of two reacting substrates is the hole carrying species, is a fundamental mechanistic aspect of hole catalyzed cross cycloadditions. The first assignment of mechanistic role sense was achieved in the context of the cyclobutanation of 3,3-dimethylindene (**7**) and phenyl vinyl ether (**8**).[41] The role sense **7**$^{\dot{+}}$/**8** was established through studies of the effect of varying substrate concentrations on the relative rates of cross addition and the two competing cyclodimerizations (**7**$^{\dot{+}}$/**7** and **8**$^{\dot{+}}$/**8**). The preference for this role sense was attributed, in the study mentioned, to the greater ionizability of **7** than

8. In a subsequent study of the hole catalyzed Diels-Alder cycloaddition of 1,3-cyclohexadiene (**2**) and 2,5-dimethyl-2,4-hexadiene (**4**), the role assignment $4^{\ddag}$ /**2** was made, based upon the far greater ionizability of **4** than **2**. However, in this and related cases it was proposed that orbital symmetry effects also have a major role in determining role selectivity.[35] Thus it was observed that the $4^{\ddag}$ /**2** role sense corresponds to an orbital symmetry allowed [4 + 1] cycloaddition, while the $2^{\ddag}$ /**4** role sense would correspond to a forbidden [3 + 2] cycloaddition.

Subsequent experimental and theoretical studies have not affirmed the concept of orbital symmetry control, and recent studies suggest that orbital symmetry effects are generally negligible in hole catalyzed pericyclic reactions. The premise that substrate ionizability alone controls role selection has also been questioned. A recent study of hole catalyzed cyclobutanation of a series of conjugated dienes (**D**) by N-methyl-N-vinylacetamide (**9**) implicates the role sense $D^{\ddag}$ /**9** for dienes which are both more and less ionizable than **9**.[42] The proposal was advanced that the highly electron rich substrate **9** is inherently reactive toward cation radicals (caticophilic) and efficiently intercepts both D^{+} and 9^{+}. This engenders cycloaddition via the role sense $D^{\ddag}$ /**9** and diverts $9^{\ddag}$ from its potential cross addition to **D**. The much greater caticophilicity of **9** than a series of typical dienes and also than other electron rich dienophiles has been confirmed experimentally. Consequently it appears that a more valid theory of role selection would include both substrate ionizability and caticophilicity and possibly other factors as well. The cross addition $7^{\ddag}$ /**8**, for example, is favored over the $8^{\ddag}$ /**7** role sense by both the greater ionizability of **7** than **8** and the greater caticophilicity of **8** than **7**. In the reaction of **2** and **4**, the $4^{\ddag}$ /**2** role sense is also favored by both factors. In particular, the caticophilicity of **4** is considered to be extremely low because of steric effects. In instances in which one substrate is both more ionizable and more caticophilic, dimerization normally dominates cross addition.

The significance of role sense is further accentuated by recognition of the potential dependence of product selectivity on role sense. Recent research has provided evidence for dual, role differentiated mechanisms in the reaction of 1,1'-dicyclopentenyl (**10**) with phenyl vinyl sulfide (**11**). The major mechanistic role sense ($10^{\ddag}$ /**11**) is found to be associated with virtually complete cyclobutane (**CB**) periselectivity, while the minor role sense ($11^{\ddag}$ /**10**) appears to have Diels-Alder periselectivity.

The recognition that role sense is not uniformly determined by substrate ionizability and that the less ionizable substrate can actually be the major or sole hole carrying species for the purposes of cross addition raises a new and basic mechanistic question: Is exoergic hole transfer faster than cycloaddition in the cation radical/neutral ion-dipole or encounter complex? If so, the role sense immediately prior to covalent bond formation (cycloaddition) is reversed from that immediately prior to collision. In this case, primary role sense, which can often be determined by kinetic studies such as those mentioned earlier, may not be directly relevant to product selectivity, which (it is assumed) should depend on the secondary role sense (the role sense in the cation radical/neutral pair just prior to covalent bond formation). The latter role sense would then have to be determined independently. Whereas the existence of discrete mechanisms of disparate periselectivity in the reaction of **10** and **11** clearly corresponds to the slow hole transfer case, it appears logical to assume that hole transfer may not always be slow relative to cycloaddition, especially where hole transfer exoergicities are large. The development of further means for identifying secondary role sense is therefore of interest. Evidence has recently been provided that regiospecificity may also be a useful criterion of secondary role sense.

In contrast to the hole catalyzed Diels-Alder reaction, hole catalyzed cyclobutanation appears to be acutely sensitive to steric effects at the vinylic carbon beta to the electron donating and/or conjugating substituent. In view of this steric sensitivity it was initially surprising to find that cross addition of *N*-methyl-*N*-vinylacetamide (**9**) to E-1,3-pentadiene (**12**) occurs at both the unsubstituted (84%) and the monosubstituted (16%) diene terminus (Scheme 30).[43] The formation of all four cycloadducts is strongly and equivalently quenched by 4,4′-dimethoxybiphenyl, thus confirming the involvement of a common cation radical intermediate in their formation. In view of the highly regiospecific nature of electrophilic additions to **12**,[44] these results appeared to negate a reaction of role sense **9**$^+$/**12**. The role sense **12**$^+$/**9**, however, would be nicely consonant with the tendency of cation radicals to react preferentially at the site of higher positive charge density (greater degree of alkyl substitution) observed in hole catalyzed Diels-Alder reaction. The much greater sensitivity of cyclobutanation to steric effects[45] might then explain the fact that the major site of reactivity in **12**$^+$ is not the site of higher charge density. Kinetic evidence had earlier lead to the assignment of the primary role sense **12**$^+$/**9**, and the foregoing analysis now suggests that the secondary role sense (immediately prior to covalent bond formation) is the same. Consequently exoergic hole transfer, which would yield **12**$^+$/**9**, must be slow in this system (relative to cycloaddition). The exoergicity of the hypothetical hole transfer reaction, estimated from irreversible oxidation

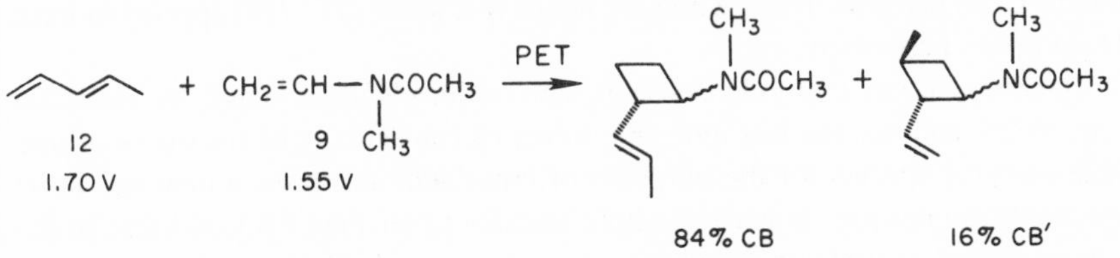

Scheme 30. Regiochemistry of the cycloaddition of N-Methyl-N-Vinylacetamide to E-1,3-Pentadiene.

potentials (**9**, 1.55 V; **12**, 1.70 V) is 0.15 eV or 3.5 kcal/mol. The electron transfer rate, calculated from the Marcus equation ($\Delta G_0^* = 7$ kcal/mol), is therefore *ca.* 5×10^8. As was seen in the previous section, it is by no means implausible that exoergic hole transfer in a cation radical/neutral encounter complex is slower than cycloaddition, especially when the neutral substrate is highly caticophilic and the hole energy of the cation radical is high.

The use of regiospecificity, or the lack thereof, as a criterion of secondary role sense, is novel and requires further scrutiny. Using the system **12**/vinylamine (**13**) as a model, MNDO reaction path calculations were carried out for both role senses $\mathbf{12}^{+}/\mathbf{13}$ and $\mathbf{13}^{+}/\mathbf{12}$ and for both regiochemical modes (H/H and H/T, Figures 2 and 3). These calculations bear out the intuitive assumption that only in the role sense $\mathbf{12}^{+}/\mathbf{13}$ is the anomalous regiochemistry competitive. The calculations further suggest that the driving force for reaction at the more highly substituted terminus of $\mathbf{12}^{+}$ is most highly developed in the pi complex which precedes cycloaddition, complexing being rather strongly favored at the more highly substituted diene terminus (Figure 2; RC = 4 − 5A). It is also evident that as covalent bond formation proceeds, and more particularly at the transition state for cycloaddition, the preference for the anomalous mode of reaction is diminished, presumably by steric effects attendant to covalent bond formation. In contrast, $\mathbf{13}^{+}$ is predicted to have the normal strong preference of electrophiles for reaction at the unsubstituted terminus of **12** (Figure 3).

The proposed relationship between secondary role sense and regiospecificity is further supported by studies of the hole catalyzed cyclobutanation of 4-isopropenyl-1-vinylcyclohexene (**14**) and ethyl vinyl ether (**15**). In this system the

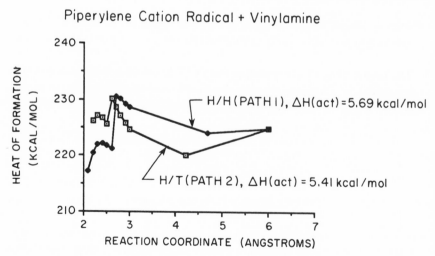

Piperylene Cation Radical + Vinylamine

Figure 2. MNDO reaction path calculations for the piperylene cation radical/ vinylamine reaction in head to head (H/H) and head to tail (H/T) regiochemistries.

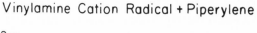

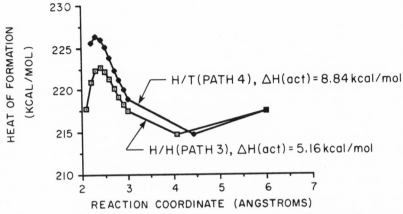

Figure 3. MNDO reaction path calculations for the vinylamine cation radical/piperylene reaction in head to head (H/H) and head to tail (H/T) regiochemistries.

role sense $14^{\overset{+}{\cdot}}$/**15** is favored by both relative caticophilicity (**15** is superior to **14**) and relative ionizability (**14**$^{\overset{+}{\cdot}}$ favored over **15**$^{\overset{+}{\cdot}}$). Further, hole transfer in the cation radical/neutral pair would be endoergic and thus, of necessity, very slow. Consequently, the secondary role sense $14^{\overset{+}{\cdot}}$/**15** is secure. The regiochemical results (Scheme 31) in this system are indeed virtually identical to those in the previous system (**12**$^{\overset{+}{\cdot}}$/**9**). Thus, 15% of the cross addition occurs at the monosubstituted diene terminus, while 85% occurs at the unsubstituted terminus.

A Marcus Semi-Classical Treatment of Hole Transfer
in the Aminium Salt Catalyzed Diels-Alder

The kinetic study of the cyclodimerization of **2** mentioned earlier derived the value $\Delta G^*_{app} = 15.6$ kcal/mol for the overall activation free energy of this reaction. Using the value $\Delta G^*_p = 2.2$ kcal/mol (the value derived from the

Scheme 31.

photochemical quenching study[17]) for the activation free energy of the pericyclic step ($2^{\ddagger}/2$), the net activation energy for the hole transfer step ($3^{\ddagger}/2 \rightarrow 2^{\ddagger}/3$) ΔG^{*}_{HT} = 13.4 kcal/mol is obtained. When Marcus theory is applied to this hole transfer with ΔG^{*}_{0} = 7 kcal/mol and $\Delta G'_{0}$ = 12.7 kcal/mol (from the oxidation potentials 1.05 and 1.60V), the activation free energy for the hole transfer step is predicted to be ΔG^{*}_{HT} = 14.8 kcal/mol, in reasonable agreement with the value derived experimentally. The approximate validity of this approach (with ΔG^{*}_{0} = 7) is further supported by the treatment of the kinetic results for the dimerization of *trans*-anethole, for which the exoergicity correction is rather small ($\Delta G'_{0}$ = 1.4 kcal/mol). The Marcus theory (ΔG^{*}_{0} = 7) predicts an activation free energy ΔG^{*}_{HT} = 7.7 kcal/mol for the analogous hole transfer, and comparison with experiment is again possible if one deducts a value of ΔG^{*}_{p} = 2.2 kcal/mol from the experimental value ΔG^{*}_{app} = 10.6 kcal/mol. The resulting value of ΔG^{*}_{HT} = 8.4 kcal/mol again agrees fairly well with that predicted by Marcus theory (7.7 kcal/mol). These results provide encouragement that rates of such endothermic hole transfer reactions can be predicted from the Marcus equation with $\Delta G^{*}_{0} \approx 7$ kcal/mol.

Hole transfer is also involved in the chain transfer step of the propagation cycle of these reactions, although these transfers are now exoergic. Assuming the oxidation potential of the simple olefinic moiety of the Diels-Alder adduct of 2 is $E_{ox} \geq 2.0$ V, the hole transfer from the adduct cation radical to 2 is predicted to occur at the maximum diffusion controlled rate.

2.3. Hole Catalyzed Cyclobutanation

The photosensitized electron transfer (PET) cyclodimerization of N-vinylcarbazole (NVC), a reaction discovered by Ellinger,[15] played a pivotal role in the historical development of cation radical cycloadditions. The subsequent careful mechanistic characterization of this reaction by the Ledwith group led to the discovery of hole catalysis. This latter group observed sensitization by a wide variety of sensitizers, and in every case quantum yields exceeded unity and ranged up to as high as 66, thus clearly documenting the chain nature of the reaction. A direct connection between cyclodimerization and the quenching of sensitizer (S) fluorescence by NVC was inferred from the fact that NVC does quench the fluorescence of these sensitizers very efficiently and that substances like DABCO, ferrocene, and iodine ion, which quench the sensitizer fluorescence even more efficiently than does NVC, selectively retard cyclodimerization. That electron transfer, giving $NVC^{+}S^{-}$ ion radical pairs, is a concomitant of fluorescence quenching was indicated by the observation that cyclodimerization rates are fastest in relatively polar solvents such as acetonitrile and acetone and quite low in nonpolar solvents. The feasibility and likelihood of complete electron transfer was further supported by applying the Weller equation, which reveals that the singlet excitation energy of each of the sensitizers which is effective in cyclodimerizing NVC exceeds the difference between the oxidation potential of NVC (1.02 V vs. SCE) and the reduction potential of the ground state sensitizer ($+0.02$ V for chloranil, -0.29 V for fluorenone). Moreover, involvement of triplet NVC in the cycloaddition is readily excluded. Since NVC has a much higher triplet energy (70 kcal/mol) than any of the sensitizers used, the former should not be accessible from sensitizer triplets *via* energy transfer. Triplet NVC formation by back electron transfer within the ion radical pair is also strongly endothermic for most of the sensitizers and in any case should preferentially form the lower energy sensitizer triplets. Indeed, a number of the sensitizers have triplet energies too low even to effect electron transfer. In these cases the involvement of the singlet excited state of the sensitizer is clearly demonstrated. An additional aspect of these mechanistic studies is of special interest, viz. the powerful acceleration of the cycloaddition rate by atmospheric oxygen. This effect is observed for all sensitizers, and in some cases is so strong that oxygen appears to be an absolute requirement. Presumably, oxygen acts to interdict electron transfer from sensitizer anion radicals to the chain carrying (e.g., $NVC^{\ddagger}$) cation radicals, instead oxidizing the sensitizer anion radicals and forming dioxygen anion radicals. In this manner, chain termination by back electron transfer to the relatively long-lived $NVC^{\ddagger}$ is averted or minimized.

Synthetically, the cyclodimerization reaction proved not to be extensible to vinylamines generally, and it was not until 1972 that the next significant extension of the scope of the cation radical chain cyclobutanation reaction was reported. In that year, the cyclodimerization of phenyl vinyl ether (PVE) under PET conditions was reported, but no explicit mention of the possibility of a cation radical chain mechanism was made.[6] In 1974, detailed studies of the reaction were reported which established a mechanism identical to that found previously for the dimerization of *N*-vinylcarbazole.[7] The subsequent observation of efficient cross addition between phenyl vinyl ether and 3,3-dimethylindene alluded to the possibility of a broader scope for PET cyclobutanation[41], and the recent observations of cross additions of vinyl ethers, vinyl sulfides, and *N*-vinylamides to conjugated dienes have brought into sharp focus the general synthetic utility of hole catalysis for effecting cycloadditions to electron rich alkenes (Scheme 32).[46,47] Further, the development of new heteroatom anion assisted vinylcyclobutane rearrangements makes such cyclobutanation reactions an extremely attractive indirect route for net Diels-Alder addition to electron rich dienophiles (Scheme 33).

Cycloadditions to conjugated dienes also permit valuable insights into the mechanistic details of hole catalyzed cyclobutanation. Since the original proposal of stepwise cyclobutanation *via* a 1,4-butanediyl cation radical intermediate in the cyclodimerization of *N*-vinylcarbazole, hole catalyzed cyclobutanation had been consistently considered to be a stepwise and therefore (rigorously speaking) a mechanistically non-pericyclic process. The circumstance that cyclobutanation predominates over Diels-Alder addition in hole catalyzed cycloaddi-

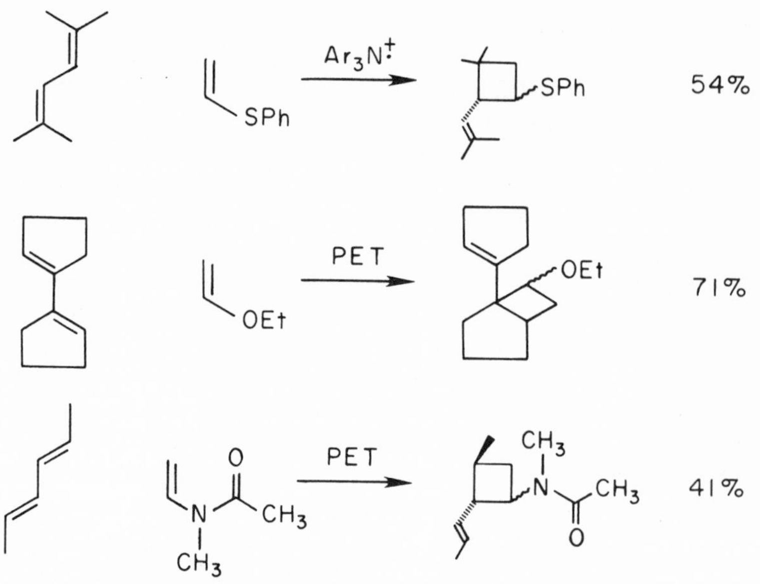

Scheme 32. Cyclobutanation of electron rich alkenes.

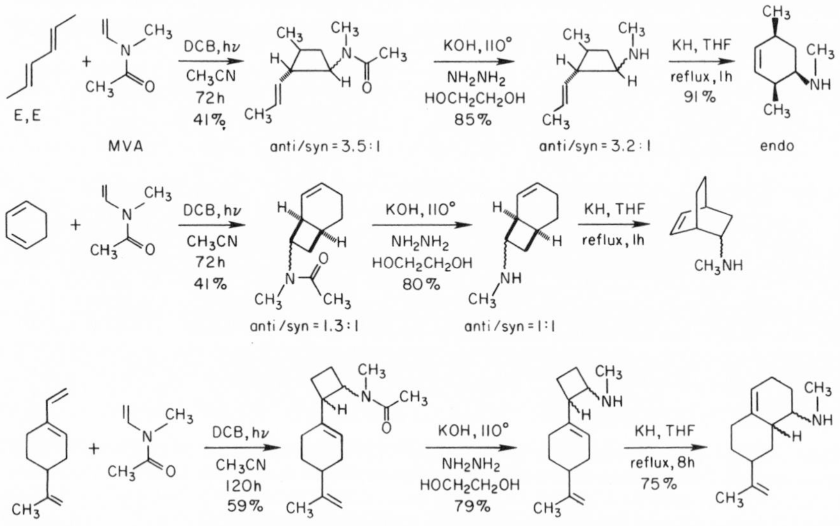

Scheme 33. Indirect Diels-Alder additions.

tions to acyclic, conjugated dienes, is, of course, consistent with the stepwise mechanistic scenario since even stepwise addition to an *s-trans* diene cannot afford Diels-Alder (*cis*-cyclohexene) adducts. The fact that many of these cyclo-additions closely approach 100% cyclobutane periselectivity even where the diene must have a substantial *s-cis* conformational population (Scheme 34), however, casts doubt upon this mechanistic scenario. More decisively, the cycloaddition of *N*-methyl-*N*-vinylacetamide to 1,3-cyclohexadiene is also 100% cyclobutane periselective (Scheme 35).[41] In this system the hypothetical acyclic cation/radical has the Z-allylic geometry which permits cyclization to either cyclobutane or Diels-Alder adducts, and the latter could perhaps even be favored by product development control. Consequently a concerted cyclobutanation mechanism is implicated for these cyclobutanations. The preference for con-certed cyclobutanation over concerted Diels-Alder addition in the case of elec-tron rich alkenes and particularly for *N*-vinylamides has been associated with a greater degree of synchronization in the Diels-Alder cycloadditions, leading to more extensive charge delocalization in this latter reaction. The lesser degree of synchrony of the cyclobutanation transition state engenders greater positive charge localization, specifically at the site adjacent to the stabilizing heteroatom substituent. Cyclobutanation is thus favored by heteroatom donor substituents.

A concerted hole catalyzed cyclobutanation mechanism had already been inferred in the aminium salt catalyzed cyclodimerization of *cis*- and *trans*-anethole on the basis of the observation of stereospecificity (Scheme 36).[48] Ab initio SCF-MO reaction path calculations for the prototype reaction (ethene cation radical/ethene) provide still further support for the suggestion of concert in hole catalyzed cyclobutanation.[49] Finally a concerted retrocyclobutanation has quite recently been observed (Scheme 37).[50]

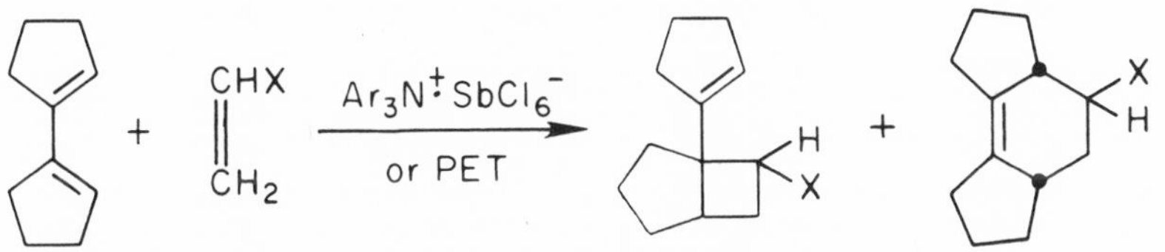

X =		
NAcMe	100	0
OEt	98	2
OCH$_2$CH$_2$Cl	97	3
OPh	82	18
SPh	69	31

Scheme 34. CB periselectivity in additions to electron rich alkenes.

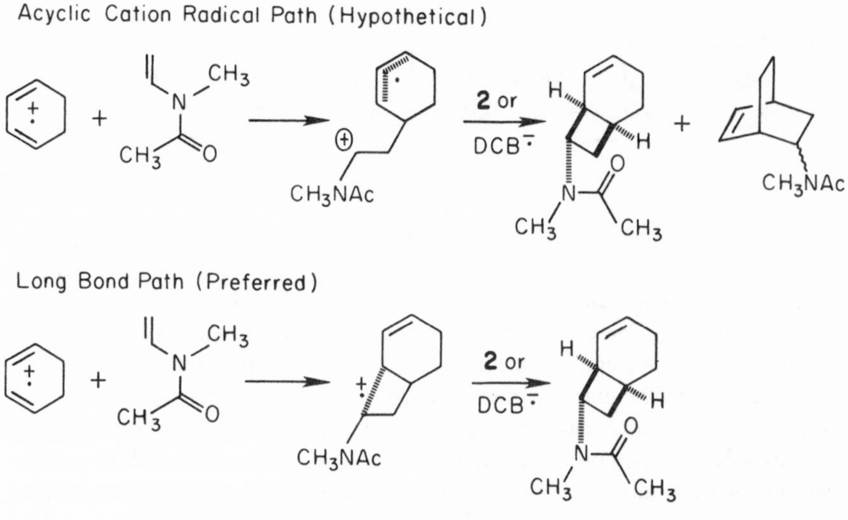

Acyclic Cation Radical Path (Hypothetical)

Long Bond Path (Preferred)

Scheme 35.   Concerted vs. stepwise cyclobutanation.

Concerted cyclobutanation could proceed directly to an intact cyclobutane cation radical or, as the prototype reaction path calculation originally suggested, *via* a long bond cyclobutane cation radical which has one completely formed bond and a second, weaker, one electron bond (quasi concerted addition). In the latter scenario, completion of the second bond accompanies hole transfer, giving a vibrationally excited cyclobutane. Indeed, a continuum of concerted mechanisms can be envisioned, depending largely upon the preferred ground state

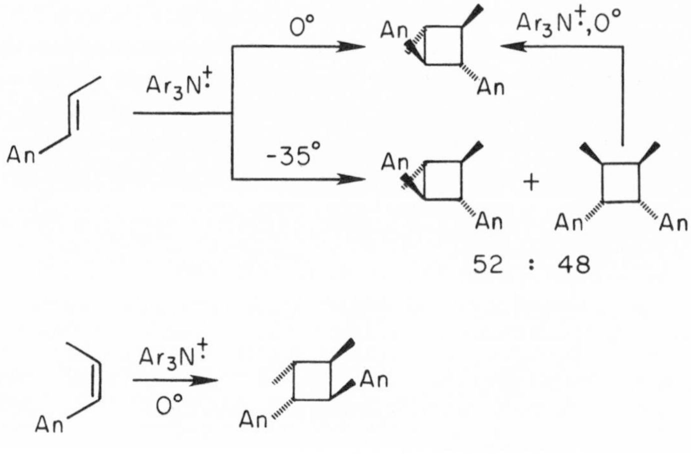

Scheme 36.   Concerted cyclobutanation.

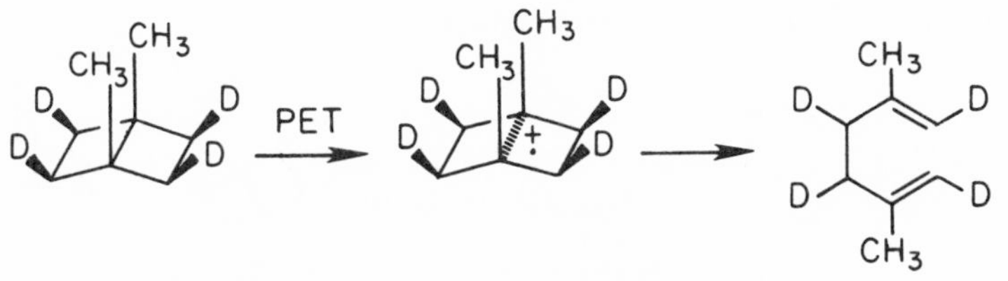

Scheme 37. A concerted retrocyclobutanation.

structure of the particular cyclobutane adduct cation radical involved. At one extreme, the long bond structure acquires predominant ion-dipole attractive character as the covalent, one electron bond becomes longer and weaker. At the other extreme, as the long bond is tightened, the hole site resides predominantly on an ionizable substituent attached to the ring (alkenyl, aryl, heteroatom), but with significant hyperconjugative loosening of an adjacent ring bond. This latter structural type is suggested by the MP2/6-31G*//3-21G optimized structure of the vinylcyclobutane cation radical, but the vinylcyclobutanol cation radical appears to represent a valid long bond structure (Scheme 38).[51]

When the attenuation of the long bond is taken to completion, the open, acyclic cation radical results and the cyclobutanation becomes stepwise. If no structural minimum exists at a long bond or intact cyclobutane cation radical structure, hole transfer must precede cyclization, which then involves a diradical. This mechanistic scenario has been established in the cyclodimerization of 1,1-diphenylethene under PET conditions.[52] A recent, excellent reaction path calculation for the addition of ethene/ketene cation radical reveals a stepwise reaction path with no minimum at all for an intact cyclobutanone cation radical.[53] In interesting contrast, the PET promoted retrocyclobutanation of the 3,3-dimethylindene dimer has been found, in CIDNP studies, to involve the sequential formation of two discrete cation radical intermediates (Scheme 39).[54] The first of these corresponds to an intact cyclobutane dimer structure with the hole site primarily located on one of the aryl rings, while the second corresponds to a *singly-linked*, acyclic structure. Thus, cycloaddition is inferred to occur, in this system, in a stepwise fashion even though an intact cyclobutane structure exists. *Mechanistic diversity* can therefore be anticipated in hole catalyzed cycloaddi-

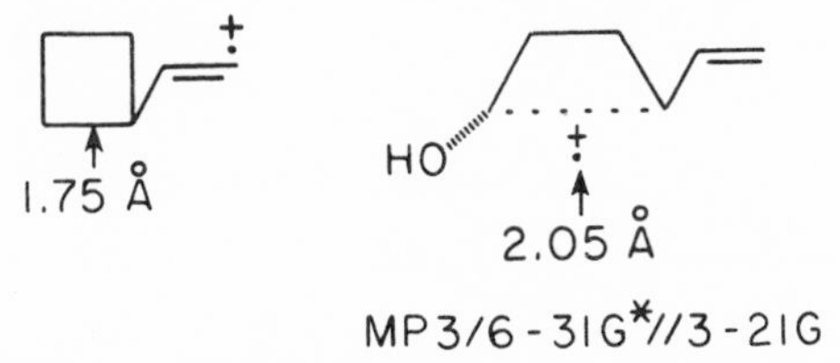

MP3/6-31G*//3-21G

Scheme 38. Long bonds in cyclobutane cation radicals.

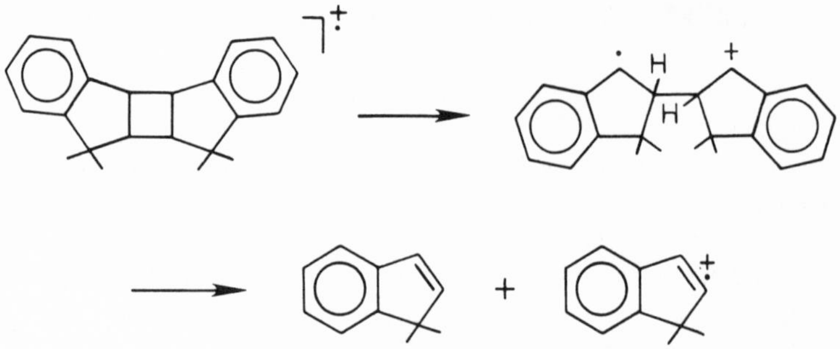

Scheme 39. Mechanistic diversity.

tions.[55] It should be noted that acetonitrile, the solvent preferred in PET promoted cyclobutanations, is effectively far more polar than dichloromethane, the solvent preferred in aminium salt promoted reactions. Stepwise cycloadditions are therefore more likely in the PET cyclobutanations.

2.4. Hole Catalyzed Dioxygenation

The 1,4- and 1,2-addition of triplet oxygen to diene and tetrasubstituted alkene cation radicals, respectively, have been known for some time and studied extensively and elegantly (Scheme 40).[56,57] Stereochemical studies on the oxygenation of *syn* and *anti*-bis(8-bicyclo[3.2.1]octylidene) indicate the intervention, to at least some extent, of an acyclic β-peroxycarbocation since, although the *syn* olefin gives only the *syn* dioxetane, the *anti* olefin gives an 80:20 mixture of the *anti* and *syn* dioxetanes.

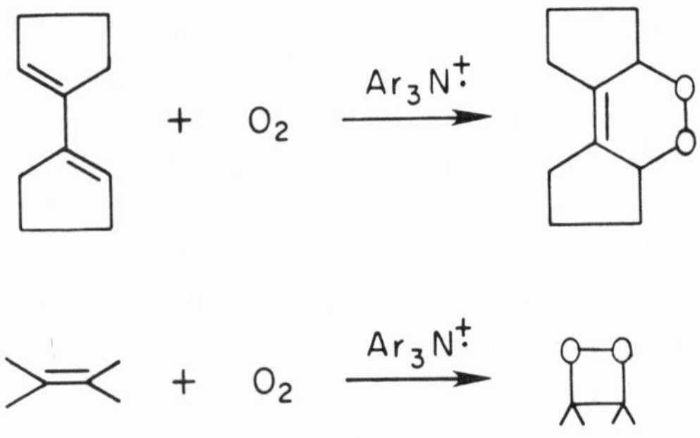

Scheme 40. Dioxidation of diene and alkene cation radicals.

3. HOLE CATALYZED SIGMATROPIC REACTIONS

3.1. Introduction

Although not prominently featured in the pioneering developments in hole catalyzed pericyclic reactions, a major current of interest in hole catalyzed sigmatropic reactions has developed during the last decade. The variety of such reactions and the extent of interest in them now easily rivals that of the cycloaddition category. Especially prevalent in this category are studies of [1,3] and [3,3] sigmatropic shifts.

3.2. [1,3] Sigmatropic Shifts

It appears that the first report of a hole promoted sigmatropic shift of any kind involved the rearrangement of 1,2-divinylcyclobutane cation radicals to 4-vinylcyclohexene cation radicals in the mass spectrometer.[58] Subsequently, many examples of hole promoted [1,3] shifts have been observed under PET conditions, including vinylcyclobutane and vinylcyclopropane as well as arylcyclobutane and arylcyclopropane rearrangements.[59,60] Light induced rearrangements of even relatively unstrained cation radicals have also been observed extensively in frozen matrices, but it is not yet completely clear whether these rearrangements involve electronically excited states of the cation radicals or their vibrationally excited ground states.[61]

Recent research has emphasized hole catalyzed (both aminium salt and PET) vinylcyclopropane and vinylcyclobutane rearrangements in solution and their mechanism, stereochemistry, and synthetic utility. Synthetically convenient and efficient vinylcyclopropane rearrangements have been observed under aminium salt hole catalytic conditions (Scheme 41).[62]

As in the case of cycloaddition, the circumstance that the original hole induced sigmatropic reaction involved a vinylcyclobutane rearrangement proves prophetic in that the hole catalyzed vinylcyclobutane rearrangement turns out to be a reaction of especially broad scope. In combination with hole catalyzed cyclobutanation, this reaction also provides an effective synthetic route for net Diels-Alder addition to electron rich alkenes. It was noted earlier that the cyclobutane dimers of 1,3-cyclohexadiene, obtained from the triplet photosensitized dimerization, are stable under typical aminium salt conditions. When, however, the more powerful hole catalyst *tris*(2,4-dibromophenyl)aminium hexachloroantimonate is employed, these cyclobutane dimers rearrange stereospecifically (s/r) to the corresponding Diels-Alder adducts (Scheme 42).[63] A mechanism involving a hole catalyzed retrocyclobutanation reaction followed by a hole catalyzed Diels-Alder addition is precluded by the observed stereospecificity. The more readily ionizable triplet cyclodimers of 2,4-dimethyl-1,3-pentadiene undergo the

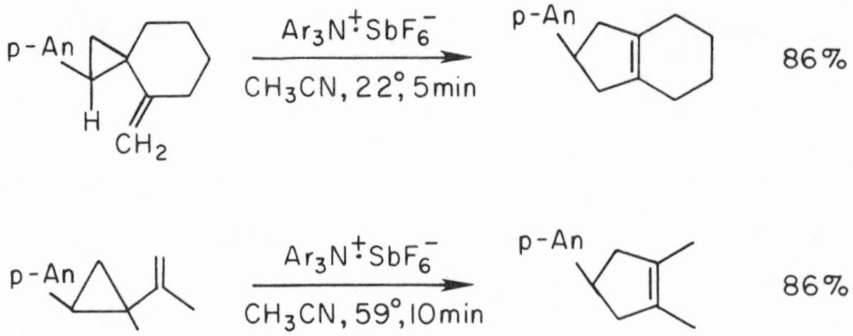

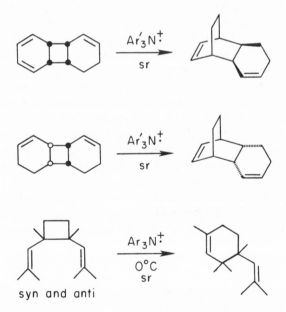

Scheme 41. The hole catalyzed vinylcyclopropane rearrangement.

analogous [1,3] shift even in the presence of *tris*(4-bromophenyl)aminium hexa-chloroantimonate. Again retrocyclobutanation/Diels-Alder addition is precluded by the circumstance the product is constitutionally isomeric with the dimer of 2,4-dimethyl-1,3-pentadiene formed under aminium salt conditions. The presence of functionality more ionizable than a simple olefinic function at the 2-position of the vinylcyclobutane renders rearrangement even more facile and efficient. The rearrangements of the *trans*-anethole/butadiene cyclobutane adducts (*syn* and *anti*; Scheme 43) occur in 90% yield using either the aminium salt

Scheme 42. Vinylcyclobutane (VCB) rearrangements.

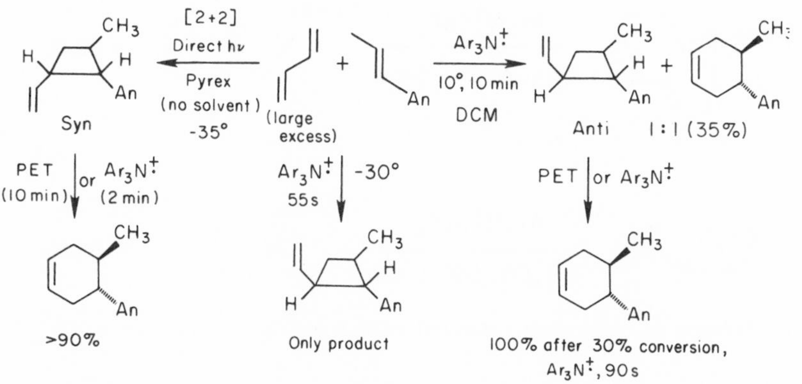

[2+2]
Direct hν
Pyrex
(no solvent)
−35°

CH₃
H
H
An
Syn

+

(large excess)

$Ar_3N^{\dot{+}}$
10°, 10 min
DCM

CH₃
H
H
An
Anti   1 : 1 (35%)

+

CH₃
An

PET
(10 min) or $Ar_3N^{\dot{+}}$ (2 min)

$Ar_3N^{\dot{+}}$ −30°
55s

PET or $Ar_3N^{\dot{+}}$

CH₃
An
>90%

CH₃
H
H   An
Only product

CH₃
An
100% after 30% conversion, $Ar_3N^{\dot{+}}$, 90 s

Scheme 43. Acceleration of the VCB rearrangement by ionizable groups.

or PET conditions. Under the latter conditions, which usually require a period of at least 2–20 hours of irradiation, the reaction is complete in 10 minutes. An efficient chain is therefore indicated. Since added 2,6-bis(*tert*-butyl) pyridine has no effect on the reaction, Bronsted acid catalysis is decisively ruled out.

The alternative mechanistic possibility of retrocyclobutanation/Diels-Alder addition was again eliminated, this time by conducting the reaction in the presence of a large excess (800 mol%) of 2,3-dimethylbutadiene, which is three times as reactive towards the *trans*-anethole cation radical as is 1,3-butadiene. No *trans*-anethole/2,3-dimethyl-1,3-butadiene adduct was formed, even though the latter reaction is known to be extremely facile and to involve reaction of the *trans*-anethole cation radical with neutral 2,3-dimethyl-1,3-butadiene. In contrast to the non-stereospecificity observed in the vinylcyclopropane rearrangement, the rearrangement of the *syn* and *anti trans*-anethole/E,E-2,4-hexadiene cyclobutane adducts (Scheme 44) is stereospecific (s/r). However, the corresponding E,Z-2,4-hexadiene adducts rearrange non-stereospecifically. It appears possible that the greater angle strain involved in a concerted vinylcyclopropane rearrangement than in a concerted vinylcyclobutane rearrangement might explain the contrasting results in the two systems.

In either type of system, it seems clear, concerted and stepwise paths are of quite similar energy, and the preferred path can readily be influenced by minor steric effects. Where concert is involved, an s/r mechanism is typically preferred.

3.3.   Other [1,n] Shifts

One of the pioneering examples of hole promoted sigmatropic shifts in solution involves a [1,16] hydrogen shift in an A/D-seco-corrin cation radical produced by electrochemical oxidation. Discussion of this interesting reaction is, however, deferred to a subsequent section on bioorganic systems.

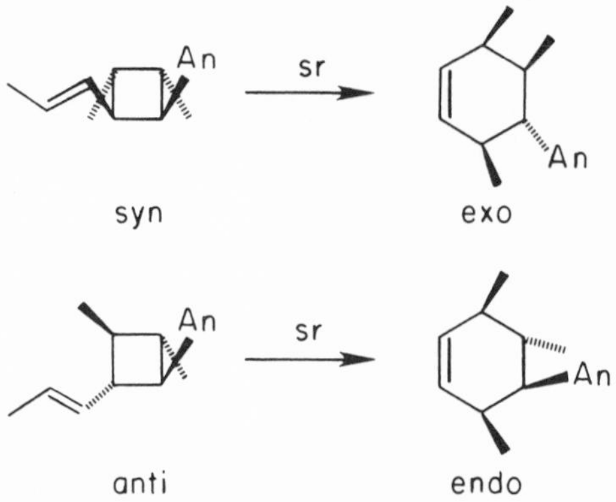

syn   exo

anti   endo

Scheme 44. A stereospecific VCB rearrangement.

3.4. [3,3] Sigmatropic Shifts

The extension of efficient hole catalysis to a variety of pericyclic reactions in solution was anticipated theoretically, and the Cope rearrangement was among the pericyclic types specifically envisioned.[64] An MNDO/3 reaction path calculation for the Cope rearrangement of the prototype Cope system (the 1,5-hexadiene cation radical) predicted a miniscule activation energy (1.4 kcal/mol) for cyclization to either a boat or chair 1,4-cyclohexanediyl cation radical, with the boat route being slightly favored (*ca.* 0.5 kcal/mol). The likelihood that the boat structure would have a 1,4 long bond was anticipated, and it was evident that in the prototype system the second stage of the Cope reaction (cleavage of the C_3-C_4 bond) would be prohibited by its large endoergicity. This latter prediction has subsequently been verified, and the 1,5- hexadiene cation radical has been observed to cyclize to the 1,4-cyclohexanediyl cation radical when generated in a matrix.[65] The latter cation radical exists in the chair form, and its rearrangement to the cyclohexene cation radical (possibly a [1,3] hydrogen shift) ensues.

To provide the exemplification of the hole catalyzed Cope reaction, a system was constructed for which the Cope second stage would be exoergic, while providing a reactant site suitably ionizable for hole formation in solution (Scheme 45).[66] The reaction stereochemistry could unfortunately not be tracked because of light induced *cis, trans* isomerization of the product. A subsequent case of a hole promoted Cope rearrangement under PET conditions has claimed to establish a preferred chair cyclization/cleavage stereochemistry.[67] The latter example appears not to have an exoergic second stage, however, and it appears much more likely that the intermediate 1,4-cation radical accepts an electron from its sensitizer anion radical gegenion to generate a 1,4-diradical, the subsequent cleavage of which (*via* the chair form) is indeed highly exoergic (Scheme

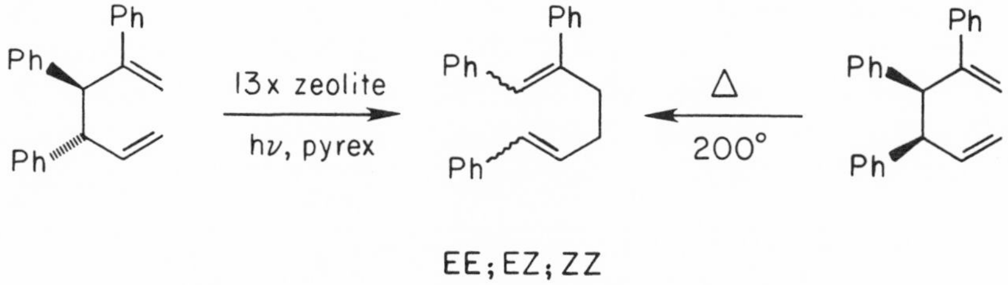

EE; EZ; ZZ

Scheme 45. A proposed hole catalyzed Cope rearrangement.

46). A Cope rearrangement occurring exclusively *via* the cation radical manifold has now finally been established (Scheme 47).[68]

4. HOLE CATALYZED CHELEOTROPIC REACTIONS

4.1. Hole Catalyzed Cyclopropanation

Previously discussed hole catalyzed reactions have provided synthetically useful methods for generating 4, 5, and 6 membered rings. Hole catalyzed cheleotropic addition of carbenoid equivalents derived from diazo compounds has recently been found to provide a convenient route to cyclopropanes (Scheme 48).[69] A varied selection of conjugated dienes, styrenes, and tetrasubstituted alkenes have been efficiently cyclopropanated under aminium salt conditions using ethyl diazoacetate as the "carbene" source.

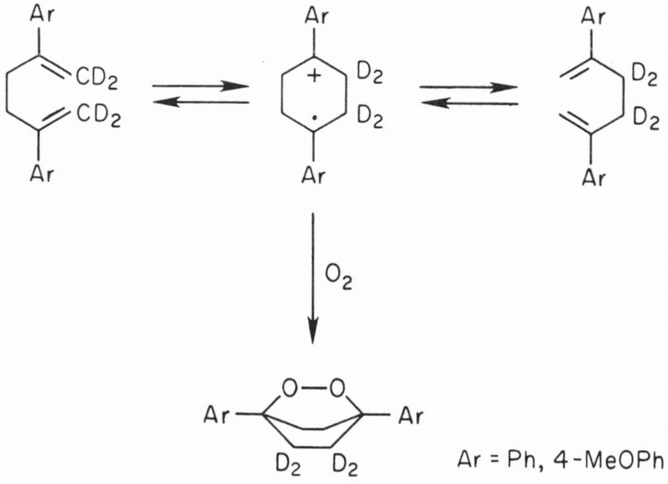

Ar = Ph, 4-MeOPh

Scheme 46. A hole catalyzed hemi-Cope with probable diradical opening.

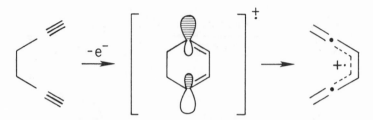

Scheme 47.   Hole catalyzed Cope in matrix isolation.

The unique selectivity of these reactions is especially well exemplified by the cyclopropanation of dihydroindane (Scheme 49).[70] The rhodium catalyzed cyclopropanation of this molecule is not very selective (5:2) and prefers the less substituted double bond.[71] Hole catalyzed cyclopropanation, in sharp contrast, occurs exclusively at the more readily ionizable site (the tetrasubstituted double bond). The hole catalyzed cyclopropanation reaction is also attractive because it works well at 1:1 substrate:diazo compound ratios, does not waste diazo compound *via* the familiar coupling reactions, and can be carried out at $-78\,°C$ where desirable for selectivity or stability.

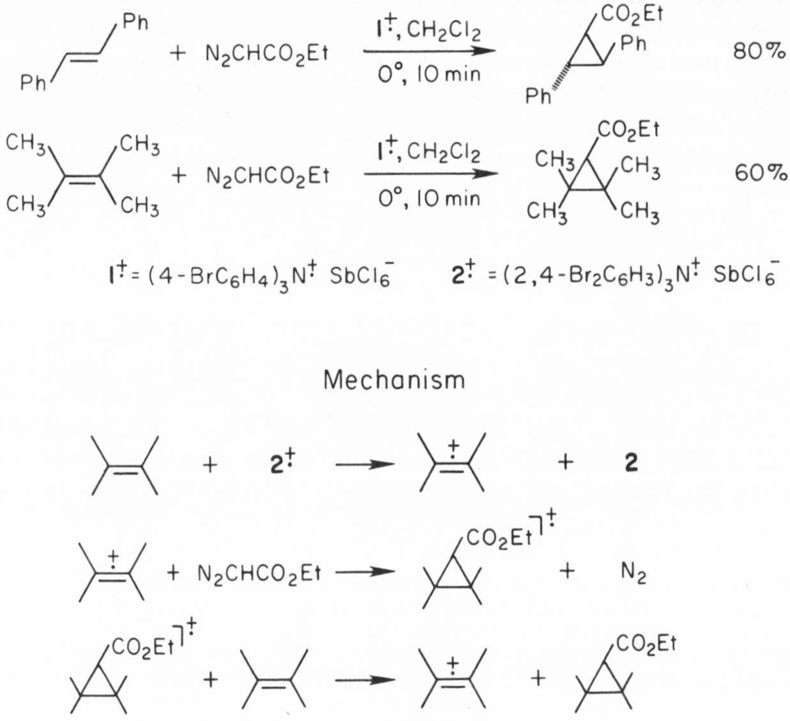

$$\text{(Ph, Ph diene)} + N_2CHCO_2Et \xrightarrow[\text{0°, 10 min}]{I^{+\cdot},\,CH_2Cl_2} \text{(product)} \quad 80\%$$

$$\text{(tetramethylethylene)} + N_2CHCO_2Et \xrightarrow[\text{0°, 10 min}]{I^{+\cdot},\,CH_2Cl_2} \text{(product)} \quad 60\%$$

$$I^{+\cdot} = (4\text{-}BrC_6H_4)_3N^{+\cdot}\ SbCl_6^- \qquad 2^{+\cdot} = (2,4\text{-}Br_2C_6H_3)_3N^{+\cdot}\ SbCl_6^-$$

Mechanism

$$\text{(alkene)} + 2^{+\cdot} \longrightarrow \text{(alkene)}^{+\cdot} + 2$$

$$\text{(alkene)}^{+\cdot} + N_2CHCO_2Et \longrightarrow \text{(cyclopropane-}CO_2Et)^{+\cdot} + N_2$$

$$\text{(cyclopropane-}CO_2Et)^{+\cdot} + \text{(alkene)} \longrightarrow \text{(alkene)}^{+\cdot} + \text{(cyclopropane-}CO_2Et)$$

Scheme 48.   Hole catalyzed cyclopropanation.

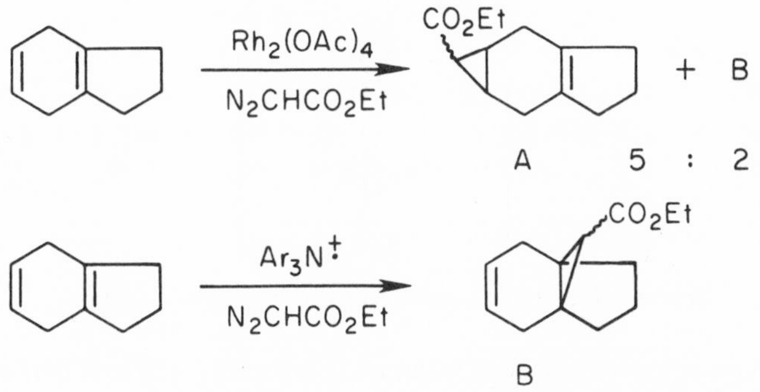

Scheme 49.   Site selectivity in hole catalyzed and transition metal catalyzed cyclopropanation.

4.2. Hole Catalyzed Epoxidation

The facility and site selectivity of hole catalyzed cyclopropanation lent encouragement to the development of an analogous cheleotropic reaction, epoxidation, and suggested that, if feasible, this reaction would be vastly more site selective than standard epoxidizing agents such as MCPBA. Equally important, a cation radical mechanism has been advocated for the biomimetic epoxidation of alkenes catalyzed by metalloporphyrins (Scheme 50).[72] The availability of an authentic cation radical epoxidation procedure would have the potential to provide valuable insights into this mechanistic possibility. The oxidant chosen for the initial studies, iodosylbenzene, is one which is frequently employed in biomimetic

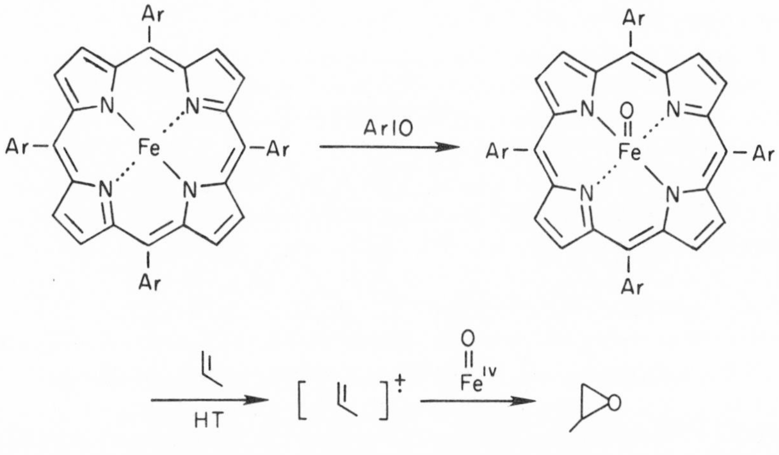

Scheme 50.   A possible hole catalyzed mechanism for biomimetric epoxidation.

epoxidations. *Trans*-Stilbene, a moderately ionizable alkene which is smoothly cyclopropanated under hole catalytic conditions, and which is not extensively dimerized under these conditions, was chosen as the substrate for the initial experiments. In the presence of $3^{\ddot{+}}$ (20 mol percent) in dichloromethane at 0 °C, a very low conversion (5%) to *trans*-stilbene oxide was achieved. The major reaction product, however, is *meso*-stilbene dichloride.

Based on the assumption that the source of electrophilic chlorine is the hexachloroantimonate anion of the catalyst, the corresponding perchlorate salt $(3^{\ddot{+}} ClO_4^-)$ was examined as the catalyst. Under these conditions, stilbene dichloride is not observed as a product and the yield of *trans*-stilbene oxide rises to 20%. Control experiments then revealed that the oxidizing agent induces rapid decomposition of the catalyst, irrespective of the counter ion, even in the absence of the pi substrate.

As a consequence of the relative incompatibility of iodosylbenzene (and various substituted iodosylbenzenes) with the hole catalyst, a variety of other potential monoxidants was surveyed for compatibility with the aminium salts. Amine oxides and sulfoxides, *inter alia*, were found to decompose the catalyst extremely effectively. The only oxidant tested which had even moderate compatibility with the catalyst was selenium dioxide. Further studies using this oxidant have, however, proved highly encouraging.

In the presence of 20 mol percent of $3^{\ddot{+}}$ at 0° in dichloromethane, *trans*-stilbene is converted by an excess (2:1) of selenium oxide to the epoxide in 80% yield (Scheme 51).[73] In control runs omitting the aminium salt, selenium dioxide did not react with this substrate even at room temperature for several hours. To confirm the hole catalytic nature of the reactions, the same oxidant and substrate were allowed to react under standard photosensitized electron transfer conditions for producing substrate cation radicals (1,4-dicyanobenzene, acetonitrile, hv, pyrex). As under aminium salt conditions, the only detectable oxidized product was *trans*-stilbene oxide.

The aminium salt reaction is especially convenient and efficient, however, and is strongly preferred for synthetic applications. This reaction is notably efficient, giving at most traces of benzil as a secondary oxidation product of the epoxide, a small amount of *trans*-stilbene dimer (< 5%), and unreacted stilbene. The stilbene dimer, however, is a clear signal of the production of stilbene cation radicals. The observation that excess 2,6-bis(*tert*-butyl) pyridine does not suppress the epoxidation further rules out a Bronsted acid catalyzed mechanism. the oxidation of *cis*-stilbene proceeds with equal efficiency, but again yields *trans*-stilbene oxide (however, *vide infra*), and the recovered unreacted stilbene is found to be preponderantly *trans*. Neither diphenylacetaldehyde nor benzyl phenyl ketone, possible carbocation rearrangement products, are formed in the epoxidation of the stilbenes. The oxidation of 1,1-diphenylethene also proceeds smoothly (70%) to the epoxide. No rearrangement products are observed, but a

10% yield of the cyclobutadimer of 1,1-diphenylethene is also observed. Diphenylacetylene furnishes benzil in 100% yield.

Trans-β-methylstyrene reacts slowly with selenium dioxide in dicloromethane at room temperature to afford exclusively allylic hydroxylation. However, at 0 °C this reaction is suppressed, and in the presence of **1**† and SeO$_2$, *trans*-β-methylstyrene is oxidized cleanly and efficiently to the epoxide (Scheme 51). Again, no rearrangement products or products of allylic hydroxylation are observed. Similarly, α-methylstyrene and indene yield exclusively the epoxide. The epoxidation of relatively difficulty ionizable, unconjugated, alkenes such a 1-octene and norbornene predictably fails, as does hole catalyzed cyclopropanation and all other hole catalyzed reactions of such alkenes. Readily ionizable substrates which are susceptible to hole catalyzed cycloaddition (e.g., the Diels-Alder) are not efficiently epoxidized as the monomers by SeO$_2$, but the epoxide of the dimer can often be obtained. Epoxidation of the monomers is frustrated by the relative insolubility of selenium dioxide.

Though more expensive and somewhat less convenient than selenium dioxide, soluble organoselenium oxidants appear to offer several advantages, including shorter reaction times, stereospecific epoxidation, and epoxidation of substrates

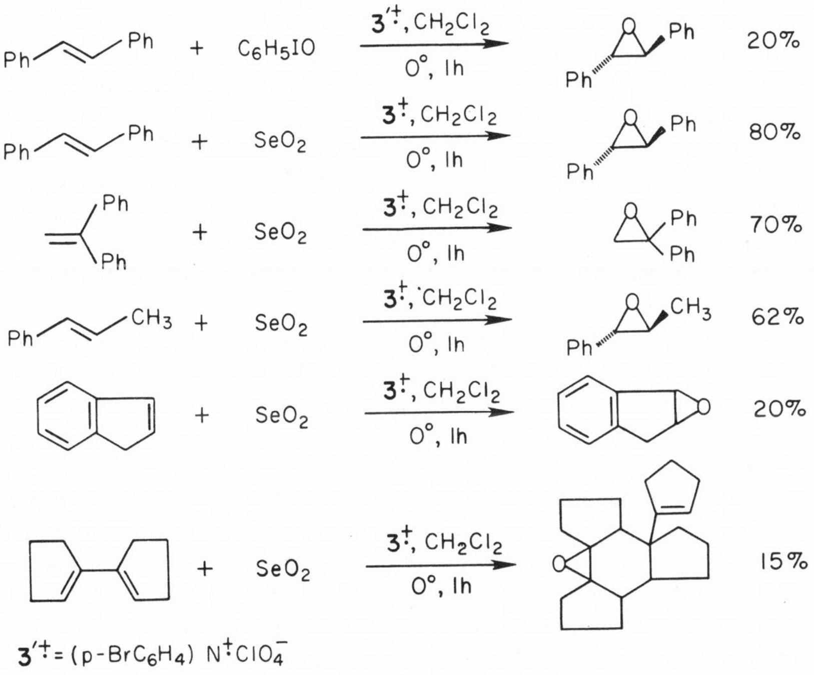

$$\mathbf{3}'^{\dagger} = (p\text{-}BrC_6H_4)\ N^{\dagger}ClO_4^-$$

Scheme 51. Hole catalyzed epoxidation.

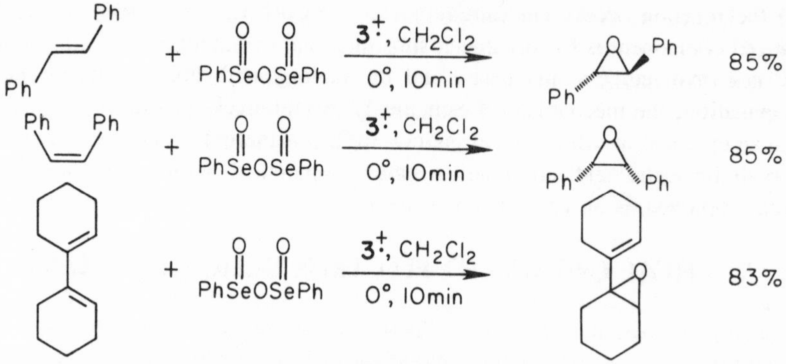

Scheme 52.

which undergo rapid hole catalyzed cyclodimerization. Benzeneselenenic any-dride (Scheme 52) appears at present to be the most effective of this class of reagents. Diphenylselenoxide, in contrast, decomposes the hole catalyst too rapidly.

The formulation of a detailed mechanism for these hole catalyzed epoxidations is still somewhat premature, but several key aspects of the mechanism are secure:

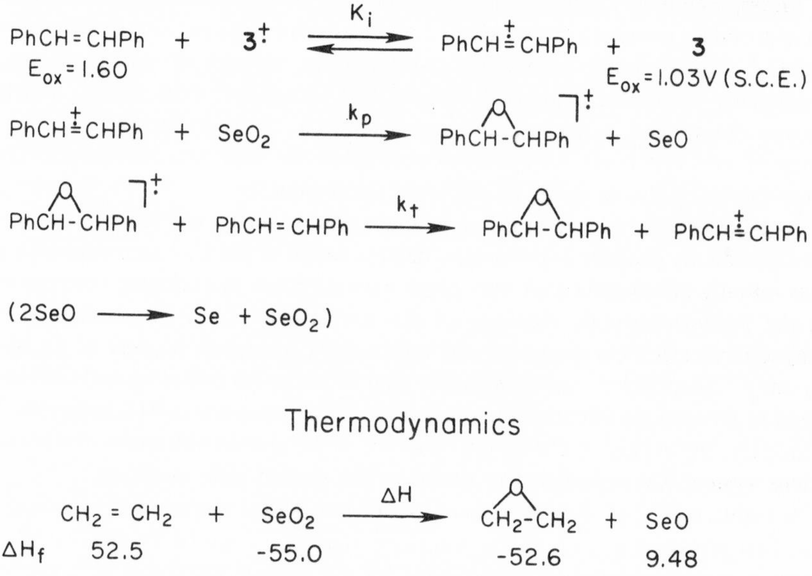

$(2SeO \longrightarrow Se + SeO_2)$

Thermodynamics

$\Delta H = -40.6$ kcal/mol $= -1.76$ ev. Corrections for the stabilization energy of stilbene (10 kcal, 0.4 ev) and for the ΔE_{ox} of stilbene vs. stilbene oxide (0.5 ev) still leaves step "k_p" exothermic by 0.7 ev.

Scheme 53. Proposed mechanism.

(1) the reaction occurs *via* cation radicals and not *via* acid catalysis; (2) the ionized component is the organic π substrate; and (3) intermediate carbocations are not involved. On this basis, and by analogy with hole catalyzed cyclopropanation, the mechanism of Scheme 53 is tentatively proposed. It is noted that an epoxidation which converts SeO_2 to SeO is thermodynamically favorable in both the neutral and cation radical states. Apparently, SeO_2 has not previously been employed as an epoxidizing reagent.

5. HOLE CATALYZED ELECTROCYCLIC REACTIONS

Ironically, the simplest category of pericyclic reactions of cation radicals was initially the most misunderstood. Woodward and Hoffman ventured the prediction that the stereochemistry of electrocyclic reactions of doublets (ion radicals and radicals) is controlled by the symmetry of the SOMO (singly occupied MO) of the reaction partner having the more extended conjugated system.[74] In the diene/cyclobutene (the C_4^{+}) reaction, e.g., the SOMO of a diene cation radical is antisymmetric and the preferred stereochemistry of the diene cation radical/cyclobutene cation radical reaction would be conrotation. In contrast, the SOMO of a diene anion radical is symmetric and the preferred C_4^{+} reaction stereochemistry would be disrotation.

An opposed theory subsequently developed by Dougherty correctly identified an appropriate transition state model (e.g., the cyclobutadiene cation radical for the C_4^{+} reaction) but improperly construed the concept of transition state aromaticity to predict disrotation for the C_4^{+} reaction.[75] With timing which proved unfortunate, a mass spectrometric study of the retroelectrocyclic reactions of *cis*- and *trans*-3,4-cyclobutenedicarboxylic acid was interpreted (far from convincingly) in terms of preferred disrotation.[76]

As a direct consequence of this apparent accord of theory and experiment, the first potentially decisive experimental determination of the C_4^{+} stereochemistry was initially misconstrued. A very clean demonstration of exclusive corrotation in the retroelectrocyclic cleavage of *cis*- and *trans*-1,2,3,4-tetramethylcyclobutene in an electrical discharge was reluctantly considered, because of the apparently "anomalous" stereochemistry, not to occur *via* cation radicals but instead to proceed *via* vibrationally excited ground electronic states (Scheme 54).[77] Similarly, the exclusive disrotation observed in the electrocyclization of a hexatriene system was considered to occur on the ground state manifold.

A viable theory of the stereochemistry of ion radical electrocyclic reactions was first proposed in 1977.[78] The transition state of a conrotatory electrocyclic reaction was considered to be modelled by the Möbius topologue of a cyclic conjugated system of n carbon atoms, where the electrocyclic reaction is of the type C_n as classified above, and having n-1 electrons for the cation radical and n + 1 for the anion radical. Correspondingly the transition state of a disrotatory electrocyclic reaction is modelled by the normal or Hückel topologue of the same monocyclic system. In the case of the diene/cyclobutene cation radical reaction,

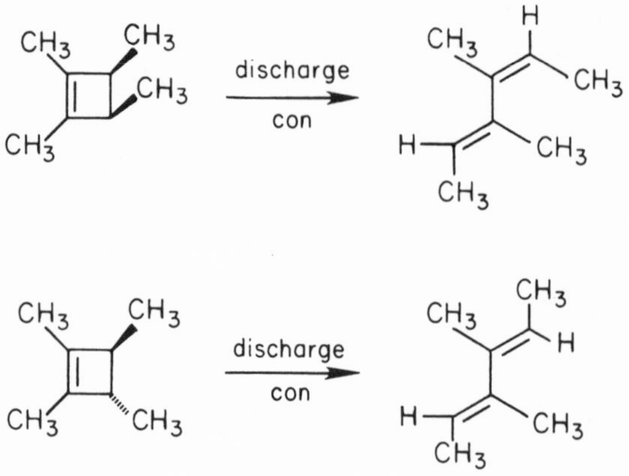

Scheme 54. Stereochemistry of electrocyclic reactions in an electrical discharge.

the transition state models are Möbius and Hückel cyclobutadiene cation radical, respectively. In the HMO approximation, the former is favored by 0.24β, and conrotation is preferred. Precisely the same result obtains for the $C_4^{-\bullet}$ reaction, and in general the preferred stereochemistry of an ion radical electrocyclic reaction is that of the corresponding neutral. Since Hückel benzene cation radical is more stable than the Mobius topologue, the $C_6^{+\bullet}$ and $C_6^{+\bullet}$ reactions should have a preferred disrotatory cleavage mode exactly as found in the electrical discharge experiments. The stereochemical preference alternates between conrotatory and disrotatory for n = even and the selectivity progressively diminishes in the manner of a damped vibration. For n = odd (e.g., allyl/cyclopropyl radical, $C_3^{\cdot}$), incidentally, the theory foresees no significant stereochemical preference.

Another element of confusion in the development of electrocyclic ion radical chemistry was the view that since typically neither reaction mode (con or dis) is allowed these reactions would necessarily be slower than those of the corresponding neutrals. However, a theoretical treatment based upon quantitative (PES) estimates of excited state energies not only concurred that the reaction stereochemistry is that of the corresponding neutral, but advanced the prediction that the ion radical reactions should be more facile than that of the corresponding neutral.[79] Corroboration of this facility initially came in the domain of anion radical electrocyclic reactions, but more recently the extremely facile stereospecific conrotatory cleavage of *cis*- and *trans*-1,2-diphenylbenzocyclobutene cation radicals, which occurs at a rate faster than highly exoergic back electron transfer (Scheme 55) has been impressively demonstrated.[80]

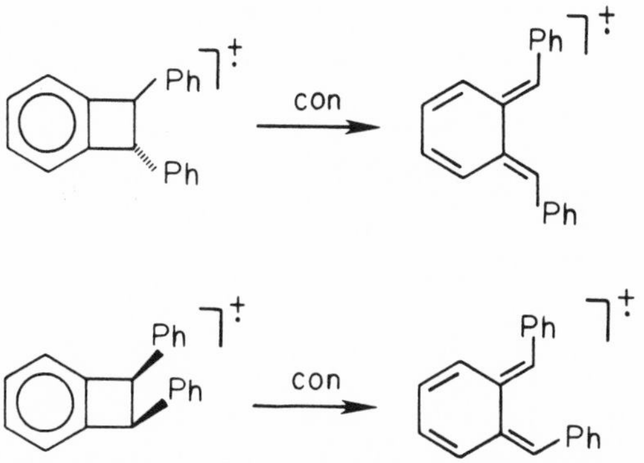

Scheme 55. Stereochemistry of electrocyclic reactions of cation radicals.

6. HOLE CATALYTIC BIOLOGICAL AND BIOMIMETIC PERICYCLIC REACTIONS

6.1. Introduction

The extraordinary kinetic impetus and selectivity of hole catalyzed pericyclic reactions and their ability to circumvent forbiddenness give credence to the claim that hole catalysis is the most powerful general catalytic form available for pericyclic reactions. Therefore, to the extent pericyclic chemistry is involved in biological systems, it would appear logical to assume that hole catalysis, under the control of an appropriate enzyme system, would be at least a reasonable catalytic option. The circumstance that electron transfer is prominent in biological systems, thereby providing ample opportunity for hole formation, lends added credence to this proposal. Recent research has begun to provide encouragement that the role of hole catalysis in biological systems is quite significant. Indeed, it could well be this area in which hole catalytic chemistry will experience its strongest growth in this decade.

6.2. Hole Promoted [1,16] Sigmatropic Hydrogen Shifts in Corrin Synthesis

One of the earliest, and certainly one of the most impressive, examples of hole catalyzed sigmatropic shifts was realized in the corrin series.[81] Electrochemical oxidation of the nickel (II)-A/D-secocorrinate in acetonitrile containing a trace of water was found to provide an almost quantitative yield of a secocorrinoxide in which a [1,16] hydrogen shift (from the methylene group at C(19) in ring D to the methylidene carbon in ring A) had occurred in the intermediate cation radical (Scheme 56). Formation of the corresponding corrin complex could be achieved in modest yield by carrying out the oxidation in acetonitrile/acetic anhydride/ acetic acid (8:1:1) followed by one electron reduction. These important experiments demonstrate a striking parallel between the hole promoted and photochemical cyclizations of A/D secocorrins to corrins.

6.3. Hole Catalyzed Cycloadditions in the Synthesis of Lignans/Neolignans

The antiinflammatory neolignans magnoshinin and magnosalin have recently been isolated from the buds of Magnolia salicifolia MAXIM. Both neolignans are produced in the cyclodimerization of E-asarone under PET conditions (Scheme 57).[82] The cyclobutanoid neolignin (magnosalin) is the initial product of a hole promoted cyclobutanation and this, in part, subsequently rearranges via a hole promoted vinylcyclobutane rearrangement to magnoshinin. The analogous cyclodimerization of methylisoeugenol, under aminium salt conditions, gives dimers closely related to the lignans galbulin and isogalbulin.[83]

6.4. Hole or Electron Promoted Retrocyclobutanation in the Repair of DNA by DNA Photolyase

The predominant DNA photolesion engendered by long wavelength ultraviolet light is pyrimidine cyclodimerization, a cyclobutanation reaction involving an excited state of the pyrimidine. One of the repair processes is an enzymatic retrocyclobutanation catalyzed by DNA photolyase in the presence of visible light and one or more cofactors (e.g., flavin). The retrocyclobutanation is generally considered to occur via either the dimer cation radical or the corresponding anion radical. In the former case, it is presumed that sequential cleavage of first the 6,6' bond (e.g., of a uracil dimer) followed by the 5,5' bond occurs. In the anion radical scenario, the sequence of predicted bond cleavages is

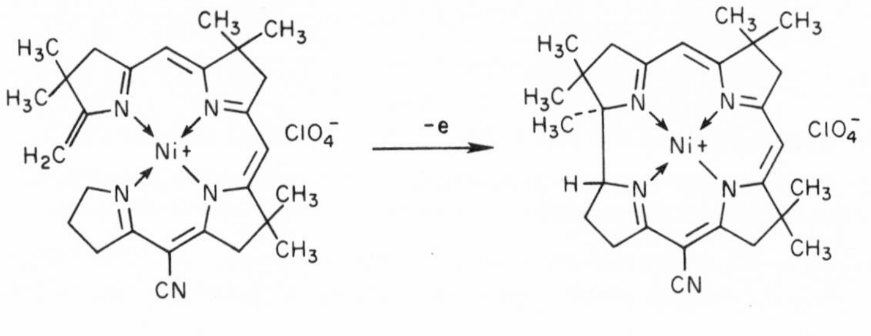

Scheme 56. A sigmatropic shift of a cation radical in the corrin series.

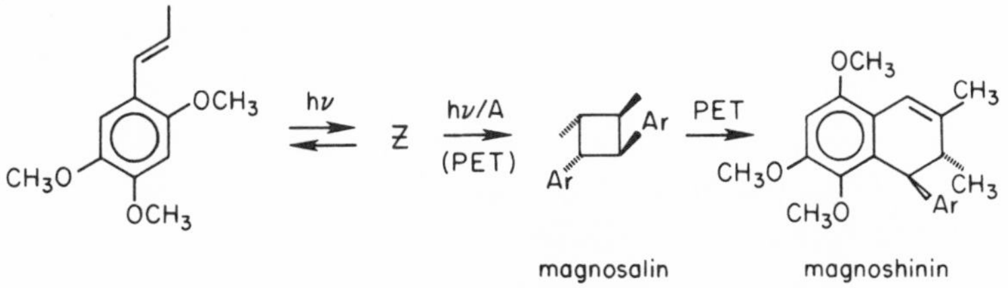

magnosalin   magnoshinin

Scheme 57. Neolignan synthesis via cation radicals.

just the reverse. A recent study of the secondary deuterium isotope effects in the 2-deoxyuridine dinucleotide photodimer (Scheme 58) reveal $k_H/k_D = 1.082$ and 1.071 for the 5,5'- and 6,6'-dideuterioderivatives, respectively.[84] These effects appear to be most consistent with a concerted cleavage of both bonds and are especially interesting in view of the established concert in many cation radical cyclobutanation reactions in simple systems.

6.5. Carotenoid Cation Radicals in Photosynthesis

The involvement of carotenoid cation radicals in the photosynthesis of green plants has been proposed and the possibility of hole promoted (or catalyzed) reactions involving these intermediates is a highly intriguing one.[85] Recent studies of cation radicals of simple carotenoid models suggests that a hemi-Cope type cyclization occurs (Scheme 59) which is somewhat reminiscent of the squalene cyclization. Further research in this area should be extremely fruitful.

6.6. Biological and Biomimetic Oxidation

Intensive research on the mechanism of monooxygenation catalyzed by cytochrome P-450 and its metalloporphyrin models has established the involvement of an oxoiron (V) porphyrin intermediate as the effective oxidizing agent.[86] This species is capable of acting as a hole transfer agent and has been shown to react with a rather wide range of substrates, including amines, polycyclic aromatics, and quadricyclane *via* hole transfer.[87,88] In the case of certain highly carcinogenic polyclic aromatic hydrocarbons such as benzo[a]pyrene, carcinogenicity has in

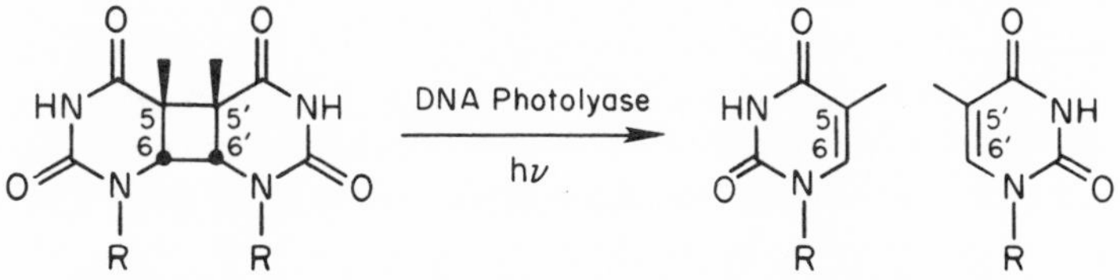

Scheme 58. Possible cation radicals in the repair of DNA.

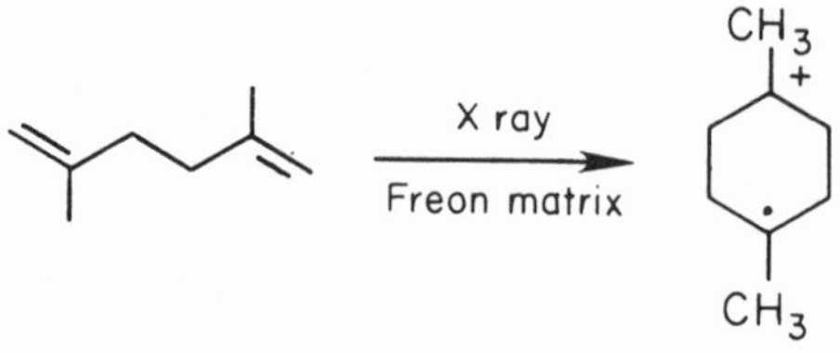

Scheme 59. Hemi-Cope cyclization of simple carotenoid models.

fact been proposed to be linked to such hole transfer[89]. The mechanism of epoxidation of alkenes catalyzed by cytochrome P-450 and its biomimetic models (metalloporphyrins) is of intense current interest, and at least one group prominently involved in that research has strongly advocated a hole transfer mechanism.[90] This proposal is based, in part, upon the correlation of epoxidation reactivity with the ionization potential of the substrate. The new research on hole catalyzed epoxidation described previously provides a model for authentic cation radical behavior and confirms that pi cation radicals can be efficiently and sterospecifically epoxidized. The observation that allylic hydroxylation and/or pinacol type rearrangement products, which often are by products in biomimetic epoxidation, are not found in hole catalyzed epoxidation suggests that at least these co-products arise via a non-cation radical mechanism. Whether biomimetic epoxidation itself proceeds *via* cation radical intermediates has not yet been established, but the availability of an authentic hole catalyzed epoxidation reaction promises to provide major assistance in this determination.

7. ORGANOMETALLIC REACTIONS BY HOLE TRANSFER

The acceleration of reactions by hole transfer is of current interest in organometallic as well as organic chemistry but catalytic processes have apparently not yet been observed in organometallic systems.[91] Of especial interest would be hole accelerated bimolecular reactions between organometallics and strictly organic molecules, whether or not catalytic or pericyclic. Such chemistry could eventually lead to a hybrid transition metal/hole catalytic concept for organic synthesis. A program intended to develop such chemistry has recently been initiated in this laboratory and has yielded preliminary results which suggest that a major corpus of chemistry awaits exploration in this area.[92]

The addition of a catalytic quantity of **3**‡ (1–10 mol %) to a solution of vinylferrocene in dichloromethane at room temperature produces the hole conjugate vinylferrocinium ion, which is stable for a modest time period (*ca.* 10 min). Subsequent to this well defined induction period, however, a rapid catalytic dimerization of vinylferrocene commences and after 1.5 hr furnishes a 73% yield of a single acyclic dimer (Scheme 60). Both the acyclic addition mode and the

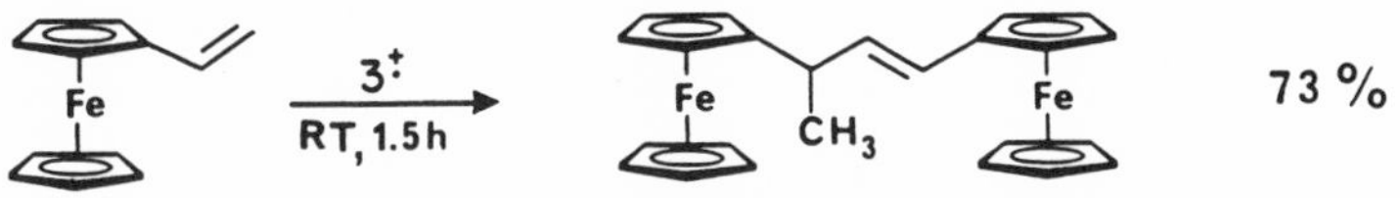

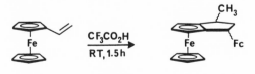

Scheme 60. Initiation of organometallic reactions by holes.

head-to-tail regiochemistry are suggestive of a Bronsted acid catalyzed mechanism, and the generation of Bronsted acid under analogous aminium salt/ionizable substrate conditions has previously been demonstrated. That the dimerization of vinylferrocene initiated by its hole conjugate is in fact *not* a Bronsted acid catalyzed reaction is demonstrated by the observation that the same dimerization occurs without appreciable loss of efficiency in the presence of an excess of 2,6-di-*tert*-butylpyridine. That the conjugate acid of the latter is not itself capable of catalyzing the dimerization was also demonstrated *via* its chloride and triflate salts. Further, the actual Bronsted acid catalyzed dimerization of vinylferrocene does occur (CF_3CO_2H, CH_2Cl_2) but produces four diastereoisomeric dimers none of which is identical to that produced via the vinylferrocene hole conjugate (Scheme 61). The dimer produced in the hole accelerated process is stable under the Bronsted acid condition.

The existence of a well defined induction period precludes a direct reaction of the vinylferrocene hole conjugate with vinylferrocene, a typical hole catalyzed mechanism, as the mechanism of the present dimerization. As noted previously, the acyclic addition mode and the regiochemistry also appear incompatible with a hole catalyzed process. Rather, the existence of an induction period indicates the formation of a catalytically active intermediate *via* some reaction involving vinylferricinium ion. The most plausible alternative reaction mechanism, especially since it would be expected to duplicate the regiochemistry of a Bronsted acid catalyzed reaction, involves iron protonated vinylferrocene as a catalytic intermediate. Such an intermediate could potentially be formed through a hydrogen abstraction by vinylferrocinium. The hole conjugates of several diene-iron complexes have indeed been reported to abstract hydrogen atoms from dichloromethane giving (ultimately) carbon protonated cationic complexes.[93] The dimerization of vinylferrocene in CD_2Cl_2, however, yields a dimer containing no detectable deuterium, and the dimerization reaction is not accelerated by added toluene, as a reaction involving hydrogen abstraction from the solvent should be.

Scheme 61.

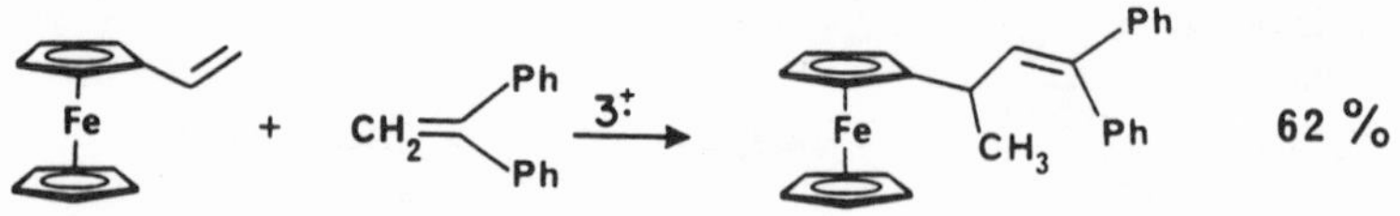

Scheme 62.

Nevertheless, the intermediacy of the iron protonated conjugate acid of vinylferrocene appears the most likely mechanistic possibility, even though the mechanism of its formation from the vinylferricinium ion remains speculative.

When an organic substrate such as 1,1-diphenylethene is included in the typical reaction mixture, a single cross adduct is formed in 62% yield (Scheme 62). This cross adduct reflects exclusive protonation of vinylferrocene as opposed to 1,1-diphenylethene. This highly developed role preference is consistent with the proposed intermediacy of the iron protonated conjugate acid of vinylferrocene, assuming the expected preference for intramolecular proton transfer and invoking a concerted addition mechanism analogous to the Ad_E3 mechanism for electrophilic addition (Scheme 63). An even more intriguing possibility is that of an agostically stabilized conjugate acid.

That the chemistry of the iron protonated conjugate acid of vinylferrocene remains wholly distinct from that of the carbon protonated conjugate acid of vinylferrocene is significant as is the observation of a hole transfer initiated route for the generation of the iron protonated conjugate acid and the novel catalytic chemistry associated with this species. The possibility that hole transfer may represent a general route to metal protonated conjugate acids, and thus to a variety of new catalytic chemistry appears promising and is being actively

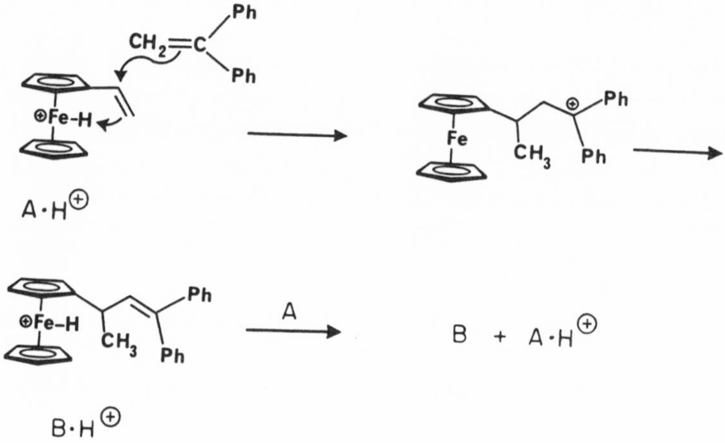

Scheme 63.

pursued. It is clear, of course, that the limited chemistry observed thus far is neither pericyclic nor hole catalytic. The role of the hole conjugate in these cases appears to be to generate efficient organometallic catalysts which are not readily accessible by other means. Whether this indirect approach to reaction acceleration is exclusively maintained in other systems will be of considerable interest.

8. ELECTRON TRANSFER CATALYZED PERICYCLIC REACTIONS

8.1. Introduction

The field of electron catalyzed/promoted pericyclic reactions has an even shorter history than that of hole catalyzed pericyclic reactions. The pioneering example of such a reaction would turn out to be in the electrocyclic domain and not, as for hole catalysis, in the realm of cycloadditions. The development of the concept of electron catalysis of pericyclic reactions just now appears to be accelerating and expectations for the future of this relatively new field are exciting.

8.2. Electron Catalyzed Electrocyclic Reactions

The pioneering example of the title reaction was provided in 1972 in the form of the conrotatorily stereospecific retroelectrocyclic reaction of the *cis-* and *trans-* 1,2-diphenylbenzocyclobutene anion radicals (Scheme 64).[94] In contrast to previous assumptions that pericyclic reactions of all doublet species are *symmetry forbidden*, it was shown in the work cited that the electrocyclic reaction of the benzocyclobutene/*o*-xylene anion radical is symmetry allowed in the conrotatory

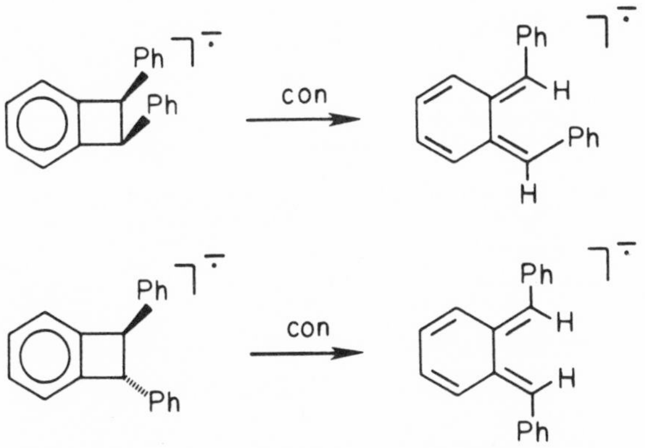

Scheme 64. Early stereochemical results on anion radical electrocyclic reactions.

mode. Quite recently, a catalytic electrocyclic reaction of a bis(allene) anion radical has been observed to occur in virtually quantitative yield (Scheme 65).[95] The preferred stereochemistry of anion radical electrocyclic reactions is the same as for the corresponding cation radical, at least in planar alternant hydrocarbon systems, as was discussed previously.

The theory of ion radical electrocyclic reactions of non-planar systems was developed further in 1977 in the context of the 1,3-cyclohexadiene/1,3,5-hexatriene (C_6^{-}) reaction.[96] Semi-empirical SCF MO calculations indicated that the closure of the all cis-2,4,6-hexatriene anion radical in the preferred conformation of C_2 symmetry to the 1,3-cyclohexadiene anion radical preferentially occurs in the conrotary mode, whereas the closure of the same triene anion radical from the C_s nonplanar or planar conformations occurs disrotatorily (Scheme 66). The latter two results conform with the earlier predictions based upon the more stable (Hückel) topology of the cyclic conjugated array (benzene

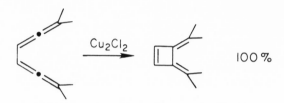

Scheme 65. A recent example of an electron catalyzed electrocyclic reaction.

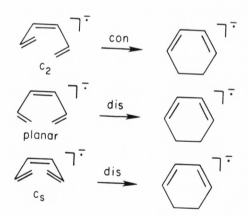

Scheme 66. Molecular vs. orbital symmetry effects on the stereochemistry of anion radical electrocyclic reactions.

anion radical model) in the transition state. In the case of the C_2 conformation, it was observed that disrotation, which is inherently a C_2 operation, cannot be superimposed upon a C_2 molecule while maintaining high pericyclicity in the transition state. On the other hand, conrotation is inherently a C_2 process, and can be superimposed upon a molecule of C_2 symmetry to maintain a symmetric and highly pericyclic transition state. Since the con/dis preference is relatively weak for ion radicals and is further attenuated for $C_6^{+\cdot}$ over $C_4^{+\cdot}$, it appeared likely that *molecular symmetry* effects were dominant over *orbital symmetry* effects in the $C_6^{+\cdot}$ electrocyclic reaction of the C_2 twisted form. Since this conformation was predicted to be the more stable one, a conrotatory $C_6^{+\cdot}$ reaction was foreseen. This prediction has subsequently been decisively verified (Scheme 67).[97] The contrary circumstance that the $C_6^{+\cdot}$ electrocyclic reaction occurs disrotatorily is in accord with predictions based upon *orbital symmetry* (idealized cyclic transition state array) and has been considered to be the consequence of a preferred planar conformation of the triene cation radical.[96] The much greater delocalization energy of a cation than an anion radical species is expected to favor the planar form in a triene cation radical.

8.3. Electron Catalyzed Diels-Alder Reactions

A most intriguing proposed example of an electron catalyzed Diels-Alder addition of 1,2,4,-triazolinediones has been observed (Scheme 68).[98] The reaction is efficiently catalyzed by sodium naphthalenide (*ca.* 1 mol%), sodium metal, and even sodium iodide and is retarded by tetracyanoethene and lead tetraacetate.

8.4. Electron Catalyzed Retrocyclobutanation

It should be recalled that retrocyclobutanations of pyrimidine dimers by DNA photolyase may possibly involve electron, as opposed to, or in addition to, hole catalysis.

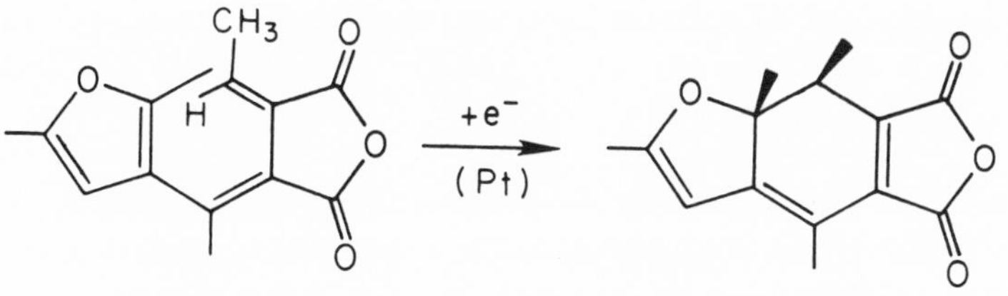

Scheme 67. A conrotatory C_6^- electrocyclic reaction.

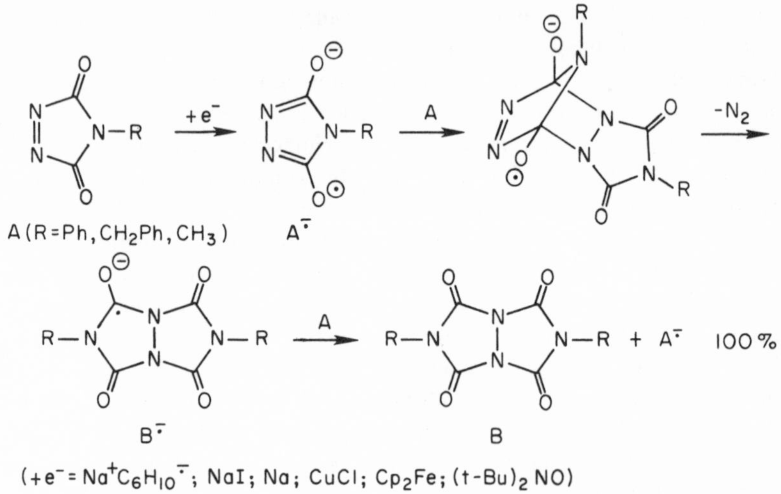

Scheme 68. An electron catalyzed Diels-Alder reaction.

9. THE KINETIC IMPETUS FOR HOLE AND ELECTRON CATALYZED PERICYCLIC REACTIONS

The kinetic impetus for hole catalyzed pericyclic reactions is impressive enough to be of general theoretical interest.[64] Three principal effects appear to operate, and the specific blend of these effects will depend upon the degree of development of product character in the transition state (Scheme 69). The major factor in reactions having a very reactant-like transition state is considered to be the development of substantial stabilizing ion-dipole attractions, in sharp contrast to the steric repulsions concomitant to the approach of two neutral molecules. In a more nearly central transition state, this effect would still be operative, but an additional effect, viz., the delocalization of the hole, becomes important. In a very product-like transition state, two sharply contrasting possibilities exist, depending upon whether the transition state is cyclic (highly synchronous reaction) or essentially acyclic (highly non-synchronous reaction). In the first case the hole energy (the negative of the energy of the SOMO) increases relative to that of the reactant, since the product typically has a less extended conjugated system, thus resulting in *negative* kinetic impetus. In the second case, the hole energy decreases in the acyclic transition state as the SOMO approaches the non-bonding level, thus generating positive kinetic impetus. Indeed in all cases studied so far, cation radical/neutral reaction paths emerge as either highly non-synchronous or stepwise. The unique facility of cation radical/neutral reactions apparently resides in the circumstance that at any point on the reaction path, whether early, medium, or late one or more substantially stabilizing effects is

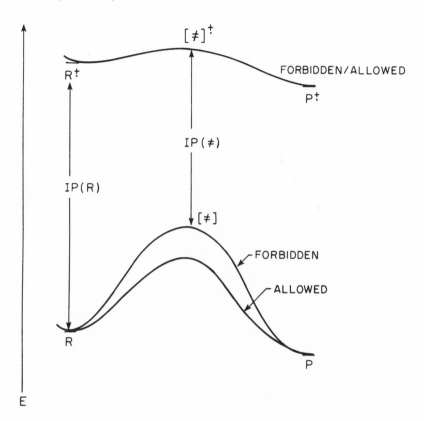

Scheme 69. The kinetic impetus for hole catalyzed reactions.

operative and no important non-thermodynamic destabilizing effect impedes progress along the reaction path. Qualitatively, the same discussion would appear to apply to anion radical/neutral reactions.

ACKNOWLEDGMENTS

The support of the National Science Foundation (CHE-8822051) and the Robert A. Welch Foundation is gratefully acknowledged. All of the art work for this chapter was expertly prepared by Eva Riley.

REFERENCES AND NOTES

1. Alder, R. W. *J. Chem. Soc. Chem. Comm.* **1980**, 1185–1186.
2. Chanon, M. *Accounts Chem. Res.* **1987**, *20*, 214.
3. Pabon, R. A.; Bauld, N. L. *J. Am. Chem. Soc.* **1984**, 1145–1146.

4. Crellin, R. A.; Lambert, M. C.; Ledwith, A. *J. Chem. Soc. Chem. Commun.* **1970**, 682.
5. Ellinger, L. P. *Polymer* **1964**, *5*, 559.
6. Kuwata, S.; Shigemitsu, Y.; Odaira, Y. *J. Org. Chem.* **1973**, *21*, 3803.
7. Farid, S.; Hartman, S. E.; Evans, T. R. In *The Exciplex*, Gordon, M.; Ware, W. R., Eds. Academic Press, New York, 1975, p. 327.
8. Evans, T. R.; Wake, R. W.; Jaenicke, O. In *The Exciplex*, Gordon, M.; Ware, W. R., Eds., Academic Press, New York, 1975, p. 345.
9. Willstatter, R.; Piccard, J. *Ber.* **1908**, *41*, 1458.
10. Weitz, E.; Schwechten, H. W. *Ber.* **1927**, *60*, 545.
11. Walter, R. I. *J. Am. Chem. Soc.* **1966**, *88*, 1923.
12. (a) Schenck, G. O.; Mannsfeld, S.-P.; Schomburg, G.; Krauch, C. H. *Z. Naturforsch.* **1964**, *19B*, 18; (b) Schutte, R.; Freeman, G. R. *J. Am. Chem. Soc.* **1969**, *91*, 3715; (c) Penner, T. L.; Whitten, D. G.; Hammond, G. S. *J. Am. Chem. Soc.* **1970**, *92*, 2861; (d) Neunteufel, R. A.; Arnold, D.R. *ibid.* **1973**, *95*, 4080; (e) Libman, J. *J. Chem. Soc. Chem. Commun.* **1976**, 361; (b) Mizuno, K.; Kaji, R.; Okada, H.; Otsuji, Y. *Ibid.* **1978**, 594.
13. Valentine, D.; Turro, N. J., Jr.; Hammond, G. S. *J. Am. Chem. Soc.* **1964**, *86*, 5202.
14. Bellville, D. J.; Wirth, D. D.; Bauld, N. L. *J. Am. Chem. Soc.* **1981**, *103*, 718.
15. Pye, R. J.; Bauld, N. L. Unpublished results.
16. Jones, C. R.; Allman, B. J.; Mooring, A.; Spahic, B. *J. Am. Chem. Soc.* **1983**, *105*, 652.
17. Calhoun, G. C.; Schuster, G. B. *J. Am. Chem. Soc.* **1984**, *106*, 6870.
18. Gassman, P. G.; Singleton, D. A. *J. Am. Chem. Soc.* **1984**, *106*, 7993.
19. Lorenz, K. T.; Bauld, N. L. *J. Am. Chem. Soc.* **1987**, *109*, 1157.
20. Eberson, L.; Olofsson, B. *Acta Chemica* Scandinavica B **1988**, *42*, 336–338.
21. Yamaguchi, K. *Chem Phys.* **1977**, *25*, 215.
22. Bellville, D. J.; Bauld, N. L.; Pabon, R.; Gardner, S. A. *Chem. Phys.* **1983**, *105*, 3584–3588.
23. Bellville, D. J.; Bauld, N. L. *Tetrahedron* **1986**, *42*, 6167–6173. Further calculations at the MP2/6-31G*/3-21G level eliminate the structural minimum for the intermediate (LBINT) in this paper.
24. Pabon, R. A.; Bellville, D. J.; Bauld, N. L. *J. Am. Chem. Soc.* **1983**, *105*, 5158.
25. Harirchian, B.; Bauld, N. L. *J. Am. Chem. Soc.* **1989**, *111*, 1826–1828.
26. Harirchian, B.; Bauld, N. L. *Tetrahedron Lett.* **1987**, *28*, 927–930.
27. Reynolds, D. W.; Harirchian, B.; Chiou, H.-S.; Marsh, B. K.; Bauld, N. L. *J. Physical-Organic Chem.* **1989**, *2*, 57–58.
28. Reynolds, D. W.; Lorenz, K. T.; Chiou H.-S.; Bellville, D. J.; Pabon, R. A.; Bauld, N. L. *J. Am. Chem. Soc.* **1987**, *109*, 4960.
29. Bauld, N. L.; Bellville, D. J.; Gardner, S. A.; Migron, Y.; Cogswell, G. *Tetrahedron Lett.* **1982**, *8*, 825–828.
30. Wright, M. E.; Jin, M. J. *J. Org. Chem.* **1989**, *54*, 965–968.
31. Ghosh, S.; Bauld, N. L. *J. Catalysis* **1985**, *95*, 300–304.
32. Laszlo, P.; Lucchetti, J. *Tetrahedron Lett.* **1984**, *25*, 1567.
33. Fox, M. A.; Sackett, D. D.; Younathan, J. N. *Tetrahedron* **1987**, *43*, 7.
34. Adheim, L.; Eberson, L. *Acta Chem. Scand. B* **1976**, *30*, 527.
35. Bellville, D. J.; Bauld, N. L. *J. Am. Chem. Soc.* **1982**, *104*, 2665–2667.
36. Mlcock, J.; Steckhan, E. *Tetrahedron Lett.* **1987**, *28*, 1081.
37. Chockalingam, K.; Pinto, M.; Bauld, N. L. *J. Am. Chem. Soc.* **1990**, *112*, 447–448.
38. Pye, R. J.; Kim, T.; Bauld, N. L. *J. Am. Chem. Soc.* In press.
39. Schlesener, C. J.; Amatore, C.; Kochi, J. K.; *J. Am. Chem. Soc.* **1984**, *106*, 3567–3577. The value $\Delta G_o^* = 6.0$ kcal/mol is found for hole transfer from tris (phenanthroline) iron (III) to arenes.
40. Johnson, M. D.; Miller, J. R.; Green, N. D.; Closs, G. L. *J. Phys. Chem.* **1989**, *93*, 1173. The value of ΔG_o^* for intramolecular long range hole transfer between organic pi moieties was found to range from 5.9–7.3 kcal/mol.

41. Farid, S.; Hartman, S. E.; Evans, T.R. *The Exciplex*, Gordon, M.; Ware, W. R., Eds., Academic Press: New York, 1975, p. 327.

42. Bauld, N. L.; Harirchian, B. J.; Reynolds, D. W.; White, J. C. *J. Am. Chem. Soc.* **1988**, *110*, 8111-8117.

43. Bauld, N. L.; Pinto, M.; Pye, R. J.; Chockalingam, K.; Kim, T. Manuscript in preparation.

44. Nordlander, J. E.; Owvor, P. O.; Haky, J. E. *J. Am. Chem. Soc.* **1979**, *101*, 1288.

45. Reynolds, D. W.; Bauld, N. L. *Tetrahedron* **1986**, *42*, 6189-6194.

46. Bauld, N. L.; Bellville, D. J.; Harirchian, B.; Lorenz, K. T.; Pabon, R. A., Jr.; Reynolds, D. W.; Wirth, D. D.; Chion, H. S.; Marsh, B. K. *Accounts Chem. Res.* **1987**, *20*, 371-378.

47. Bauld, N. L. *Tetrahedron* **1989**, *45*, 5307-5363.

48. Pabon, R. A.; Bauld, N. L. *J. Am. Chem. Soc.* **1983**, *105*, 633-634.

49. Pabon, R. A.; Bauld, N. L. *ibid.* **1984**, *106*, 1145-1146.

50. Tsuji, T.; Muira, T.; Sugiura, K.; Nishida, S. *J. Am. Chem. Soc.* **1990**, *112*, 1998-1999.

51. Bauld, N. L. *J. Computational Chem.* **1990**. In press.

52. Mattes, S. L.; Farid, S. *J. Am. Chem. Soc.* **1983**, *105*, 1386.

53. Heinrich, N.; Koch, W.; Morrow, J. C.; Schwarz, H. *J. Am. Chem. Soc.* **1988**, *110*, 6332.

54. Roth, H. D.; Schilling, M. L. *J. Am. Chem. Soc.* **1981**, *103*, 7210-7217.

55. Roth, H. D.; Schilling, M. L.; Abelt, C. J. *Tetrahedron* **1986**, *42*, 6157.

56. Barton, D. H. R.; Leclerc, G.; Magnus, P. D.; Menzies, I. D. *J. Chem. Soc. Chem. Commun.* **1972**, 447.

57. Nelson, S. F. *Accounts Chem. Res.* **1987**, *20*, 276.

58. Paisley, H. M.; Brittain, E. F. H.; Wells, C. H. J. *J. Chem. Soc.* (B) **1969**, 185-187.

59. Padiva, A.; Chou, C. S.; Rieker, W. F. *J. Org. Chem.* **1980**, *45*, 4555.

60. Asuname, T.; Yamamoto, M.; Nishijima, Y. *J. Chem. Soc. Chem. Commun.* **1975**, 608.

61. (a) Dunkin, I. R.; Andrews, L.; Lurito, J. T.; Kelsall, B. J. *J. Phys. Chem.* **1985**, *89*, 1701; (b) Shida, T.; Momose, T.; Ono, N. *J. Phys. Chem.* **1985**, *89*, 815.

62. Dinnocenzo, J. P.; Conlon, D. A. *J. Am. Chem. Soc.* **1988**, *110*, 2324.

63. Reynolds, D. W.; Harirchian, B.; Chiou, H.-S.; Marsh, B. K.; Bauld, N. L. *J. Physical Organic Chem.* **1989**, *2*, 57-88.

64. Bauld, N. L.; Bellville, D. J.; Pabon, R.; Chelsky, R.; Green, G. *ibid.* **1983**, *105*, 2378.

65. Guo, Q.-X.; Quin, X.-Z.; Wang, J.T.; Williams, F. *J. Am. Chem. Soc.* **1988**, *110*, 1974.

66. Lorenz, K.; Bauld, N. L. *J. Catalysis* **1985**, *95*, 613-616.

67. Miyashi, T.; Konno, A.; Takahashi, Y. *J. Catalysis* **1988**, *110*, 3676.

68. Dai, S.; Pappas, R. S.; Chen, G.-F.; Guo, Q.-X.; Wang, J. T.; Williams, F. *J. Am. Chem. Soc.* **1989**, *111*, 8759-8761.

69. Bauld, N. L.; Stufflebeme, G. W.; Lorenz, K. T. *J. Physical Organic Chem.* **1989**, *2*, 585-601.

70. Bauld, N. L; Chockalingam, K. Unpublished.

71. Doyle, M. P. *Chem. Rev.* **1986**, *86*, 919.

72. Traylor, T. G.; Miksztal, A. R. *J. Am. Chem. Soc.* **1989**, *111*, 7443-7448.

73. Mirafzal, G.; Bauld, N. L. Unpublished research.

74. Woodward, R. B.; Hoffmann, R. *J. Am. Chem. Soc.* **1965**, *87*, 395.

75. Dougherty, R. C. *J. Am. Chem. Soc.* **1968**, *90*, 5780.

76. Hoffman, M. K.; Bursey, M. M.; Winter, R. E. K. *J. Am. Chem. Soc.* **1970**, *92*, 727.

77. Kim, J. H.; Thornton, E. R. *J. Am. Chem. Soc.* **1975**, *97*, 1865.

78. Bauld, N. L.; Cessac, J. *J. Am. Chem. Soc.* **1977**, *99*, 23-26.

79. Haselbach, E.; Bally, T.; Lanyiova, Z. *Helv. Chim. Acta.* **1979**, *62*, 577.

80. Takahashi, Y.; Kochi, J. K. *Chem. Ber.* **1988**, *121*, 253-9.

81. Krautler, B.; Pfaltz, A.; Nordmann, R.; Hodgson, K. O.; Dunitz, J. D.; Eschenmoser, A. *Helv. Chim, Acta.* **1976**, *59*, 924-937.

82. Kadota, S.; Tsubono, K.; Makino, K.; Takeshita, M.; Kibuchi, T. *Tetrahedron Lett.* **1987**, *28*, 2857.

83. Wilson, R. M.; Dietz, J. G.; Shepherd, T. A.; Ho, D. M.; Schnapp, K. A.; Elder, R. C.; Watkins, J. W. II, Geraci, L. S.; Campana, C. F. *J. Am. Chem. Soc.* **1989**, *111*, 1749–1754.

84. Witmer, M.; Altmann, E.; Young, H.; Sancar, A.; Begley, T. P. *J. Am. Chem. Soc.* **1989**, *111*, 9264–9265.

85. Prasad, L. S.; Ding, R.; Bradford, E. G.; Kispert, L. D.; Wang, H. *Israel J.Chem.* **1989**, *29*, 33–38.

86. Groves, J. T.; Nemo, T. E.; Myers, R. S. *J. Am. Chem. Soc.* **1979**, *101*, 1032–1033.

87. Stearns, R. A.; Ortiz de Montellano, P. R. *J.Am. Chem. Soc.* **1985**, *107*, 4081–4082.

88. Macdonald, T. L.; Zirvi, K.; Burka, L. T.; Peyman, P.; Guengerich, F. P. *ibid.* **1982**, *104*, 2050–2052.

89. Cremonesi, P.; Cavalieri, E. L.; Rogan, E. G. *J. Org. Chem.* **1989**, *54*, 3561–3570.

90. Traylor, T. G.; Miksztal, A. R. *J. Org. Chem.* **1989**, *111*, 7443–7448.

91. Connelly, N. G. *Chem. Soc. Rev.* **1989**, *18*, 155–185.

92. Mirafzal, G.; Bauld, N. L. Unpublished research.

93. Connelly, N. G.; Kelly, R. L. *J. Organomet. Chem.* **1976**, *120*, C16.

94. (a) Bauld, N. L.; Chang, C. S.; Farr, F. R. *J. Am. Chem. Soc.* **1972**, *94*, 7164; (b) Bauld, N. L.; Cessac, J.; Chang, C.S.; Farr, F. R.; Holloway, R. *J. Am. Chem. Soc.* **1976**, *98*, 4561–4567.

95. Pasto, D. J.; Yang, S.-H. *J. Org. Chem.* **1989**, *54*, 3544–3549.

96. Bauld, N. L.; Cessac, J. *J. Am. Chem. Soc.* **1977**, *99*, 23–26.

97. Fox, M. A.; Hurst, J. R. *ibid.* **1984**, *106*, 7626–7627.

98. Borhani, D. W.; Greene, F. D. *J. Org. Chem.* **1986**, *51*, 1563–1570.

MECHANISMS AND CATALYSIS
IN ELECTRON TRANSFER CHEMISTRY
OF REDOX COENZYME ANALOGUES

Shunichi Fukuzumi

Advances in Electron Transfer Chemistry,
Volume 2, pages 67–175
Copyright © 1992 by JAI Press Inc.
All rights of reproduction in any form reserved.
ISBN: 1-55938-168-X

1. INTRODUCTION

Most biological redox reactions are mediated by redox coenzymes such as NAD(P)H (NAD$^+$ = nicotinamide adenine dinucleotide; NADP$^+$ = nicotinamide adenine dinucleotide phosphate; NADH, NADPH = the reduced forms of NAD$^+$ and NADP$^+$, respectively) and flavins.[1] In particular, electrons are not transferred directly from fuel molecules and their breakdown products to the ultimate electron acceptor O_2. Instead, these substrates transfer electrons to the redox coenzymes, and the reduced forms then transfer their high potential electrons to O_2 by means of an electron-transport chain located in the inner membrane of mitochondria.[2,3] Alternatively, the high potential electrons derived from the oxidation of fuel molecules can be used in biosyntheses that require reducing power in addition to ATP.[1,4] In these cases transfer of electrons is accompanied with that of protons.

For example, NAD(P)H coenzymes as well as the analogues act as the source of two electrons and a proton, thus formally transferring a hydride ion to a suitable substrate (S) (Eq. 1).[5,6] On the other hand, flavin coenzymes (Fl) can act as the acceptor of two electrons and two protons, equivalent to two hydrogens

NADH: R = H; NADPH: R = PO_3H_2

$$NADH + S \underset{-H^+}{\overset{+H^+}{\rightleftharpoons}} NAD^+ + SH_2 \tag{1}$$

from a number of reduced substrates ($S'H_2$) including NADH (Eq. 2).[7] These reactions are only made possible to proceed efficiently by the action of appropri-

R = H: riboflavin

R = $-\overset{O}{\underset{O^-}{\overset{\|}{P}}}-O^-$: FMN

R = $-\overset{O^-}{\underset{O}{\overset{\|}{P}}}-O-\overset{O^-}{\underset{O}{\overset{\|}{P}}}-OCH_2$: FAD

$$Fl + S'H_2 \rightleftharpoons FlH_2 + S' \tag{2}$$

ate enzymes, although the reactions must be thermodynamically allowed to occur in the absence of enzymes. Then, how can the enzymes reduce the activation barriers of the reactions (Eqs. 1 and 2)?

In the case of the forward reaction in Eq. 1 this question may be related to a classic controversy: whether the hydride transfer occurs in a one-step or consists of sequential transfer of two electrons and a proton, perhaps in a e^--H^+-e^- sequence.[8-10] In the former case the action of enzyme may be regarded as the activation of substrates which may enhance the oxidizing ability to make it possible to accept a hydride ion from NAD(P)H. Such description of the reaction is, however, qualitative and provides no further mechanistic insight, certainly none of any quantitative aspects. In contrast, the latter approach permits us to focus on electron transfer from NAD(P)H to substrates as the step which is required to reduce the activation barrier, since the subsequent transfer of hydrogen (or proton and electron) is highly exergonic and therefore it should occur spontaneously without help of catalysis.[10] In particular, acid-base catalysis may play an essential role to decrease the activation barriers of electron transfer reactions, since both the interactions of acids and bases with oxidants (electron acceptors) and reductants (electron donors), respectively may accelerate the electron transfer from reductants to oxidants. However, little attempts have been made heretofore to assess the enzymatic redox reactions along this line or to shed light on catalysis in electron transfer reactions of redox coenzyme analogues.

Here I have attempted to delineate mechanisms and catalysis in electron transfer chemistry of redox coenzyme analogues in relation with those of overall redox chemistry. Such attempts may hopefully provide simple chemical bases in understanding the excellent but mysteriously complex actions of enzymes.

2. ELECTRON TRANSFER REACTIONS OF NADH ANALOGUES

First, let us examine mechanism of thermal and photoinduced electron transfer reactions of NADH analogues in order to see how the NADH analogues being formal hydride donors act as electron donors and also compare electron transfer and hydride transfer reactions in a quantitative manner.

2.1. Transfer of Two Electrons and a Proton

A typical NADH model compound, 1-benzyl-1,4-dihydronicotinamide (BNAH) can be readily oxidized by strong inorganic oxidants such as $[Fe(N-N)_3]^{3+}$ $[N-N = 2,2'$-bipyridine (bpy) and 1,10-phenanthroline (phen)] in acetonitrile (MeCN) at 298 K.[11] The stoichiometry of the oxidation of BNAH by $[Fe(N-N)_3]^{3+}$ determined by the spectral titration indicates that BNAH acts as a one-electron donor towards $[Fe(N-N)_3]^{3+}$ (Eq. 3), and the radical cation $BNAH^{+\cdot}$, which may disappear by the disproportionation, is not further oxidized

$$BNAH + [Fe(N-N)_3]^{3+} \longrightarrow BNAH^{+\cdot} + [Fe(N-N)_3]^{2+} \qquad (3)$$

by $[Fe(N-N)_3]^{3+}$.[11] In the presence of excess pyridine, however, the number of equivalents of $[Fe(N-N)_3]^{3+}$ reduced per mole of BNAH changes from one in the absence of pyridine to two.[11] The change of the stoichiometry on addition of a base can be explained by reactions (Eqs. 4 and 5), where **B** denotes a base. Such a multistep electron transfer is confirmed by the kinetics of the formation of

$$BNAH^{+\cdot} + B \xrightarrow{k_B} BNA^{\cdot} + BH^{+} \qquad (4)$$

$$BNA^{\cdot} + [Fe(N-N)_3]^{3+} \xrightarrow{fast} BNA^{+} + [Fe(N-N)_3]^{2+} \qquad (5)$$

$Fe(N - N)_3]^{3+}$ in the presence of a base as shown in Figure 1, which exhibits a two-step oxidation by $[Fe(N - N)_3]^{3+}$.[11] The first step corresponds to the initial electron transfer from BNAH to $[Fe(N - N)_3]^{3+}$ (Eq. 3). The rate constants of the first step were too fast to be determined by using a stopped flow spectrophotometer; $k_{et} > 1 \times 10^7$ M^{-1} s^{-1}. Indeed, such fast electron transfer is expected from the largely negative values of the Gibbs energy change of electron transfer; $\Delta G^0_{et} = -44$ and -45kJ mol^{-1} for $[Fe(bpy)_3]^{3+}$ and $[Fe(phen)_3]^{3+}$, respectively, obtained from Eq. 6, where E^0_{ox} and E^0_{red} are the one-electron oxidation potential of BNAH (0.57 V vs. SCE)[12] and the one-electron reduction

$$\Delta G^0_{et} = F(E^0_{ox} - E^0_{red}) \qquad (6)$$

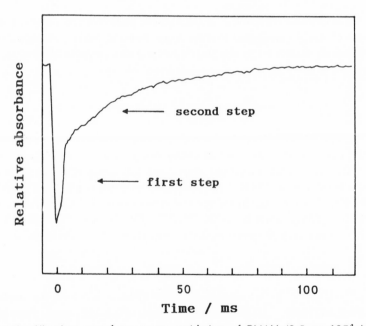

Figure 1. Kinetic curve for two-step oxidation of BNAH (2.0 × 10^{-4} M) by Fe(bpy)$_3$]$^{3+}$ (7.45 × 10^{-4} M) in the presence of 3-cyanopyridine (6.3 × 10^{-3} M), followed by the increase in absorbance at 520 nm due to [Fe(bpy)$_3$]$^{2+}$.[11]

potentials of $[Fe(bpy)_3]^{3+}$ (1.06 V) or $[Fe(phen)_3]^{3+}$ (1.07 V).[13] When the weaker oxidants such as ferricenium ions[14] and ferricyanide ions[15] are employed in the oxidation of NADH and analogues, the rate constants of initial electron transfer can be determined by the conventional methods. The second step in Figure 1 is ascribed to the reactions (4) and (5), in which the deprotonation of $BNAH^{+\cdot}$ by a base (Eq. 4) is rate-determining. The rate of electron transfer from $BNA^{\cdot}$ to $[Fe(N-N)_3]^{3+}$ (Eq. 5) may be diffusion-limited since the ΔG^0_{et} value is largely negative (-218 and $-219\,kJ\,mol^{-1}$ for $[Fe(bpy)_3]^{3+}$ and $[Fe(phen)_3]^{3+}$ respectively), which are obtained from the E^0_{ox} value of $BNA^{\cdot}$ (-1.1 V)[16] and the E^0_{red} values of $[Fe(N-N)_3]^{3+}$ as described above. In such a case rates of the second step correspond to those of proton transfer from $BNAH^{+\cdot}$ to a base Thus, BNAH acts as an apparent two-electron donor in the presence of a base when transfer of two electrons proceed via a electron-proton-electron sequence It should be emphasized that the presence of a base is required for transfer of the second electron to occur.

A strong organic oxidant such as tetracyanoethylene (TCNE) can also oxidize BNAH in MeCN at 298 K.[11,17] The stoichiometry is given by Eq. 7. Such an unusual stoichiometry indicates that the reduction of TCNE by BNAH occurs via

$$BNAH + (3/2)TCNE \longrightarrow BNA^+ + TCNE^{-\cdot} + (1/2)TCNEH_2 \qquad (7$$

a transfer of a hydride ion (two-electron and proton) from BNAH to TCNE (Eq 8), followed by fast electron transfer from $TCNEH^-$ to TCNE (Eq. 9), and the subsequent disproportionation of $TCNEH^{\cdot}$ (Eq. 10). In the presence of a base

$$BNAH + TCNE \longrightarrow BNA^+ + TCNEH^- \qquad (8$$

$$TCNEH^- + TCNE \xrightarrow{\text{fast}} TCNEH^{\cdot} + TCNE^{-\cdot} \qquad (9$$

$$2TCNEH^{\cdot} \xrightarrow{\text{fast}} TCNEH_2 + TCNE \qquad (10$$

the stoichiometry changes from Eq. 7 to Eq. 11, when the observed second-order rate constant increases linearly with the base concentration.[11] Such an enhance

$$BNAH + 2TCNE + B \longrightarrow BNA^+ + 2TCNE^{-\cdot} + BH^+ \qquad (11$$

ment of the rate by the addition of a base can hardly be reconciled by the hydride transfer from BNAH to TCNE (Eq. 8) being a one-step process, since neither BNAH nor TCNE interact with a base. A possible intermediate in the reduction of TCNE by BNAH may be $BNAH^{+\cdot}$, which is deprotonated by a base. Thus,

$$BNAH + TCNE \rightleftharpoons (BNAH^{+\cdot} \ TCNE^{-\cdot}) \tag{12}$$

$$(BNAH^{+\cdot} \ TCNE^{-\cdot}) \longrightarrow (BNA^{\cdot} \ TCNEH^{\cdot}) \longrightarrow BNA^{+} + TCNEH^{-} \tag{13}$$

the hydride transfer may occur via the electron-proton-electron sequence shown in Eqs. 12 and 13. In the absence of an external base, $TCNE^{-\cdot}$ formed by the electron transfer acts as a base to accept a proton from $BNAH^{+\cdot}$ (Eq. 13). In the presence of a stronger base than $TCNE^{-\cdot}$ (e.g., pyridine) the deprotonation of $BNAH^{+\cdot}$ by the base (Eq. 14) may exceed the intramolecular deprotonation in

$$(BNAH^{+\cdot} \ TCNE^{-\cdot}) + B \xrightarrow{k'_B} BNA^{\cdot} + TCNE^{-\cdot} + BH^{+} \tag{14}$$

$$BNA^{\cdot} + TCNE \xrightarrow{fast} BNA^{+} + TCNE^{-\cdot} \tag{15}$$

the radical ion pair, followed by the fast electron transfer from $BNA^{\cdot}$ ($E^{0}_{ox} = -1.1$ V)[16] to TCNE ($E^{0}_{red} = 0.23$ V) (Eq. 15) as in the case of the electron transfer reactions with $[Fe(N-N)_3]^{3+}$ in the presence of a base (Eq. 5).

The rate constants of proton transfer from $BNAH^{+\cdot}$ to various bases (k_B), determined from the electron transfer reactions from BNAH to $[Fe(N-N)_3]^{3+}$ agree with those determined from the reactions with TCNE (k'_B) as shown in Figure 2, where the $\log(k_B$ and $k'_B)$ values are plotted against pK_a of the bases.[11] Proton transfer between normal acids and bases are known to give biphasic Brönsted plots with breaks at $\Delta pK_a = 0$.[17] In fact, such a break is observed in Figure 2 at $pK_a = 3.6 \pm 0.3$, which should correspond to the pK_a value of $BNAH^{+\cdot}$.[18] In this manner the pK_a values of radical cations of various NADH analogues are determined as listed in Table 1, where the pK_a value of radical cation of 9,10-dihydro-10-methylacridine ($AcrH_2$) (2.0) is less than those of BNAH derivatives, 1-(X-benzyl)-1,4-dihydronicotinamides (X-BNAH: X = 4-Cl and 2,4-Cl_2).[16] The pK_a value of $BNAH^{+\cdot}$ can also be obtained from the primary kinetic isotope effects determined from the ratio of the rate constant of BNAH to that of $[4,4-^{2}H_2]BNAH$ on the proton transfer reactions.[11] In general, primary kinetic isotope effects on proton transfer reactions are known to show a maximum at the break in the Brönsted plot in Figure 2, i.e., at $\Delta pK_a = 0$.[17] The plot of k_H/k_D against pK_a indeed shows a maximum at $pK_a = 3.5 \pm 0.3$, which agrees well with the break point in Figure 2, as illustrated in Figure 3.[11] Such

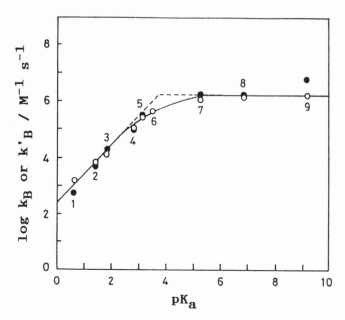

Figure 2. Brönsted plot of log k_B (○) or log k'_B (●) vs pK_a of bases: 1 = 3,5-dichloropyridine, 2 = 3-cyanopyridine, 3 = 4-cyanopyridine, 4 = 3-bromopyridine, 5 = 3-acetylopyridine, 6 = 4-acetylpyridine, 7 = pyridine, 8 = 2-aminopyridine, 9 = 4-aminopyridine.[11]

Table 1. pK_a Values of Radical Cations of NADH Analogues[16]

NADH analogue	pK_a
BNAH	3.6
4-ClBNAH	3.4
2,4-Cl$_2$BNAH	3.3
AcrH$_2$	2.0

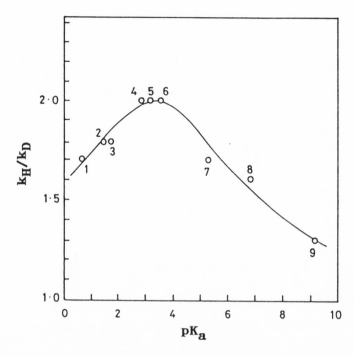

Figure 3. Variation of the primary kinetic isotope effect k_H/k_D for the proton transfer rate constant k'_B as a function of pK_a of base. Numbers refer to pyridine derivatives in Figure 2.[11]

agreements between the k_B as well as the pK_a values in Figures 2 and 3 provide strong evidences for the k'_B values as electron-transfer mechanism (Eqs. 12–15) of the hydride transfer reaction.

A series of p-benzoquinone derivatives (Q) can also be reduced by BNAH as well as other NADH analogues (X-BNAH and $AcrH_2$) via hydride transfer from BNAH to Q (Eq. 16) in the same manner as TCNE.[19] The stoichiometry (Eq. 17)

$$BNAH + Q \longrightarrow BNA^+ + QH^- \qquad (16)$$

$$BNAH + (3/2)Q \longrightarrow BNA^+ + Q^{-\cdot} + (1/2)QH_2 \qquad (17)$$

is therefore the same as that of TCNE (Eq. 7). The plots of k_H/k_D against pK_a of semiquinone radicals ($QH\cdot$) also show maxima which agree well with the pK_a values of radical cations of NADH analogues in Table 1 as shown in Figure 4.[20] Such variation of k_H/k_D with ΔpK_a has been well expressed in the context of Marcus theory of proton transfer[21] as is evident from the simulation curves in Figure 4.[20] The smaller maximum k_H/k_D value for $AcrH_2$ in an aqueous solution

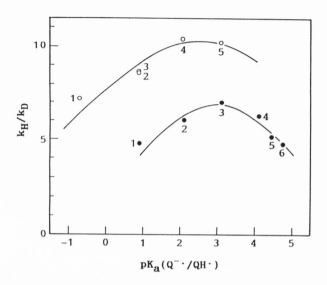

Figure 4. Plots of the primary kinetic isotope effects for the acid-independent rate constants k_H/k_D vs $pK_a(Q^{-\cdot}/QH^{\cdot})$ in the reduction of p-benzoquinone derivatives by AcrH$_2$ and AcrD$_2$ in H$_2$O-EtOH (5:1 v/v) (●) and MeCN (○) at 298 K. Numbers refer to p-benzoquinone derivatives; 1 = p-chloranil, 2 = 2,6-dichloro-p-benzoquinone, 3 = chloro-p-benzoquinone, 4 = p-benzoquinone, 5 = methyl-p-benzoquinone, 6 = 2,6-dimethyl-p-benzoquinone.[20]

than that in MeCN may be ascribed to the much larger solvation energy for proton as compared to MeCN, which may result in the more stabilization of the transition state of proton transfer. The pK_a value of AcrH$_2^{+\cdot}$ appears to be rather insensitive to the solvents (H$_2$O and MeCN) since the pK_a values of QH$^{\cdot}$ in the plots are taken as those in H$_2$O for both cases. This means that the difference in the pK_a values of AcrH$_2$ in H$_2$O and MeCN is approximately the same as that of QH$^{\cdot}$.

2.2.   Comparison with an NAD Dimer Analogue

As described above, cleavage of the C-H bond by proton transfer following the initial electron transfer is essential for NADH analogues to act as hydride donors (two electrons and proton). In this context, it may be interesting to compare the reactions of AcrH$_2$ and the dimer, 10,10'-dimethyl-9,9'-biacridine [(AcrH)$_2$] with a typical hydride acceptor, trityl cation (Ph$_3$C$^+$) since in the latter case cleavage of the C-C bond may also be possible following the initial electron transfer (*vide infra*).

Mixing (AcrH)$_2$ with Ph$_3$C$^+$ in deaerated acetonitrile (MeCN) at 298 K results in the one-electron reduction of Ph$_3$C$^+$ as is evident from the formation of Ph$_3$C$^{\cdot}$ (g = 2.0024) as shown in Figure 5.[22] The stoichiometry is given by Eq. 18,

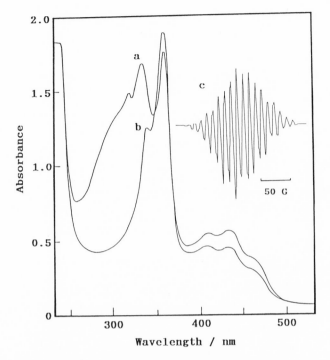

Figure 5. (a) Electronic absorption spectrum observed in the reaction of (AcrH)$_2$ (5.0 × 10^{-5} M) with Ph$_3$C$^+$ (1.0 × 10^{-4} M) in deaerated MeCN and (b) that after introducing dioxygen to the solution. (c) ESR spectrum observed in the reaction of (AcrH)$_2$ (1.5 × 10^{-3} M) with Ph$_3$C$^+$ (1.5 × 10^{-3} M) in deaerated MeCN.[22]

where (AcrH)$_2$ acts as a pure two electron donor instead of a hydride (two electrons and a proton) donor.[22] The triphenylmethyl radical is stable in MeCN at 298 K,[23] but disappears by introducing dioxygen to the deaerated solution to yield triphenylmethyl peroxide (Eqs. 19 and 20).[25] In this contrast, the corresponding

$$\text{(AcrH)}_2 + 2Ph_3C^+ \longrightarrow 2\ (AcrH^+) + 2Ph_3C\cdot \tag{18}$$

$$Ph_3C\cdot + O_2 \longrightarrow Ph_3COO\cdot \tag{19}$$

$$Ph_3COO\cdot + Ph_3C\cdot \longrightarrow Ph_3COOCPh_3 \tag{20}$$

monomer ($AcrH_2$) acts as a normal hydride donor in the two-electron reduction Ph_3C^+ to yield triphenylmethane selectively (Eq. 21).[24]

$$\text{(structure)} + Ph_3C^+ \longrightarrow AcrH^+ + Ph_3CH \qquad (21)$$

The rate of the oxidation of $(AcrH)_2$ by Ph_3C^+ is unaffected by the presence of dioxygen, although the product is changed from $Ph_3C^{\cdot}$ to $Ph_3COOCPh_3$ as mentioned above.[22] Thus, the rate determining step of the formation of $AcrH^+$ may be electron transfer from $(AcrH)_2$ to Ph_3C^+ (Eq. 22), followed by the facile cleavage of the C-C bond of $(AcrH)_2^{+\cdot}$ to yield $AcrH^+$ and $AcrH^{\cdot}$ (Eq. 23). In fact, no ESR signal has been detected in the electron transfer reaction from

$$(AcrH)_2 + Ph_3C^+ \longrightarrow (AcrH)_2^{+\cdot} + Ph_3C^{\cdot} \qquad (22)$$

$$(AcrH)_2^{+\cdot} \xrightarrow{\text{fast}} AcrH^{\cdot} + AcrH^+ \qquad (23)$$

$(AcrH)_2$ to Fe^{3+} by applying a rapid-mixing technique, indicating that the lifetime of $(AcrH)_2^{+\cdot}$ is shorter than 10 ms.[22] Taken together, the second electron transfer from $AcrH^{\cdot}$ to Ph_3C^+ (Eq. 24) may be much faster than the initial electron transfer from $(AcrH)_2$ to Ph_3C^+, since the electron transfer may

$$AcrH^{\cdot} + Ph_3C^+ \longrightarrow AcrH^+ + Ph_3C^{\cdot} \qquad (24)$$

be highly exergonic, judging from the one-electron oxidation potential of $AcrH^{\cdot}$ ($E_{ox}^0 = -0.43$ V vs. SCE)[16] and the one-electron reduction potential of Ph_3C^+ (0.27 V vs. SCE).[26]

The facile cleavage of the C-C bond upon the one-electron oxidation of $(AcrH)_2$ is reminiscent of organometallic compounds containing metal-metal σ bonds, which are readily cleaved by the one-electron oxidation to produce metal radical species (Eq. 25).[27] Thus, the C-C bond of the dimer $[(AcrH)_2]$ possesses a

$$M-M' \xrightarrow{-e} M-M'^{+\cdot} \xrightarrow{M^+} M'^{\cdot} \xrightarrow{-e} M'^+ \qquad (25)$$

character of the metal-metal bond acting as a two-electron donor, while the C-H bond of the monomer ($AcrH_2$) does that of the metal-hydrogen bond acting as a hydride donor.

2.3.   Radical Cations of NADH Analogues

The radical cation of NADH which should be formed upon one-electron oxidation of NADH appeared to be too unstable to detect by conventional techniques, until Czochralska and Lindqvist[28] reported the direct observation of the absorption spectrum (λ_{max} = 540 nm) of NADH$^{+\cdot}$, generated by biphotonic one-electron oxidation of NADH upon laser excitation. Peters et al.[29] also succeeded in observing the absorption spectrum (λ_{max} = 640 nm) of radical cation of an NADH model compound ($AcrH_2^{+\cdot}$), by applying picosecond laser technology. The $AcrH_2^{+\cdot}$ (λ_{max} = 640 nm) can be detected also in thermal electron transfer from $AcrH_2$ to Fe^{3+} in MeCN (Eq. 26) by using a stopped flow technique.[30] In the $AcrH_2$-Fe^{3+} system, the ESR spectrum is observed in the

$$AcrH_2 + Fe^{3+} \longrightarrow AcrH_2^{+\cdot} + Fe^{2+} \tag{26}$$

reaction of $AcrH_2$ with Fe^{3+} in deaerated MeCN by applying a rapid-mixing technique shown in Figure 6a.[31] The g-value is 2.0027, indicating the contribution of spin-orbit coupling due to electron spin at nitrogen nucleus.

Deuterium substitution at appropriate known sites permit us to determine the hyperfine splitting (hfs) values by the computer simulation, since hyperfine pattern and the deuteron splitting should decrease by the magnetogyric ratio of proton to deuterium (0.153).[32] In fact, deuterium substitution of two hydrogen atoms at C-9 position and that of three hydrogen atoms at N-CH$_3$ position of $AcrH_2$ results in drastic changes in the splitting patterns as shown in Figure 6b and 6c.[31] The substitution of one hydrogen atom with isopropyl group at C-9 position also causes the change in the splitting pattern as shown in Figure 6d.[31] The hfs values determined by the computer simulation (parts e–h in Figure 6) are listed in Table 2.[31] The larger $a_N(N-CH_3)$ value of $AcrH_2^{+\cdot}$ than $a_H(N-CH_3)$ value suggests the non-planarity of $AcrH_2^{+\cdot}$ at nitrogen, since the deviation from planarity may result in the increase in the $2s$ population on nitrogen and thereby the $a_N(N-CH_3)$ value may increase as compared to the $a_H(N-CH_3)$ value. The degree of non-planarity of $AcrH_2^{+\cdot}$ may be in between the reduced form $AcrH_2$ being a boat conformation and the oxidized form $AcrH^+$ being planar, since the best fit between the MO calculation and observed hfs values is achieved by using the folding angle between the planes of the two benzene rings of $AcrH_2^{+\cdot}$ (164°) in comparison with that of the fully reduced form (150°).[31] In such a case the hfs value of axial C-9 proton (a_{Hax} = 23.9 G) is calculated to be larger than that of equatorial C-9 proton (a_{Heq} = 19.8 G).[31] In the ESR spectrum of $AcrH_2^{+\cdot}$, however, the two C-9 protons are equivalent, $a_H(C-9)$ = 23.4 G (Table 2), which shows a reasonable agreement with the average value (21.9 G) of a_{Hax} and a_{Heq}. Thus, the inversion of the boat structure may occur rapidly in

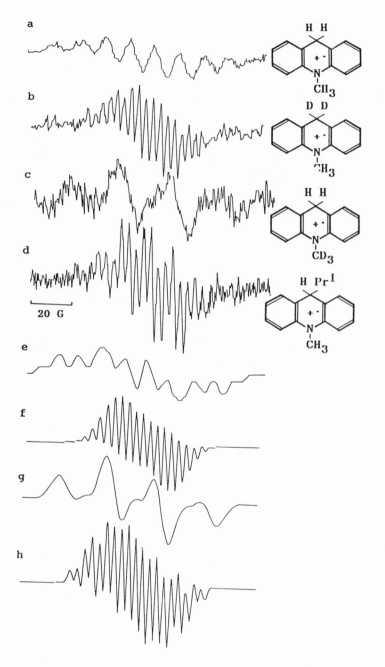

Figure 6. ESR Spectra of transient radical cations of NADH analogues observed in electron transfer from (**a**) $AcrH_2$ (1.2×10^{-3} M), (**b**) $AcrD_2$ (2.0×10^{-3} M), (**c**) $AcrH_2-CD_3$ (1.2×10^{-3} M), and (**d**) $AcrH(Pr^i)$ (1.5×10^{-3} M) to $Fe(ClO_4)_3$ (1.0×10^{-3} M) in MeCN. (**e–h**) Computer simulation spectra of $AcrH_2^{+\cdot}$, $AcrD_2^{+\cdot}$, $AcrH_2-CD_3^{+\cdot}$, and $AcrH(Pr^i)^{+\cdot}$, using the parameters in Table 2, respectively.[31]

Table 2. Hyperfine Splitting (hfs) Values of Radical Cations
of NADH Analogues[31]

radical cation	hfs,[a] G				
AcrH$_2$$^{+\cdot}$	a$_H$(C-9)	a$_N$(N-CH$_3$)	a$_H$(N-CH$_3$)	a$_H$(C-2)	a$_H$(C-7)
	23.4	10.1	7.4	3.4	3.4
AcrD$_2$$^{+\cdot}$	a$_D$(C-9)	a$_N$(N-CH$_3$)	a$_H$(N-CH$_3$)	a$_H$(C-2)	a$_H$(C-7)
	3.6	10.1	7.4	3.4	3.4
AcrH$_2$-CD$_3$$^{+\cdot}$	a$_H$(C-9)	a$_N$(N-CD$_3$)	a$_D$(N-CD$_3$)	a$_H$(C-2)	a$_H$(C-7)
	23.4	10.1	1.1	3.4	3.4
AcrH(Pr^i)$^{+\cdot}$	a$_H$(C-9)	a$_N$(N-CH$_3$)	a$_H$(N-CH$_3$)	a$_H$(C-2)	a$_H$(C-7)
	14.2	10.1	7.4	3.4	3.4

[a] The ΔH_{msl} values of AcrH$_2$$^{+\cdot}$, AcrD$_2$$^{+\cdot}$, AcrH$_2$-CD$_3$$^{+\cdot}$, and AcrH(Pr^i)$^{+\cdot}$ are 2.1, 1.4, 4.0, and 1.4 G, respectively.

solution in the ESR time scale. In the case of AcrH(Pr^i) the isopropyl group is in a boat-axial conformation with respect to the central acridine ring. This may be the reason why the a$_H$(C-9) value of AcrH(Pr^i)$^{+\cdot}$ (14.3 G), which may be ascribed to the equatorial proton, is smaller than the averaged a$_H$(C-9) value of AcrH$_2$$^{+\cdot}$ (23.4 G).

Unfortunately, application of this method to observe the ESR spectra of radical cations of NADH and other analogues has been unsuccessful because of the instability of the radical cations, indicating that the spin delocalization on the tricyclic ring of AcrH$_2$ is essential for stabilizing the radical cation. Nonetheless the large hfs value of the C-9 proton of AcrH$_2$$^{+\cdot}$ (Table 2) indicates that the C-9 hydrogen which is removed by the two-electron oxidation is indeed activated by the one-electron oxidation and thereby subjected to the cleavage of the C-H bond following electron transfer. The larger spin density on the carbon atom attached to the C-9 position of AcrH(Pr^i)$^{+\cdot}$ than that of the C-9 hydrogen (*vide supra*) suggests the possibility of the cleavage of the C-C bond instead of the C-H bond as observed in the case of (AcrH)$_2$$^{+\cdot}$ (Eq. 23).

2.4. Photoinduced Electron Transfer

The NADH model compounds (X-BNAH and AcrH$_2$) can act as electron donors in photoinduced electron transfer reactions as well.[10,16] An advantage of such photoinduced electron transfer reactions is that the fast rate of initial electron transfer can be easily determined by the emission quenching by electron donors provided that the emission lifetime τ is known. A number of rate constants of photoinduced electron transfer reactions have been determined by the emission quenching of a dicationic complex $[Ru(bpy)_3]^{2+}*$ (* denotes the excited state, τ 850 ns) and a neutral complex $[Ru(bpy)_2L]$ (L = 4,4'-dicarbethoxy-2,2'-bipyridine) by BNAH (Eq. 27) and other NADH model compounds as well as the emission quenching of BNAH* and $AcrH_2*$ by various oxidants (ox) in MeCN at 298 K (Eq. 28).[16] The addition of $HClO_4$ to the $AcrH_2$-$[Ru(bpy)_3]^{2+}*$ system in MeCN results in the significant decrease of the k_{et} value as shown in Figure 7.[33] The inhibitory effect of $HClO_4$ may be ascribed to the protonation on $AcrH_2$ (Eq. 29) by which the electron donor ability becomes much weaker as compared to that of unprotonated $AcrH_2$.[34] A similar inhibitory effect is observed by the addition of $Mg(ClO_4)_2$ to the BNAH-$[Ru(bpy)_3]^{2+}*$ system (Eq. 27).[16] Such a retarding effect may also be caused by the complex formation of NADH model compounds with Mg^{2+} ion (Eq. 30),[35] since the donor ability of the complex is much weaker than that of the uncomplexed NADH model compound as is evident from the appreciable positive shift

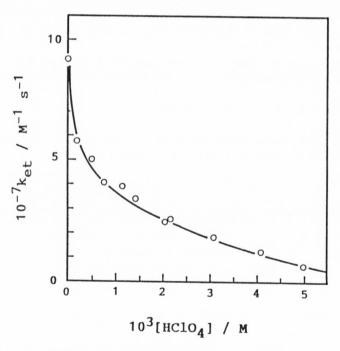

Figure 7.   Dependence of the electron transfer rate constant (k_{et}) on the $HClO_4$ concentration for the reductive quenching of $[Ru(bpy)_3]^{2+}*$ by $AcrH_2$ in the presence of $HClO_4$ in MeCN at 298 K.[33]

$$\text{BNAH} + [\text{Ru(bpy)}_3]^{2+*} \longrightarrow \text{BNAH}^{+\cdot} + [\text{Ru(bpy)}_3]^{+} \qquad (27)$$

$$\text{AcrH}_2^{*} + \text{ox} \longrightarrow \text{AcrH}_2^{+\cdot} + \text{ox}^{-\cdot} \qquad (28)$$

$$\text{AcrH}_2 + \text{H}^{+} \rightleftharpoons \text{AcrH}_3^{+} \qquad (29)$$

$$\text{BNAH} + \text{Mg}^{2+} \rightleftharpoons (\text{BNAH Mg}^{2+}) \qquad (30)$$

of the one-electron oxidation potentials due to the complex formation with Mg^{2+} (Table 3).[16] The carbonyl group of BNAH may interact with Mg^{2+}, since $AcrH_2$ has no carbonyl group and shows no interaction with Mg^{2+}. As such, no shift of the oxidation potential of $AcrH_2$ is observed in the presence of Mg^{2+} (Table 3). In fact, no retarding effect of Mg^{2+} is observed on the electron transfer reactions of $AcrH_2$.[16]

These electron transfer reactions of NADH analogues are classified into three groups using differently charged oxidants (neutral, monocation,and dication); photoinduced electron transfer reactions of X-BNAH with various neutral organic oxidants and $[Ru(bpy)_2L]$ in MeCN, electron transfer reactions of NADH with organic monocations[14] and ferricenium cations (Fc^{+}) in H_2O,[35] and photoinduced electron transfer reactions of X-BNAH with a dication complex $[RuL_3]^{2+}$ in MeCN are shown in Figure 8a, 8b, and 8c, respectively.[16] The ΔG_{et}^{0} values are obtained from the one-electron oxidation potentials of reductants $E^0(red^{+}/red)$ (X-BNAH, NADH, and BNAH*) and the one-electron reduction potentials of

Table 3. One-Electron Oxidation Potentials (vs. SCE) of PyH_2 in the Absence and Presence of Mg^{2+} Ion in MeCN at 298 K[16]

PyH_2	$E^0(PyH_2^{+\cdot}/PyH_2)$,[a] V	$E^0(PyH_2^{+\cdot}/PyH_2)$,[b] V
4-MeOBNAH	0.50	0.68
4-MeBNAH	0.54	0.70
BNAH	0.57	0.80
4-ClBNAH	0.62	0.77
2,4-Cl$_2$BNAH	0.59	0.78
Hantzch's ester	0.72	0.94
AcrH$_2$	0.80	0.79

[a] In the presence of 0.10 M $NBu^n_4ClO_4$. [b] In the presence of 5.0×10^{-2} M $Mg(ClO_4)_2$ and $NBu^n_4ClO_4$.

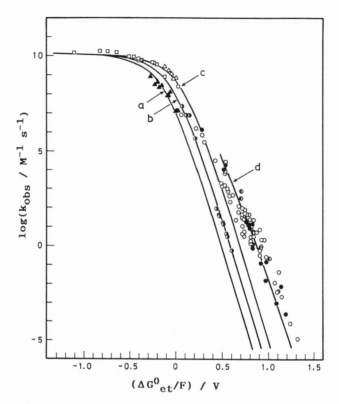

Figure 8. Plots of log k_{obs} vs the Gibbs energy change of the electron transfer reactions of NADH analogues for (**a**) the electron transfer reactions from X-BNAH to $[Ru(bpy)_3]^{2+*}$ in the absence and presence of Mg^{2+} ion $(1.0 \times 10^{-2}$ M) in MeCN (▲), (**b**) those from NADH to ferricenium ions[35] and organic monocations[14] in H_2O (◑), (**c**) those from X-BNAH to $[Ru(bpy)_2L]^*$ in MeCN (△) and those from $^1BNAH^*$ to organic oxidants in the absence and presence of Mg^{2+} ion $(5.0 \times 10^{-2}$ M) in MeCN (▢), and (**d**) the hydride transfer reactions from X-BNAH (○) and $AcrH_2$ (●) to Q in the absence and presence of Mg^{2+} ion (0.10 M) in MeCN at 298 K and those from NADH to Q in H_2O at 303 K[8b] (◐).[16] The solid lines in Figure 8a–c are drawn based on Eqs. 33–35 by using the work terms w_p -0.10, 0. $+0.10$ eV, respectively, and the simulated solid line in Figure 8d is drawn based on Eq. 35 by using the work term -0.31 eV.[16]

oxidants $E^0_{(ox/ox^-)}$ ($[Ru(bpy)_3]^{2+*}$, $[Ru(bpy)_2L]^*$, and organic oxidants) by using Eq. 6.

By applying the general scheme for the emission quenching by an outer-sphere electron transfer in MeCN to the present system (Eq. 31),[37] the observed rate constant is given by Eq. 32, where k_{30} comprises all possible modes by which the

$$\text{red}^* + \text{ox} \underset{k_{21}}{\overset{k_{12}}{\rightleftarrows}} (\text{red}^* \text{ ox}) \underset{k_{32}}{\overset{k_{23}}{\rightleftarrows}} (\text{red}^{+\cdot} \text{ ox}^{-\cdot}) \xrightarrow{k_{30}} \text{decay} \quad (31)$$

$$k_{obs} = \cfrac{k_{12}}{1 + \cfrac{k_{21}}{k_{30}}\left(\cfrac{k_{30}}{k_{23}} + \cfrac{k_{32}}{k_{23}}\right)} \quad (32)$$

radical ion pair disappears, in particular *via* the back electron transfer to the ground state, being approximately equal to the frequency factor. Under such a condition, Eq. 32 is rewritten by Eq. 33,[37] where $\Delta G^{\neq}_{23}$ and ΔG_{23} are the activation Gibbs energy and the Gibbs energy change of the actual electron transfer

$$k_{obs} = \frac{2.0 \times 10^{10}}{1 + 0.15[\exp(\Delta G^{\neq}_{23}/RT) + \exp(\Delta G_{23}/RT)]} \quad (33)$$

process, (red* ox) → (red$^{+\cdot}$ ox$^{-\cdot}$), respectively. The relation between $\Delta G^{\neq}_{23}$ and ΔG_{23} is well expressed by the Rehm-Weller equation (Eq. 34),[28] where $\Delta G^{\neq}_0$ is the activation Gibbs energy when $\Delta G_{23} = 0$. On the other hand, the relation

$$\Delta G^{\neq}_{23} = (\Delta G_{23}/2) + [(\Delta G_{23}/2)^2 + (\Delta G^{\neq}_0)^2]^{1/2} \quad (34)$$

between ΔG_{23} and ΔG^0_{et} is shown in Scheme 1. and given by Eq. 35, where w_p and w_r are the work terms required to bring the products (red$^{+\cdot}$ and ox$^{-\cdot}$) and the

$$\Delta G_{23} = \Delta G^0_{et} + w_p - w_r \quad (35)$$

reactants (red* and ox) together to the mean separation in the activated complex, which are largely coulombic, and w_r may be neglected since the reactants in the

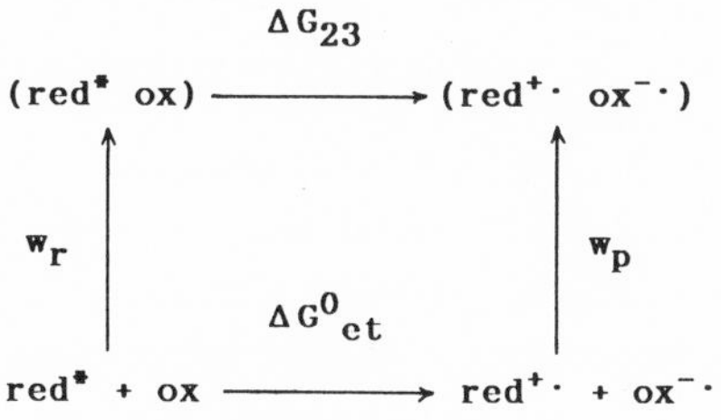

$$\begin{array}{ccc}
 & \Delta G_{23} & \\
(\text{red}^* \text{ ox}) & \longrightarrow & (\text{red}^{+\cdot} \text{ ox}^{-\cdot}) \\
\uparrow & & \uparrow \\
w_r & \Delta G^0_{et} & w_p \\
| & & | \\
\text{red}^* + \text{ox} & \longrightarrow & \text{red}^{+\cdot} + \text{ox}^{-\cdot}
\end{array}$$

Scheme 1.

present case include neutral species. Thus, the k_{obs} value can be calculated as a function of ΔG_{et}^0 by using Eqs. 32–35.

The calculated dependence of log k_{obs} on ΔG_{et}^0 by assuming that $w_p = 0$ and $\Delta G_0^{\neq} = 4.0$ kcal mol^{-1} agrees well with the experimental results for the electron transfer reactions of NADH with organic monocations[14] and ferricenium ions (Fc$^+$)[35] as shown by the solid line in Figure 8b.[16] Such an agreement indicates that the work term w_p is in fact negligible when the products upon the electron transfer include a neutral species such as Fc. On the other hand, when the calculated curve of log k_{obs} vs. $\Delta G_{et}^0/F$ is shifted to -0.1 and $+0.1$ V in the abscissa, the shifted curves agree well with the experimental results for the electron transfer reactions between X-BNAH and a dication complex [RuL$_3$]$^{2+}$* and those for the reactions between neutral reactants (the BNAH*-organic oxidant and X-BNAH-[Ru(bpy)$_2$L]* systems) as shown by the solid lines in Figure 8a and 8c, respectively.[16] Such agreements indicate that the w_p/F values of the radical ion pairs of the like charges (X-BNAH$^{+\cdot}$ [Ru(bpy)$_3$]$^+$) and the opposite charges [(BNAH$^{+\cdot}$ ox$^-$) and (X-BNAH$^{+\cdot}$ [Ru(bpy)$_2$L]$^-$] are $+0.1$ and -0.1 eV, respectively.

The plots in Figure 8a and 8c include the data in the presence of Mg^{2+} ion, which agree with the data in the absence of Mg^{2+} ion in the calculated dependence of log k_{obs} on $\Delta G_{et}^0/F$.[16] Thus, the retarding effect of Mg^{2+} ion on the photoinduced electron transfer reactions of X-BNAH corresponds to the positive shift of ΔG_{et}^0 in the presence of Mg^{2+} ion, which is attributed to the positive shift of the one-electron oxidation potentials of the ground and excited states of X-BNAH (Table 3) due to the complex formation with Mg^{2+} ion (Eq. 30).

2.5. Energetic Comparison between Electron Transfer and Hydride Transfer

In Figure 8d, the log k_{obs} values for the hydride transfer reactions from PyH$_2$ (X-BNAH, AcrH$_2$, NADH) to a series of p-benzoquinone derivatives (Q) in MeCN (eg., Eq. 16) are plotted against the Gibbs energy change of the electron transfer from PyH$_2$ to Q, $\Delta G_{et}^0/F$, which is obtained by Eq. 6. An important point to note in Figure 8d is that there is an approximately single correlation between log k_{obs} and $\Delta G_{et}^0/F$ for different kinds of dihydropyridine compounds (X-BNAH, AcrH$_2$, and NADH shown by the open, closed, and half-closed circles, respectively) in the absence and presence of Mg^{2+} ion, indicating that the activation barrier of the hydride transfer reactions is well correlated with the energetics of the electron transfer ΔG_{et}^0. Thus, the hydride transfer from PyH$_2$ to Q may proceed via electron transfer (Eq. 36) as indicated also by the dependence of k_H/k_D on pK_a (vide supra, Figure 4).

$$\text{PyH}_2 + \text{Q} \rightleftharpoons (\text{PyH}_2^{+\cdot} \text{ Q}^{-\cdot}) \longrightarrow (\text{PyH}\cdot \text{ QH}\cdot) \longrightarrow \text{PyH}^+ + \text{QH}^- \quad (36)$$

However, when the plot in Figure 8d is compared with the calculated dependence of log k_{obs} on $\Delta G_{et}^0/F$ for the electron transfer reactions of X-BNAH (the solid line in Figure 8c), the rate constants for the hydride transfer reactions are greater than those of the electron transfer reactions, although they become closer to each other with a decrease in ΔG_{et}^0. Such a difference in the reactivity has been taken to argue against the involvement of an electron transfer process in the hydride transfer reactions by assuming that the work term w_p of the radical ion pair produced upon electron transfer can be neglected.[8b,c] However, the work term w_p of the radical ion pair of the opposite charges produced by inner-sphere electron transfer reactions *via* the charge-transfer (CT) complexes is expected to be much more negative than w_p in the case of outer-sphere electron transfer reactions,[38,39] such as photoinduced electron transfer reactions of X-BNAH with organic oxidants and [Ru(bpy)$_2$L] (Figure 8c) in which the w_p value is obtained as -2.3 kcal mol^{-1} ($w_p/F = -0.1$ eV) as described above. In fact, the solid line in Figure 8d which is calculated as electron transfer with $w_p = -7.1$ kcal mol^{-1} shows reasonable agreements with the experimental results of the hydride transfer reactions. Such a large w_p value indicates the involvement of the more contact ion pair in Eq. 36 than that of outer-sphere electron transfer in Eq. 31.

2.6. Charge-Transfer Interaction in Inner-Sphere Electron Transfer

The appreciable interaction in the radical ion pair may be originated from the interaction between the redox pair before the electron transfer.[38,39] Such intermolecular interaction is reminiscent of the charge-transfer (CT) complexes formed between electron donors and acceptors.[40] In fact, the existence of the CT complex formed between BNAH and Q (Eq. 37) has been proved by the isolation

$$\text{BNAH} + \text{Q} \rightleftharpoons (\text{BNAH}^{\delta+} \text{Q}^{\delta-}) \tag{37}$$

in a nonpolar solvent such as benzene, in which no further reaction occurs and the observation of the CT band as shown in Figure 9.[19] The $h\nu_{CT}$ values of the BNAH-Q complexes are consistent with those of other known CT complexes in the correlation with the ΔG_{et}^0 values of electron transfer (Figure 10).[19]

In a polar solvent such as MeCN the CT complex is unstable to undergo the complete electron transfer, followed by proton transfer and the subsequent electron transfer, resulting in the overall hydride transfer from BNAH to Q (Eq. 36).[19] Thus, mixing of high concentrations of BNAH with *p*-chloranil in MeCN by using a stopped flow spectrophotometer displays the instant rise of the CT band in the long-wavelength region. The plot of the absorbance against the wavelength shows essentially the same spectrum (Figure 9d) as that observed for

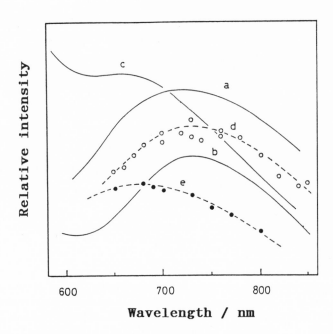

Figure 9. Reflectance spectra (——) of the 1:1 complexes of BNAH with (a) p-chloranil, (b) p-bromanil, and (c) 2,6-dichloro-p-benzoquinone, and the transient CT spectra (---) obtained by plotting the initial absorbances in the kinetic curves against the wavelengths in the reactions of (d) BNAH (7.37×10^{-2} M) with p-chloranil (1.01×10^{-1} M) and (e) BNAH (1.45×10^{-1} M) with 2,6-dichloro-p-benzoquinone (2.22×10^{-2} M) in MeCN at 298 K.[19]

the isolated CT complex (Figure 9a). Such agreement is also observed for the CT complex of 2,6-dichloro-p-benzoquinone (Figure 9c and 9e). The decay of the transient CT spectrum coincides with the formation of the product, indicating that the CT complex is indeed a reaction intermediate for the reaction.[19]

The addition of Mg^{2+} ion to the BNAH-Q system results in a significant blue shift of the CT spectra as shown in Figure 11.[41] Such a blue shift is caused by the formation of a ternary complex involving BNAH, Mg^{2+}, and Q as a reaction intermediate for the hydride transfer reaction (eq. 38). The magnitude of the blue-shift is compatibile with the positive shift of the E_{ox}^0 value of BNAH by

$$ \text{BNAH} + \text{Mg}^{2+} + \text{Q} \rightleftharpoons (\text{BNAH Mg}^{2+} \text{ Q}) \longrightarrow \text{BNA}^+ + \text{Mg}^{2+} + \text{QH}^- \quad (38) $$

the complex formation with Mg^{2+} (Table 3). In such a case Mg^{2+} ion acts as an inhibitor for the hydride transfer reactions.[35,41]

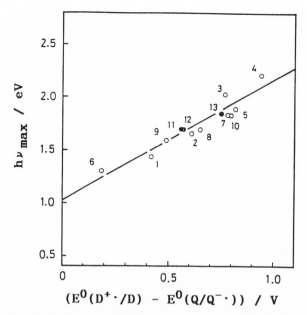

Figure 10. Correlation between the CT transition energies $h\nu_{CT}$ of BNAH-Q complexes (●) as well as other known CT complexes of Q (○) with aromatic amines (D) and the Gibbs energy change of electron transfer $E^0(D^{+\cdot}/D) - E^0(Q/Q^{-\cdot})$.[19]

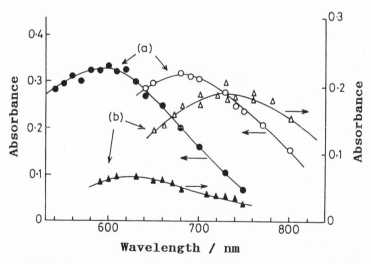

Figure 11. Transient charge-transfer spectra obtained by plotting the initial absorbances of the kinetic curves against the wavelengths (a) in the reaction of BNAH (2.22×10^{-2} M) with 2,6-dichloro-p-benzoquinone (1.45×10^{-2} M) in the absence of Mg^{2+} ion (○) and that of BNAH (4.29×10^{-2} M) with 2,6-dichloro-p-benzoquinone (9.68×10^{-2} M) in the presence of Mg^{2+} ion (1.0×10^{-1} M) (●); (b) in the reaction of BNAH (7.35×10^{-2} M) with p-chloranil (1.01×10^{-2} M) in the absence of Mg^{2+} ion (△) and that of BNAH (9.68×10^{-2} M) with p-chloranil (1.03×10^{-2} M) in the presence of Mg^{2+} ion (1.0×10^{-1} M) (▲) in MeCN at 298 K.[41]

3. ACID CATALYSIS IN REDUCTION OF SUBSTRATES BY AN ACID-STABLE NADH ANALOGUE

In Section 2, we successfully demonstrated how transfer of a hydride ion (equivalent of two electrons and proton) from NADH analogues to substrates is related with the electron transfer reactions. The initial electron transfer step, which is followed by transfer of proton and electron, constitutes the main activation barrier for the overall hydride transfer. In the absence of an appropriate catalyst, however, the reducible substrates are limited to rather strong oxidants such as p-benzoquinone derivatives, TCNE, and TCNQ. Since acid catalysis is known to play an essential role in the enzyme-catalyzed reduction of substrates by NADH,[42] let us examine acid catalysis in electron transfer reactions in relation with that in hydride transfer reactions of NADH analogues.

3.1. Mechanism of Acid-Catalyzed Reduction of p-Benzoquinone Derivatives

The substrates we first examine are p-benzoquinone derivatives, since the redox and acid-base properties of p-benzoquinone derivatives and the one-electron and two-electron reduced forms have well been established and they are important thermodynamic parameters in biological redox systems.[43,44] Figure 12 shows the pH dependence of both the one-electron and two-electron reduction potentials of p-benzoquinone (Q).[43-45] The variations of the reduction potentials with pH are governed by the acid-base properties of the reduced species. As such, the one-electron reduction potential of Q (E_{red}^1) is determined by the standard one-electron reduction potential of Q, $E^0(Q/Q^-)$, and the acid dissociation constant of QH$\cdot$ (pK_1). At high pH values (pH > pK_1), Q$^-$ predominates as the reduced species, and thereby E_{red}^1 (vs. NHE) is independent of pH, equal to $E^0(Q/Q^-)$ as shown by line **a** in Figure 12. In the region pH < pK_1, QH$\cdot$ predominates as the reduced species when the E_{red}^1 value is shifted to the positive direction with the slope of 2.3RT/F (F is the Faraday constant) which corresponds to 0.0592 at 298 K (line b, Figure 12). The one-electron reduction potential of the one-electron reduced species (Q$^-$ and QH$\cdot$), E_{red}^2 (vs. NHE), also varies depending on the acid dissociation constants of QH$^-$ (pK_2) and QH$_2$ (pK_3) as shown by lines c–f in Figure 12. The two-electron reduction potential of Q (E_{red}^m vs. NHE) is obtained by Eq. 39. The pH dependence of E_{red}^m is shown by

$$E_{red}^m = (E_{red}^1 + E_{red}^2)/2 \qquad (39)$$

the middle line in Figure 12, where the E_{red}^m value is shifted to the positive direction in the region pH < pK_3. Thus, the pH dependence of the energetics of the two-electron reduction of Q (E_{red}^m) is quite different from that of the one-

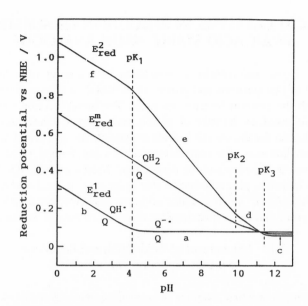

Figure 12. Dependence of the reduction potentials of *p*-benzoquinone (Q) in H₂O.[43–45] The lower line is the one-electron reduction process of Q. The upper line is the one-electron reduction process of Q⁻· and QH·. The middle line is the two-electron reduction process of Q (Eq. 39).

electron reduction (E_{red}^1). If the two-electron reduction of Q proceeds by a one-step process, the pH dependence of the rate would be correlated directly with the pH dependence of E_{red}^m, and thereby the rate would increase in the region pH < pK_3. On the other hand, if the two-electron reduction of Q proceeds *via* the one-electron reduction, the pH dependence of the rate would be correlated with the pH dependence of E_{red}^1, and thereby the rate would increase in the region pH < pK_1. Thus, examination of the pH dependence of the rate of the two-electron reduction of Q by an NADH model compound will provide an unequivocal basis to determine whether the activation barrier is determined by the one-electron or two-electron process.

Since NADH and ordinary NADH model compounds are known to be subjected to the acid-catalyzed hydration,[46] 9,10-dihydro-10-methylacridine (AcrH₂), which is stable in the presence of HClO₄,[34] is used as an NADH model compound. The pH dependencies of the observed second-order rate constants (log k_{obs}) are shown in Figure 13.[45] The log k_{obs} value of each Q in Figure 13 exhibits variation with pH in agreement with the pH dependence of the one-electron reduction potential of Q (E_{red}^1) in Figure 12. The log k_{obs} value of each Q is independent of pH in the region pH > pK_{obs}, but increases with decreasing pH in the region pH < pK_{obs}. The pK_{obs} values, thus determined for five different

p-benzoquinone derivatives, agree well with the corresponding pK_1 values of QH·, which are clearly different from the pK_2 and pK_3 values as shown in Table 4.[45] In the case of TCNQ, the log k_{obs} value is independent of pH. The TCNQ⁻· (λ_{max} 842 nm) is stable in the pH region examined in Figure 13, when no protonation of TCNQ⁻· occurs.[35]

Thus, the pH dependence of both k_{obs} and E_{red}^l strongly indicate that the activation barrier of the two-electron reduction of Q by $AcrH_2$ is correlated with the energetics of the one-electron pathway but not with the two-electron pathway. This can be shown more clearly by the plots of the log k_{obs} values of various p-benzoquinone derivatives (Q) vs. the one-electron reduction potentials of Q (E_{red}^l) and the two-electron potentials (E_{red}^m) as shown in Figure 14 and Figure 15, respectively.[45] All the data of k_{obs} in Figure 13 are unified as a single correlation between log k_{obs} and E_{red}^l (Figure 14). On the contrary, the plot in Figure 14 shows no single correlation between log k_{obs} and E_{red}^m. Closer examination of the plots in Figure 14 reveals that a correlation between k_{obs} and E_{red}^m exists only in the region pH $<$ pK_1 where the E_{red}^l values are in parallel with the E_{red}^m values (Figure 13).

As demonstrated above, the acid-catalyzed two-electron reduction of Q by $AcrH_2$ proceeds by a one-electron pathway. In the region pH $>$ pK_1 no acid catalysis is observed since the electron transfer from $AcrH_2$ to Q is not accelerated when Q⁻· remains unprotonated. In contrast, the one-electron reduction

Table 4. Comparison of the Observed Acid Dissocation Constants pK_{obs} of Reduced p-Benzoquinone Derivatives (Q) with pK_1 of QH·, pK_2 of QH_2, and pK_3 of QH⁻ [45]

p-benzoquinone derivative	pK_{obs}[a]	pK_1[b]	pK_2[b]	pK_3[b]
p-chloranil	0.9	0.9[c]	5.6	8.2
2,6-dichloro-p-benzoquinone	1.8	2.1	7.9	10.0
chloro-p-benzoquinone	2.9	3.1[c]	8.9	10.7[d]
p-benzoquinone	4.1	4.1	9.9	11.4
methyl-p-benzoquinone	4.5	4.45	10.1	11.5

[a] Determined from the results in Figure 13. [b] Taken from ref 43 unless otherwise noted. [c] Taken from ref 44.
[d] Assumed to be the average of 2,6-dichloro-p-benzoquinone and p-benzoquinone.

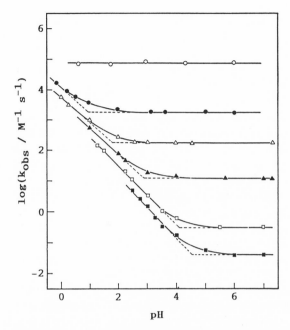

Figure 13. Plots of log k_{obs} vs pH for the reduction of TCNQ (○), *p*-chloranil (●), 2,6-dichloro-*p*-benzoquinone (△), chloro-*p*-benzoquinone (▲), *p*-benzoquinone (□), and methyl-*p*-benzoquinone (■) in H_2O-EtOH (5:1 v/v) at 298 K.[45]

gives QH in the region pH < pK_1 (Figure 12), when acid-catalyzed electron transfer from AcrH$_2$ to Q becomes energetically more favorable as pH decreases. In such a case, the acid-catalyzed electron transfer from AcrH$_2$ to Q (k_{cet}) results in the formation of a radical pair (AcrH$_2$$^{+ \cdot}QH^{\cdot}$) as shown in Eq. 40. Without a subsequent exergonic reaction, no net reaction would occur, since the acid-

$$AcrH_2 + Q + H^+ \underset{k_{cb}}{\overset{k_{cet}}{\rightleftharpoons}} (AcrH_2^{+ \cdot} \cdot QH^{\cdot}) \overset{k_H}{\longrightarrow} AcrH^+ + QH_2 \quad (40)$$

catalyzed electron transfer may be endergonic judging from the one-electron reduction potentials of various *p*-benzoquinone derivatives in the presence of acid (e.g., Figure 12) which are more negative than the one-electron oxidation potential of AcrH$_2$ (E^0_{ox} 1.04 V vs. NHE).[47] The proton affinity of QH is known to be much less than for Q$^{- \cdot}$.[44] For example, the pK_a value of AcrH$_2$$^{+ \cdot}$ (pK_a = 2.0)[16] is larger than the pK_a value of QH$_2$$^{+ \cdot}$ (pK_a = 0.3),[44] and thereby the proton transfer from AcrH$_2$$^{+ \cdot}$ to QH is endergonic. On the other hand, the pK_a value of AcrH$_2$$^{+ \cdot}$ is smaller than the pK_1 value of QH (pK_1 = 4.1; see Table 4), and thereby the proton transfer from AcrH$_2$$^{+ \cdot}$ to Q$^{- \cdot}$ is exergonic. Thus, the subse-

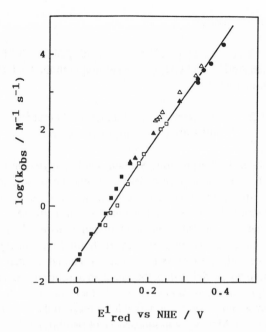

Figure 14. Plots of log k_{obs} vs the one-electron reduction potentials of Q (E_{red}^1) for the reduction of *p*-benzoquinone derivatives by AcrH$_2$ in H$_2$O-EtOH (5:1 v/v) at 298 K.[45] The symbols are the same as those used in Figure 13.

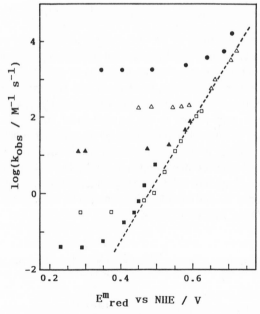

Figure 15. Plots of log k_{obs} vs the two-electron reduction potentials of Q (E_{red}^m) for the reduction of *p*-benzoquinone derivatives by AcrH$_2$ in H$_2$O-EtOH (5:1 v/v) at 298 K.[45]

94

quent exergonic reaction may proceed by the hydrogen transfer from $AcrH_2^{+\cdot}$ to $QH^{\cdot}$ (k_H) to yield $AcrH^+$ and QH_2 in competition with the back electron transfer (k_{cb}) as shown in Eq. 40.

3.2. Nonenzymatic Reduction of Acetaldehyde and Other Carbonyl Compounds

As demonstrated in the previous Section, acid catalysis on the one-electron reduction of *p*-benzoquinone derivatives (Q) in an aqueous solution can facilitate the electron transfer from $AcrH_2$ to Q, resulting in the acceleration of the overall hydride transfer which consists of the initial electron transfer being the main activation barrier and the subsequent hydrogen transfer. In biological redox systems, such acid catalysis operates in hydrophobic environment where the acid strength may be enhanced significantly as compared to that in an aqueous solution. Thus, in the model system the use of an aprotic solvent may be essential to achieve a high activity of acid catalysis. In fact, the electron-acceptor ability of carbonyl compounds shows a remarkable increase in the presence of $HClO_4$ in MeCN.[44] As such, in MeCN the luminescence of $[Ru(bpy)_3]^{2+}*$ can be quenched by acid-catalyzed electron transfer to acetaldehyde and other carbonyl compounds (Eq. 41), although no quenching occurs in the corresponding aqueous

$$[Ru(bpy)_3]^{2+*} + \ \overset{}{\underset{}{>}}C=O \ + \ H^+ \ \xrightarrow{k_{et}} \ [Ru(bpy)_3]^{3+} \ + \ -\overset{\cdot}{\underset{|}{C}}OH \quad (41)$$

system.[48–50] Such enhancement of the one-electron reduction of carbonyl compounds by acid catalysis in MeCN is expected to cause significant reduction of the activation barrier for the two-electron reduction as well, since the subsequent reduction by hydrogen (equivalent to electron and proton) is usually highly exergonic. In fact, the two-electron reduction of acetaldehyde, which is the most important substrate with regard to the physiological significance of ethanol metabolism as well as ethanol fermentation, by an acid-stable NADH analogue ($AcrH_2$) is made possible in the presence of $HClO_4$ in MeCN.[50] When $AcrH_2$ is replaced by the 9,9'-dideuteriated compound, 9,9'-[$^2H_2$]-9,10-dihydro-10-methylacridine ($AcrD_2$), deuterium is introduced to ethanol (Eq. 42).[50] Other aliphatic and aromatic ketones as well as aldehydes can also be reduced by $AcrH_2$ in the presence of $HClO_4$ in MeCN at 333 K.[48–50]

$$\text{(AcrD}_2\text{)} + CH_3CHO + H^+ \xrightarrow{k_{obs}} \text{(AcrD}^+\text{)} + CH_3CH(D)OH \quad (42)$$

When the k_{et} values of acid-catalyzed photoinduced electron transfer (Eq. 41) are compared with the observed second-order rate constants (k_{obs}) of the acid-catalyzed reduction of aliphatic aldehyde and ketones by AcrH$_2$ in the presence of HClO$_4$, there exists a linear correlation between k$_{et}$ and k$_{obs}$ as shown in Figure 16.[50] Similar linear correlations are obtained for aromatic aldehydes and ketones.[48,49] Such linear correlations demonstrate the important contribution of acid-catalyzed electron transfer step in decreasing the activation barrier for the reduction by an NADH model compound as shown in Eq. 43. The hydrogen transfer following the initial acid-catalyzed electron transfer (Eq. 43) in the reduction of aliphatic aldehydes and ketones may be only partially rate-determining, since the observed k$_H$/k$_D$ values are uniformly small (k$_H$/k$_D$ < 2).[50]

Remarkable acid catalysis is also observed in thermal electron transfer from mild inorganic one-electron reductants, 1,1'-dimethylferrocene [Fe(MeC$_5$H$_4$)$_2$] and decamethylferrocene [Fe(Me$_5$C$_5$)$_2$] to a series of α-haloketones such as phenacyl halides (PhCOCH$_2$X) in the presence of HClO$_4$ in MeCN at 335 K (Eq. 44).[49] No reaction is observed in the absence of HClO$_4$ or in the presence of

$$\text{AcrH}_2 + \text{\Large$>$}\text{C=O} + \text{H}^+ \rightleftharpoons (\text{AcrH}_2{}^{+\cdot} \ \ -\overset{\cdot}{\underset{|}{\text{C}}}\text{OH}) \longrightarrow \text{AcrH}^+ + \ -\text{CHOH} \qquad (43)$$

$$2\text{Fe(MeC}_5\text{H}_4)_2 + \text{PhCOCH}_2\text{X} + \text{H}^+ \longrightarrow 2\text{Fe(MeC}_5\text{H}_4)_2{}^+ + \text{PhCOCH}_3 + \text{X}^- \qquad (44)$$

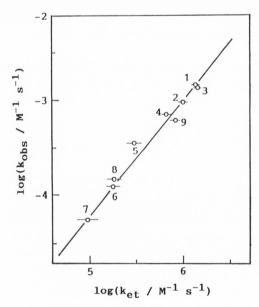

Figure 16. Plot of log k$_{obs}$ for the acid-catalyzed reduction of aliphatic aldehydes and ketones by AcrH$_2$ in the presence of HClO$_4$ (2.7 × 10^{-2} M) in MeCN at 333 K vs log k$_{et}$ for the acid-catalyzed electron transfer from [Ru(bpy)$_3$]$^{2+*}$ to the same series of substrates in the presence of HClO$_4$ (2.0 M) at 298 K; 1 = acetaldehyde, 2 = propionaldehyde, 3 = buryraldehyde, 4 = isovaleraldehyde, 5 = isobutyraldehyde, 6 = pivalaldehyde, 7 = acetone, 8 = fluoroacetone, 9 = cyclohexanone.[50]

$HClO_4$ in an aqueous solution. The second-order rate constants (k_{et}) increase linearly with an increase in the $HClO_4$ concentration. In this case no hydrogen transfer process is involved, and thus the second electron transfer yields the dehalogenated products (Eq. 44). In contrast to the one-electron reductants, $AcrH_2$ being a two-electron reductant reduces the series of α-haloketones to yield the corresponding α-haloalcohols (Eq. 45) as well as the dehalogenated products (Eq. 46).[49] The product ratios between ketones and α-haloalcohols vary depend-

$$AcrH_2 + PhCOCH_2X + H^+ \longrightarrow AcrH^+ + PhCH(OH)CH_2X \qquad (45)$$

$$AcrH_2 + PhCOCH_2X \xrightarrow[H^+]{} AcrH^+ + X^- + PhCOCH_3 \qquad (46)$$

ing on α-haloketones as shown in Table 5.[49] When $AcrH_2$ is replaced by the 9,9′-dideuteriated analogue ($AcrD_2$), no deuterium is incorporated into acetophenone, but it is introduced to each α-haloalcohol.[49]

Comparison of the observed second-order rate constants (k_{obs}) for the acid-catalyzed reduction of various α-haloketones by $AcrH_2$ with the rate constants (k_{et}) for the acid-catalyzed electron transfer reactions from ferrocene derivatives and $[Ru(bpy)_3]^{2+}*$ to the same series of α-haloketones is shown in Figure 17.[49] There are linear correlations between the k_{obs} values and the k_{et} values, despite the apparent difference in the products between the reduction by a two-electron reductant ($AcrH_2$) and one-electron reductants (ferrocene derivatives) as shown in Table 5. Such correlations strongly suggest that the acid-catalyzed reduction of α-haloketones by $AcrH_2$ to yield the corresponding α-haloalcohols (Eq. 45) and ketones (Eq. 46) involves a common activation process, i.e., the acid-catalyzed electron transfer from $AcrH_2$ to α-haloketones as shown in Scheme 2 for the $AcrD_2$-$PhCOCH_2X$ system. The electron transfer transfer from $AcrD_2$ to $PhCOCH_2X$ is subject to acid catalysis to generate the radical pair ($AcrD_2^{+\cdot}$ Ph$\dot{C}$(OH)CH_2X), which disappears either by deuterium (or hydrogen) transfer from $AcrD_2^{R+\cdot}$ to Ph$\dot{C}$(OH)CH_2X or second electron transfer from $AcrD\cdot$, which is formed by the deprotonation of $AcrD_2^{+\cdot}$, to Ph$\dot{C}$(OH)CH_2X (Scheme 2). The deuterium transfer yields $PhCD(OH)CH_2X$, while the second electron transfer yields $PhCOCH_3$, accompanied by the reductive dehalogenation (Scheme 2). This may be the reason why the deuterium is incorporated into α-haloalcohol, but not into acetophenone. The observed primary kinetic isotope effects shown in

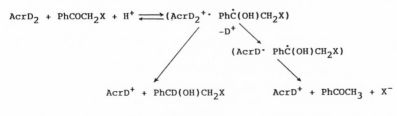

Scheme 2.

Table 5. Acid-Catalyzed Reduction of α-Haloketones by $AcrH_2$ (0.10 M), $AcrD_2$ (0.10 M), and $Fe(MeC_5H_4)_2$ (5.0×10^{-2} mol dm^{-3}) in the Presence of $HClO_4$ (0.30 M) in Acetonitrile at 335 K

no.	substrate[a]	reductant	k_H/k_D[b]	product yields (%)[c]
1	$C_6H_5COCH_2Cl$	$AcrH_2$	5.0	$C_6H_5COCH_3$(36) $C_6H_5CH(OH)CH_2Cl$(49)
	$C_6H_5COCH_2Cl$	$AcrD_2$		$C_6H_5COCH_3$(57) $C_6H_5CD(OH)CH_2Cl$(27)
	$C_6H_5COCH_2Cl$[d]	$Fe(MeC_5H_4)_2$		$C_6H_5COCH_3$(100)
2	$C_6H_5COCH_2Br$	$AcrH_2$	3.0	$C_6H_5COCH_3$(82) $C_6H_5CH(OH)CH_2Br$(14)
	$C_6H_5COCH_2Br$	$AcrD_2$		$C_6H_5COCH_3$(90) $C_6H_5CD(OH)CH_2Br$(7)
	$C_6H_5COCH_2Br$[d]	$Fe(MeC_5H_4)_2$		$C_6H_5COCH_3$(100)
3	$4\text{-MeOC}_6H_4COCH_2Br$	$AcrH_2$	2.7	$4\text{-MeOC}_6H_4COCH_3$(48) $4\text{-MeOC}_6H_4CH(OH)CH_2Br$(46)
	$4\text{-MeOC}_6H_4COCH_2Br$	$AcrD_2$		$4\text{-MeOC}_6H_4COCH_3$(72) $4\text{-MeOC}_6H_4CD(OH)CH_2Br$(24)
	$4\text{-MeOC}_6H_4COCH_2Br$[d]	$Fe(MeC_5H_4)_2$		$4\text{-MeOC}_6H_4COCH_3$(100)
4	$4\text{-MeC}_6H_4COCH_2Br$	$AcrH_2$	1.9	$4\text{-MeC}_6H_4COCH_3$(82) $4\text{-MeC}_6H_4CH(OH)CH_2Br$(14)
	$4\text{-MeC}_6H_4COCH_2Br$	$AcrH_2$		$4\text{-MeC}_6H_4COCH_3$(91) $4\text{-MeC}_6H_4CD(OH)CH_2Br$(4)
5	$2,4\text{-Cl}_2C_6H_3COCH_2Br$	$AcrH_2$		$2,4\text{-Cl}_2C_6H_3COCH_3$(84) $2,4\text{-Cl}_2C_6H_3CH(OH)CH_2Br$(9)
6	$4\text{-BrC}_6H_4COCH_2Br$	$AcrH_2$		$4\text{-BrC}_6H_4COCH_3$(87) $4\text{-BrC}_6H_4CH(OH)CH_2Br$(9)
7	$4\text{-(CN)}C_6H_4COCH_2Br$	$AcrH_2$		$4\text{-(CN)}C_6H_4COCH_3$(95) $4\text{-(CN)}C_6H_4CH(OH)CH_2Br$(trace)
8	$C_6H_5COCH(Br)C_2H_5$	$AcrH_2$		$C_6H_5COC_3H_7$(92) $C_6H_5CH(OH)CH(Br)C_2H_5$(6)
9	$C_6H_5COCH(Br)C_8H_{17}$	$AcrH_2$		$C_6H_5COC_9H_{19}$(55) $C_6H_5CH(OH)CH(Br)C_8H_{17}$(45)
10	$COCH_2Br$ (naphthyl)	$AcrH_2$		$COCH_3$ (98) $CH(OH)CH_2Br$ (trace)
11	$COCH_2Br$[c] (anthryl)	$AcrH_2$	1.4	$COCH_3$ (98) $CH(OH)CH_2Br$ (trace)

a The substrate concentration is 0.30 M unless otherwise noted. b Determined from the ratio of the rate constants of AcrH₂ to AcrD₂. c The alcohol

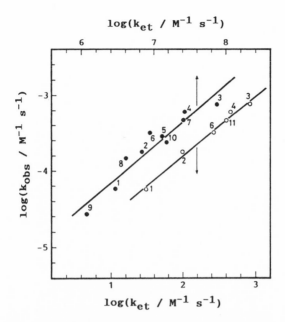

Figure 17. Plots of the rate constants (log k_{obs}) for the acid-catalyzed reduction of α-haloketones by AcrH$_2$ in the presence of HClO$_4$ (0.30 M) in MeCN at 335 K vs the rate constants (log k_{et}) for the acid-catalyzed electron transfer reactions from Fe(Me$_5$C$_5$)$_2$ (O) and [Ru(bpy)$_3$]$^{2+}$* (●) to α-haloketones in the presence of HClO$_4$ (0.30 M) at 298 K. Numbers refer to α-haloketones in Table 5.[49]

Table 5 may be ascribed to the hydrogen transfer process as well as the deprotonation process (Scheme 2). In the case of one-electron reductants (ferrocene derivatives), no hydrogen transfer process is involved and thus the second electron transfer yield only PhCOCH$_3$.

3.3. One-Electron Reduction of Nitrite

Both the two-electron reductant (AcrH$_2$) and one-electron reductant [Fe (MeC$_5$H$_4$)$_2$] can reduce nitrite to nitric oxide in the presence of HClO$_4$ in MeCN at 298 K as shown in Eqs. 47 and 48, respectively.[51] In the acid-catalyzed one-electron reduction of nitrite to nitric oxide in MeCN containing H$_2$O, the

$$AcrH_2 + 2NO_2^- + 3H^+ \longrightarrow AcrH^+ + 2NO + 2H_2O \qquad (47)$$

$$Fe(C_5H_4Me)_2 + NO_2^- + 2H^+ \longrightarrow Fe(C_5H_4Me)_2^+ + NO + H_2O \qquad (48)$$

observed second-order rate constants k_{obs} increase with an increase in the HClO$_4$ concentration and both k_{obs} values of AcrH$_2$ and Fe(MeC$_5$H$_4$)$_2$ show a first-order

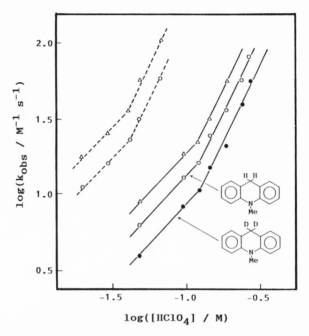

Figure 18. Dependence of the observed second-order rate constants (log k_{obs}) on log[HClO$_4$] for the reduction of NaNO$_2$ by AcrH$_2$ (○),AcrD$_2$ (●), and Fe(MeC$_5$H$_4$)$_2$ (△) in the presence of HClO$_4$ in MeCN containing 5.6 M (——) and 2.8 M (---) H$_2$O at 298 K.[51]

dependence on [HClO$_4$] in the low concentration region, changing to second-order dependence in the higher concentration region, as shown in Figure 18.[51] The identical change in the order with respect to [HClO$_4$] depending on the H$_2$O concentration may reflect the common activation barrier for the acid-catalyzed electron transfer of the two-electron and one-electron reductants.

In the presence of O$_2$, the stoichiometry of the reaction (Eq. 47) is changed to Eq. 49, where AcrH$_2$ reacts with equivalent NO$_2^-$ to yield HNO$_3$.[51] In this case,

$$\text{AcrH}_2 + \text{NO}_2^- + \text{O}_2 + 2\text{H}^+ \longrightarrow \text{AcrH}^+ + \text{HNO}_3 + \text{H}_2\text{O} \qquad (49)$$

the two-electron oxidation of AcrH$_2$ is accompanied by the two-electron oxidation of NO$_2^-$ to HNO$_3$ and the four-electron reduction of O$_2$ to H$_2$O. Such a clean change of the stoichiometry in the presence of O$_2$ may be caused by the following reaction sequence; the facile oxidation of NO by O$_2$ occurs to yield NO$_2$ (Eq. 50) which dimerizes and hydrolyzes to nitrous and nitric acid (Eq. 51).[51]

$$\text{NO} + (1/2)\text{O}_2 \longrightarrow \text{NO}_2 \qquad (50)$$

$$2\text{NO}_2 + \text{H}_2\text{O} \longrightarrow \text{HNO}_2 + \text{HNO}_3 \qquad (51)$$

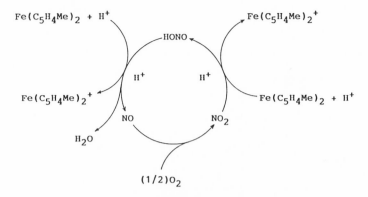

Scheme 3.

The combination of Eqs. 47, 50, and 51 gives the net stoichiometry (Eq. 49). In contrast, the four-electron reduction of dioxygen by $Fe(MeC_5H_4)_2$ occurs efficiently in the presence of a catalytic amount of nitrite in MeCN containing $HClO_4$. In the case of $Fe(MeC_5H_4)_2$ electron transfer to NO_2 may be exergonic judging from the one-electron reduction potential of NO_2 ($E^0_{red} = 0.320$ V vs. ferrocene),[52] although the electron transfer from $AcrH_2$ ($E^0_{ox} = 0.80$ V vs. SCE)[16] may be endergonic. Thus, electron transfer from $Fe(C_5H_4Me)_2$ to NO_2 may proceed efficiently before the dimerization and hydrolysis occur, accompanied by the regeneration of nitrite as shown in Scheme 3.

3.4. Multi-Electron Reduction of Nitrobenzene Derivatives *via* Radical Chain Reactions

The acid catalysis observed in the one-electron and two-electron reduction of substrates described above is also effective for multi-electron reduction of nitrobenzene derivatives.[53] As such nitrobenzene ($PhNO_2$) is readily reduced by $AcrH_2$ in the presence of $HClO_4$ in MeCN at 313 K to yield the four-electron reduction product, phenylhydroxylamine (PhNHOH) as shown in Eq. 52.[53] The two-electron reduction of nitrosobenzene (PhNO) by $AcrH_2$ in the presence of

$$2AcrH_2 + PhNO_2 + 2H^+ \longrightarrow 2AcrH^+ + PhNHOH + H_2O \quad (52)$$

$HClO_4$ in MeCN also occurs to yield PhNHOH (Eq. 53) with the much faster rate at a lower temperature (298 K) than the four-electron reduction of $PhNO_2$. Thus,

$$AcrH_2 + PhNO + H^+ \longrightarrow AcrH^+ + PhNHOH \quad (53)$$

the rate-determining step of the four-electron reduction of nitrobenzene may be the two-electron reduction of $PhNO_2$ to PhNO.[52] When *p*-nitrotoluene is used a

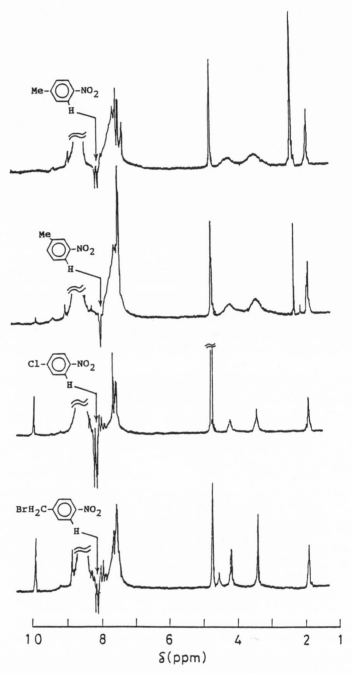

Figure 19. CIDNP Spectra observed in the acid-catalyzed reduction of nitro-benzene derivatives (4.0×10^{-2} M) by $AcrH_2$ (0.15 M) in the presence of 2.0 M $HClO_4$ (70%) in CD_3CN at 338 K.[53]

substrate, the acid-catalyzed reduction by $AcrH_2$ yields the six-electron reduction product, i.e., *p*-methylaniline (Eq. 54).[53] The reduction of *p*-ethylnitrobenzene

$$3AcrH_2 + p\text{-}MeC_6H_4NO_2 + 3H^+ \longrightarrow 3AcrH^+ + PhNH_2 + 2H_2O \quad (54)$$

and *p*-nitrobenzyl bromide also gives the corresponding six-electron reduction products, *p*-ethylaniline and *p*-aminobenzyl bromide.[53]

In the acid-catalyzed reduction of nitrobenzene derivatives by $AcrH_2$ CIDNP spectra are observed as shown in Figure 19, where the emission signals due to the ortho protons of nitrobenzene derivatives are seen in the first scan (250 s).[53] Since the reaction rates at 338 K are fast, each reaction is completed in several scans. As the temperature is lowered, the rates are slowed down, and the emission intensities decrease. On the other hand, the absorption signals due to $AcrH_2$ [δ 3.44 (s,3H), 4.20 (s,2H), 7.5 (m,8H)] show significant broadening when the emission signals of nitrobenzene derivatives are observed (Figure 18). In addition, the reaction is strongly inhibited by the presence of oxygen.[53] It is interesting to note that such strong oxygen inhibition is recognized as the most unique characteristic of nitroreductase.[54] The inhibition effect of oxygen, the observation of CIDNP spectra and the signal broadening in Figure 19 strongly suggest that the acid-catalyzed reduction of nitrobenzene derivatives by $AcrH_2$ proceed by free radical chain reactions.

The chain propagation step may include the hydrogen abstraction from $AcrH_2$ (Eq. 55), since large primary kinetic isotope effects are observed (k_H/k_D 6.0 and

$$AcrH_2 + X\text{-}C_6H_4NO_2H \cdot \longrightarrow AcrH \cdot + X\text{-}C_6H_4NO + H_2O \quad (55)$$

6.8 for $p\text{-}MeC_6H_4NO_2$ and $PhNO_2$, respectively) when $AcrH_2$ is replaced by the 9,9'-dideuteriated analogue ($AcrD_2$).[53] The AcrH· radical being a strong reductant,[16] may be readily oxidized by $X\text{-}C_6H_4NO_2$ in the presence of $HClO_4$ to yield $AcrH^+$, accompanied by regeneration of $X\text{-}C_6H_4NO_2H$· (Eq. 56).

$$AcrH \cdot + X\text{-}C_6H_4NO_2 + H^+ \longrightarrow AcrH^+ + X\text{-}C_6H_4NO_2H \cdot \quad (56)$$

A chain carrier radical AcrH· is readily trapped by oxygen to yield $AcrH^+$ in the presence of $HClO_4$ in MeCN.[10] This is the reason why oxygen can inhibit the reaction strongly. The exchange reaction between AcrH· and $AcrH_2$ may cause the signal broadening of the ^1H NMR spectra as observed in Figure 19. The facile reduction of $X\text{-}C_6H_4NO$ may follow to yield $X\text{-}C_6H_4NHOH$ which is further reduced to $X\text{-}C_6H_4NH_2$ depending on X.

3.5. Catalysis by Lewis Acids

Homogeneous System

As shown above, $HClO_4$ being a Brönsted acid in MeCN acts an efficient catalyst for the reduction of carbonyl compounds, nitrates, and nitrobenzene derivatives by an acid-stable NADH analogue (AcrH$_2$). However, the catalytic center of the enzyme, zinc ion, is believed to act as a Lewis acid rather than a Brönsted acid.[42] Here let us compare the reactivities as well as the products in the reduction of 2-haloacetophenone derivatives by AcrH$_2$ in the presence of a Lewis acid (TiCl$_4$) with those in the presence of a Brönsted acid (HClO$_4$).[49,55]

Phenacyl halide is reduced by AcrH$_2$ efficiently even at 298 K in the presence of TiCl$_4$ in dichloromethane, and the corresponding halohydrin, α-(halomethyl)benzenemethanol is obtained selectively in 70–80% yield with no dehalogenated compound in 2 min, when the reaction is quenched by water.[55] Such selective formation of halohydrin seems interesting since the model systems that have so far been reported for the reduction of α-haloketones undergo the reductive dehalogenation to yield parent ketones,[56] although the enzyme-mediated reduction of phenacyl halide is known to yield the corresponding halohydrin selectivity.[57] The reaction conditions and the yields of products for the reduction of various α-haloketones by AcrH$_2$ in the presence of TiCl$_4$ are shown in Table 6.[55] The much higher reaction temperature and more prolonged reaction time are required for the reactions in the presence of HClO$_4$ brought to completion than those in the presence of TiCl$_4$ (c.f. Table 5).[49] In the reduction of PhCOCH$_2$X (X = Br, Cl) by AcrH$_2$ in the presence of TiCl$_4$, the yield of the oxidized product AcrH$^+$ is about the same as that of the reduced product, PhCH(OH)CH$_2$X (Table 6). In general, a Lewis acid such as TiCl$_4$ is known to activate carbonyl compounds in the reduction by various reductants.[58] Thus, a hydride transfer from AcrH$_2$ to 2-haloacetophenone may be mediated by TiCl$_4$ and facilitated by the interaction of α-haloketones with TiCl$_4$.

Heterogeneous System

Compared with the homogeneous system described above, a heterogeneous system has an advantage to control the acid strength as well as the acidity, since many solid acids including solid superacids are known, and the surface acid strength and acidity can be finely tuned by various means of activation.[59] In fact, on the activated alumina prepared by calcination at various temperature, the two-electron and four-electron reduction of dioxygen by both AcrH$_2$ and Fe(MeC$_5$H$_4$)$_2$ in dichloromethane proceed efficiently as given by Eqs. 57 and 58,

$$\text{AcrH}_2 + \text{O}_2 + \text{H}^+ \xrightarrow[\text{Al}_2\text{O}_3]{} \text{AcrH}^+ + \text{H}_2\text{O}_2 \tag{57}$$

$$4[\text{Fe}(\text{MeC}_5\text{H}_4)_2] + \text{O}_2 + 4\text{H}^+ \xrightarrow[\text{Al}_2\text{O}_3]{} 4[\text{Fe}(\text{MeC}_5\text{H}_4)_2] + 2\text{H}_2\text{O} \tag{58}$$

respectively.[60] Such direct reduction of dioxygen would otherwise be difficult to occur. The dependencies of the product yields/alumina (mol g^{-1}) as well as the acidity of the activated alumina (mol g^{-1}), titrated by a Hammet indicator

Table 6. Reduction of 2-Haloacetophenone Derivatives $(2.0 \times 10^{-3}$ mol) by AcrH$_2$ and AcrD$_2$ $(5.0 \times 10^{-4}$ mol) in the Presence of TiCl$_4$ $(1.3 \times 10^{-3}$ mol) in Dichloromethane $(0.05$ cm$^3)$ at 298 K[55]

substrate	reductant	product (yield,[a] %)
PhCOCH$_2$Br	AcrH$_2$	PhCH(OH)CH$_2$Br(80) AcrH$^+$(80)
PhCOCH$_2$Cl	AcrH$_2$	PhCH(OH)CH$_2$Cl(70) AcrH$^+$(77)
PhCOCH$_2$Br	AcrD$_2$	PhCD(OH)CH$_2$Br(75) AcrD$^+$(80)
PhCOCH$_2$Cl	AcrD$_2$	PhCD(OH)CH$_2$Cl(44) AcrD$^+$(70)
4'-MeOC$_6$H$_4$COCH$_2$Br	AcrH$_2$	4'-MeOC$_6$H$_4$CH(OH)CH$_2$Br(52) AcrH$^+$(60)
4'-CNC$_6$H$_4$COCH$_2$Br	AcrH$_2$	4'-CNC$_6$H$_4$CH(OH)CH$_2$Br(50) AcrH$^+$(68)
PhCOCH(C$_2$H$_5$)Br	AcrH$_2$	PhCH(OH)CH(C$_2$H$_5$)Br(6) AcrH$^+$(80)
PhCOCH(C$_8$H$_{17}$)Br	AcrH$_2$	PhCH(OH)CH(C$_8$H$_{17}$)Br(10) AcrH$^+$(73)
none	AcrH$_2$	AcrH$^+$ (50)

[a] Reaction time 2 min.

Methyl Red $(pK_a = 4.8)$, on the calcination temperature of alumina are shown in Figure 20, where the product yields and the acidity exhibit the same maxima at 400 and 800 °C.[60] The reactivity of dioxygen towards AcrH$_2$ as well as Fe (MeC$_5$H$_4$)$_2$ also varies in parallel with the variation of the acidity (Figure 20).

Alumina surfaces after removal of adsorbed H$_2$O are known to have a layer of hydroxyl groups.[59] The removal of two neighboring hydroxyl groups from the surface by calcination may be accompanied by the formation and desorption of H$_2$O to leave an oxide ion in the outermost surface layer and an exposed incompletely coordinated aluminium ion in the next lower layer, as shown by Eq. 59.[58] The exposed aluminium ion, acting as a Lewis acid site, can thus

$$\begin{array}{cc} \text{H} & \text{H} \\ | & | \\ \text{O} & \text{O} \\ | & | \\ \text{-Al-O-Al-} \end{array} \quad + \quad \begin{array}{c} \text{O}^- \\ | \\ \longrightarrow \ \text{-Al-O-Al-} \end{array} \ + \ \text{H}_2\text{O} \qquad (59)$$

activate dioxygen to make it possible to accept an electron from AcrH$_2$ and Fe(MeC$_5$H$_4$)$_2$. The decrease in the acidity as well as the product yields as the calcination temperature is raised from 500° to 600 °C (Figure 20) may be caused by the surface sintering effects since migration of oxide and aluminium ion may occur at this temperature.[59] The migration of protons may also occur above 600 °C to result in further dehydroxylation, creating more defects, and thereby the

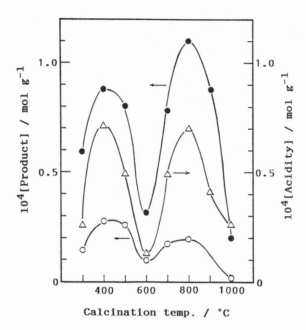

Figure 20. Plots of the amounts of products [AcrH$^+$ ($\bigcirc$) and Fe(MeC$_5$H$_4$)$_2^+$ ($\bullet$)] formed in the heterogeneous oxidation of AcrH$_2$ and Fe(C$_5$H$_4$Me)$_2$, respectively, by dioxygen in the presence of alumina in CH$_2$Cl$_2$ [mol / g (Al$_2$O$_3$)], and the acidity (H$_0$ < 4.8) of alumina ($\triangle$) vs the calcination temperature of alumina (5 hr in air).[60]

acidity as well as the product yields increases again from 600 to 800 °C (Figure 20). The considerable decrease of the acidity as well as the product yields above 800 °C (Figure 20) may be due mainly to the decrease in the surface area, caused by the irreversible change of the alumina phase from γ-Al$_2$O$_3$ to α-Al$_2$O$_3$.[60]

4. ELECTRON TRANSFER CATALYTIC SYSTEMS OF NADH ANALOGUES

In Section 3, we demonstrated that acid catalysis on electron transfer from NADH analogues to substrates in aprotic media plays an essential role in reducing activation barrier for the two-electron and multi-electron reduction of substrates. By using such simple acid catalyzed system, various NADH-dependent substrates, which would otherwise be activated only by the action of appropriate enzymes, were shown to be readily reduced by an acid-stable NADH analogue. On the other hand, NADH also plays a vital role as the electron source in the respiratory chain where the four-electron reduction of dioxygen by NADH is achieved by the step-by-step transfer of electrons through a number of electron carriers such as the cytochrome.[2,3] However, NADH and analogues are stable against dioxygen showing no direct interaction. Although an acid-stable NADH analogue can reduce dioxygen on the solid acids (*vide supra*), it is desired to construct more efficient electron transfer catalytic systems for the reduction of dioxygen in the homogeneous systems. In this Section, we describe such nonenzymatic electron transfer catalytic systems for the reduction of dioxygen by NADH analogues.

4.1. Interaction with Metalloporphyrins

First let us examine the interaction between NADH analogues with metalloporphyrins which are important components of the biological electron transport systems.[2,3] Addition of BNAH (λ_{max} = 350 nm) to a CH_2Cl_2 solution of FeTPPClO$_4$ results in a significant change of the visible spectrum as shown in Figure 21, which indicates the step-wise formation of complexes between FeTPPClO$_4$ and BNAH; the first step is the formation of a 1:1 complex (Eq. 60) and the second step is an additional axial ligand addition to form a 1:2 complex (Eq. 61).[62] Thus, the absorption maxima of FeTPPClO$_4$ (λ_{max} 399, 528, and 664

$$FeTPP^+ + BNAH \underset{}{\overset{K_1}{\rightleftharpoons}} FeTPP(BNAH)^+ \qquad (60)$$

$$FeTPP(BNAH)^+ + BNAH \underset{}{\overset{K_2}{\rightleftharpoons}} FeTPP(BNAH)_2^+ \qquad (61)$$

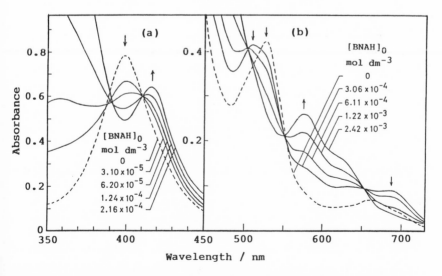

Figure 21. Visible spectroscopic change observed upon addition of BNAH to a CH_2Cl_2 solution of FeTPPClO$_4$; (a) 6.4 × 10^{-6} M, (b) 4.0 × 10^{-5} M.[62]

nm) are changed to those of FeTPP(BNAH)ClO$_4$ (λ_{max} 417, 511, and 690 nm), and then those of FeTPP(BNAH)$_2$ClO$_4$ (λ_{max} 417, 576, and 630(sh) nm) with increasing the BNAH concentration (Figure 21). Similar spectral changes are observed by the addition of other NADH model compounds (4-MeOBNAH, 4-MeBNAH, 4-ClBNAH, 2,4-Cl$_2$BNAH, and AcrH$_2$) to CH$_2$Cl$_2$ solutions of MnTPPClO$_4$ as well as FeTPPClO$_4$. The K$_1$ and K$_2$ values determined by the analyses of the spectral changes are listed in Table 7,[62] together with the one-electron oxidation potentials (E$^0_{ox}$) of the NADH model compounds in MeCN.[16] Both the K$_1$ and K$_2$ values increase with an negative shift in E$^0_{ox}$, when the donor ability as well as the basicity of NADH model compounds is increased.

The ^{1}H NMR signals of pyrrole protons of iron(III) porphyrin complexes, which are quite sensitive to the spin states, indicate that these two BNAH complexes are high-spin paramagnetic molecules with S 5/2.[62] It should be noted that formation of such a six-coordinate high-spin iron(III) porphyrin complex FeTPP(BNAH)$_2$$^+$ is unusual, since most synthetic high-spin iron(III) porphyrin complexes are known to be five-coordinate,[63] although six-coordinate high-spin

Table 7. Formation constants K$_1$ and K$_2$ for the Complexes Formed between Metalloporphyrins (FeTPPClO$_4$, FeTPPCl, MnTPPClO$_4$, CoTPPClO$_4$) and NADH Analogues in CH$_2$Cl$_2$ at 298 K, and the One-Electron Oxidation Potentials of NADH Analogues in MeCN at 298 K[62]

metallo-porphyrin	ligand	E$^0_{red}$ vs. SCE,[a] V	K$_1$,[b] M	K$_2$,[b] M
FeTPPClO$_4$	4-MeOBNAH	0.50	1.6 x 10^4	7.6 x 10^2
FeTPPClO$_4$	4-MeBNAH	0.54	9.3 x 10^3	7.0 x 10^2
FeTPPClO$_4$	BNAH	0.57	7.9 x 10^3	6.7 x 10^2
FeTPPClO$_4$	4-ClBNAH	0.62	5.4 x 10^3	3.6 x 10^2
FeTPPClO$_4$	2,4-Cl$_2$BNAH	0.59	4.9 x 10^3	2.3 x 10^2
FeTPPClO$_4$	AcrH$_2$	0.80	2.1 x 10^3	2.4 x 10^2
FeTPPCl	BNAH	0.57	2.6 x 10	c
MnTPPClO$_4$	BNAH	0.57	2.5 x 10^2	8.5 x 10^1
CoTPPClO$_4$	BNAH	0.57	c	c

[a] Taken from ref 16. [b] The experimental errors are within ± 10%. [c] Too small to be determined accurately.

complexes are often observed in naturally occurring systems such as methemo-globin and metmyoglobin.[64] The high-spin state of FeTPP(BNAH)$_2$$^+$ is further confirmed by the ESR spectrum at 77 K, which showed the characteristic anisotropic signals at g = 5.7 and g = 2.0, as expected for high-spin iron(III) species.[65] The measurements of the solution magnetic susceptibilities using the Evans n.m.r. method also support the formation of the high-spin iron(III) species.[62]

The dependence of the half-wave potentials (E$_{1/2}$) of FeTPPClO$_4$ on the BNAH concentration indicates that not only FeTPP$^+$ but also FeTPP forms bis coordination complexes with BNAH, as shown in Figure 22, where the simula-tion curves according to the redox processes of FeTPP$^+$/FeTPP and their com-plex formation with BNAH in Scheme 4 agree well with the experimental results.[62] The E$_{1/2}$ value for the Mn^{III}/Mn^{II} couple exhibits a different dependence on [BNAH]$_0$ from that for the Fe^{III}/Fe^{II} couple as also shown in Figure 21,[62] where the E$_{1/2}$ value of Mn^{III}/Mn^{II} redox couple is shifted cathodically by 60 mV/log[BNAH]$_0$. Thus, on the contrary to FeTPP, MnTPP forms only a monoligand adduct with BNAH. Such preferences of FeTPP and MnTPP to form mono- and bis-coordination complexes, respectively, are well known for the corresponding pyridine complexes.[66] The redox processes of MnTPP$^+$/MnTPP and their com-plex formation with BNAH are summarized in Scheme 5.

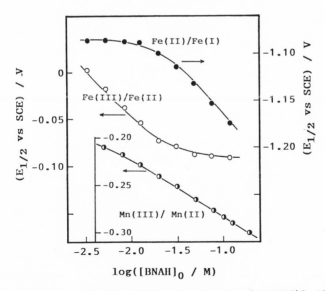

Figure 22. Plots of E$_{1/2}$ vs log[BNAH]$_0$ for the reduction of FeTPPClO$_4$ (○), FeTPP (●), and MnTPPClO$_4$ (◐) in a CH$_2$Cl$_2$ solution containing various concentrations of BNAH at 298 K. The solid lines are drawn by the simulation based on Schemes 4 and 5.[62]

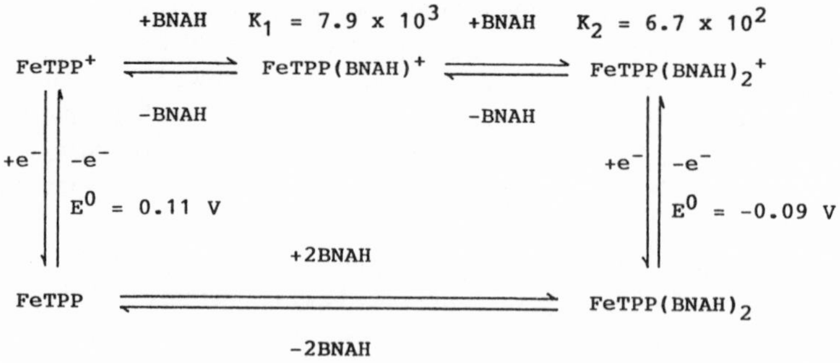

$$+\text{BNAH} \quad K_1 = 7.9 \times 10^3 \quad +\text{BNAH} \quad K_2 = 6.7 \times 10^2$$

$$\text{FeTPP}^+ \rightleftarrows \text{FeTPP}(\text{BNAH})^+ \rightleftarrows \text{FeTPP}(\text{BNAH})_2^+$$

$-\text{BNAH}$ $\quad\quad\quad\quad\quad$ $-\text{BNAH}$

$+e^- \quad -e^-$ $\quad\quad\quad\quad\quad\quad\quad\quad\quad\quad$ $+e^- \quad -e^-$

$E^0 = 0.11$ V $\quad\quad\quad\quad\quad\quad\quad\quad\quad\quad$ $E^0 = -0.09$ V

$+2\text{BNAH}$

$$\text{FeTPP} \rightleftarrows \text{FeTPP}(\text{BNAH})_2$$

-2BNAH

Scheme 4.

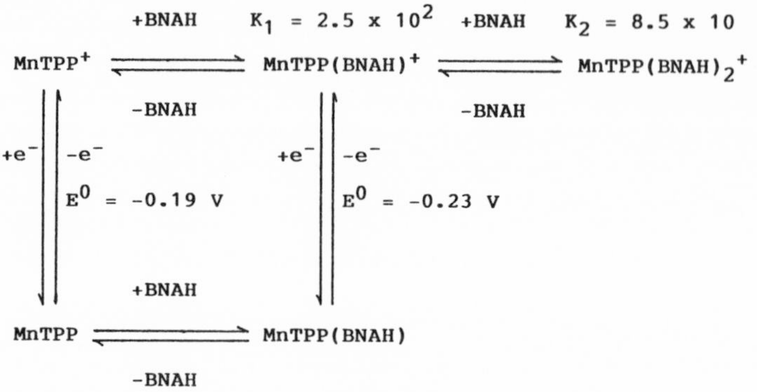

$$+\text{BNAH} \quad K_1 = 2.5 \times 10^2 \quad +\text{BNAH} \quad K_2 = 8.5 \times 10$$

$$\text{MnTPP}^+ \rightleftarrows \text{MnTPP}(\text{BNAH})^+ \rightleftarrows \text{MnTPP}(\text{BNAH})_2^+$$

$-\text{BNAH}$ $\quad\quad\quad\quad\quad\quad$ $-\text{BNAH}$

$+e^- \quad -e^-$ $\quad\quad\quad\quad\quad$ $+e^- \quad -e^-$

$E^0 = -0.19$ V $\quad\quad\quad\quad$ $E^0 = -0.23$ V

$+\text{BNAH}$

$$\text{MnTPP} \rightleftarrows \text{MnTPP}(\text{BNAH})$$

$-\text{BNAH}$

Scheme 5.

4.2. Metalloporphyrin-Catalyzed Reduction of Dioxygen

Metalloporphyrin-catalyzed reduction of dioxygen has been extensively studied in the electrochemical system in conjunction with the search of an inexpensive cathode material for dioxygen fuel cell,[67] and four-electron reduction of dioxygen to water has been achieved by using various dimeric metalloporphyrins[68] as well as monomeric indium porphyrins.[69] Here we show that an NADH analogue can be used as an electron source in the metalloporphyrin-catalyzed reduction of dioxygen. Four-electron reduction of dioxygen by an NADH analogue can also be achieved by using an appropriate electron carrier.

Two-Electron Reduction

Addition of a catalytic amount of CoTPP^+ (the perchlorate salt, TPP = tetraphenylporpyrin) to the aerated MeCN solution of AcrH_2 in the presence of HClO_4 at 298 K results in the facile oxidation of AcrH_2 by O_2 to yield AcrH^+

(λ_{max} = 358 nm) as shown in Figure 23,[70] where the concentration of CoTPP$^+$ (λ_{max} = 434 nm) remains constant with reaction time. The stoichiometry is given by Eq. 62, which is confirmed by the detection of the equivalent amounts

$$AcrH_2 + O_2 + H^+ \xrightarrow[CoTPP^+]{} AcrH^+ + H_2O_2 \qquad (62)$$

of AcrH$^+$ and H$_2$O$_2$.[70] Thus, CoTPP$^+$ acts as an efficient and stable catalyst for the two-electron reduction of dioxygen in the presence of HClO$_4$ in MeCN. Such a catalytic function can be replaced by FeTPP$^+$. In this case, however, the catalytic activity decreases gradually during the reaction due to demetallation of FeTPP$^+$ to give H$_3$TPP$^+$.[70]

In the absence of dioxygen, AcrH$_2$ is readily oxidized by CoTPP$^+$ to yield AcrH$^+$ and CoTPP.[70] The stoichiometry of the reaction is given by Eq. 63. When

$$AcrH_2 + 2CoTPP^+ \longrightarrow AcrH^+ + H^+ + 2CoTPP \qquad (63)$$

HClO$_4$ is added to the AcrH$_2$ – CoTPP$^+$ system in MeCN, the second-order rate constant decreases with an increase in the HClO$_4$ concentration as shown in Table 8. Such a decrease in the rate constant is accompanied by the decrease of the absorbance of AcrH$_2$ due to the protonation equilibrium in MeCN (Eq. 29).[34,60] Thus, only free AcrH$_2$ may be active for the reduction of CoTPP$^+$ and this is the reason why the k_{obs} value decreases with an increase of the HClO$_4$ concentration

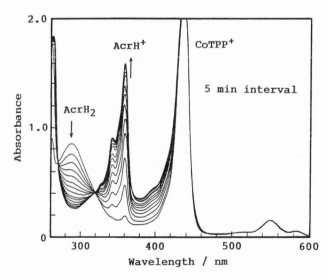

Figure 23. Oxidation of AcrH$_2$ (8.0 × 10^{-4} M) with dioxygen (2.6 × 10^{-3} M), catalyzed by CoTPP$^+$ (8.0 × 10^{-5} M) in the presence of HClO$_4$ (2.0 × 10^{-3} M) in MeCN at 298 K.[70]

Table 8.   Rate Constants (k_{obs}) for the Oxidation of AcrH$_2$ and AcrD$_2$
by CoTPP$^+$ in the Absence and Presence of HClO$_4$ in MeCN at 298 K[70]

[HClO$_4$], M	k_{obs}(AcrH$_2$),[a] $M^{-1} s^{-1}$	k_{obs}(AcrD$_2$),[a] $M^{-1} s^{-1}$	k^H_{obs}/k^D_{obs}
0	5.7	1.3	4.4
1.0×10^{-4}	4.9	1.1	4.5
1.0×10^{-3}	2.6×10^{-1}	5.9×10^{-2}	4.4
1.0×10^{-2}	b	b	

[a] The experimental errors are within ±5%. [b] Too slow to be determined accurately.

(Table 8). The observation of the primary kinetic isotope effect, which is constant with the change in [HClO$_4$] as also shown in Table 8 (k_H/k_D = 4.4 ± 0.4) may be ascribed to that of the deprotonation step of AcrH$_2$$^{+\cdot}$, which is required for two-electron oxidation of AcrH$_2$ as discussed in Section 2.1.

On the other hand, CoTPP is readily oxidized by dioxygen in the presence of HClO$_4$ in MeCN (Eq. 64),[70] although no reaction occurs in the absence of

$$2CoTPP + O_2 + 2H^+ \longrightarrow 2CoTPP^+ + H_2O_2 \qquad (64)$$

HClO$_4$. Thus, the simplest reaction scheme of the catalytic two-electron reduction of dioxygen by AcrH$_2$ may be given by Scheme 6. The rate determining step may be the oxidation of AcrH$_2$ by CoTPP$^+$ by AcrH$_2$, since the oxidation of CoTPP by dioxygen is much faster than the oxidation of AcrH$_2$ by CoTPP in the presence of HClO$_4$ in MeCN.[70] However, the dependence of rates of the oxidation for AcrH$_2$ by CoTPP$^+$ on the HClO$_4$ concentration are different in the absence and presence of dioxygen; the rate in the absence of dioxygen decreases with an increase in the HClO$_4$ concentration (Table 8), but the rate in the presence of dioxygen increases with an increase in the HClO$_4$ concentration to

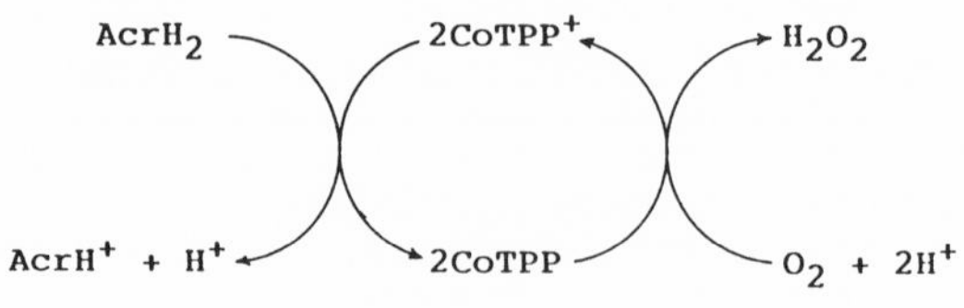

Scheme 6.

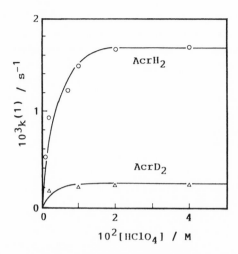

Figure 24. Plots of pseudo-first-order rate constants $k^{(1)}$ vs [HClO$_4$] for the oxidation of 2.0×10^{-4} M AcrH$_2$ (○) and AcrD$_2$ (△) with dioxygen (2.6×10^{-3} M), catalyzed by CoTPP$^+$ (2.0×10^{-4} M) in the presence of HClO$_4$ in MeCN at 298 K.[70]

reach a constant value as shown in Figure 24.[70] Moreover, the kinetic isotope effects (k^H_{obs}/k^D_{obs}) are different in the absence (4.4 in Table 8) and presence of dioxygen (7.1 in Figure 24). Such differences indicate that the mechanisms of oxidation of AcrH$_2$ by CoTPP$^+$ in the presence of HClO$_4$ are different in the absence and presence of dioxygen and that the acid-catalyzed reduction of O$_2$ by CoTPP should also be involved in the rate determining step in the catalytic two-electron reduction of O$_2$ by AcrH$_2$. Thus, the actual mechanism may be given by Scheme 7,[70] where electron transfer from AcrH$_2$ to CoTPP$^+$ occurs in concert with the reduction of O$_2$ by CoTPP in the presence of HClO$_4$. In such a case, electron transfer from AcrH$_2$ to CoTPP$^+$ in the presence of O$_2$ and HClO$_4$ may produce a radical pair (AcrH$_2^{+\cdot}$CoTPPO$_2$H$^{+\cdot}$) which may disappear by the facile hydrogen transfer from AcrH$_2^{+\cdot}$ to CoTPPO$_2$H$^{+\cdot}$ to yield AcrH$^+$ and H$_2$O$_2$, accompanied by regeneration of CoTPP$^+$ (Scheme 7). According to Scheme 7, the catalytic rate is proportional to the concentrations of CoTPP$^+$ and dioxygen

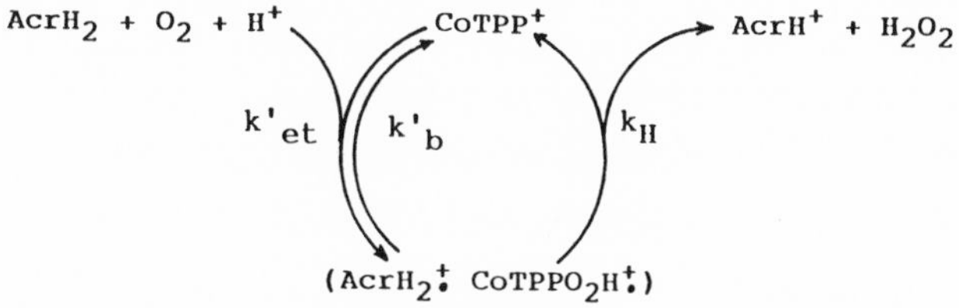

$$AcrH_2 + O_2 + H^+ \quad \overset{CoTPP^+}{\underset{(AcrH_2^{\cdot+}\ CoTPPO_2H_2^+)}{\bigvee}} \quad AcrH^+ + H_2O_2$$

$$k'_{et} \quad k'_b \quad k_H$$

Scheme 7.

and it may increase with an increase in [$HClO_4$] to reach a constant value due to the cancellation of the acid-catalyzed effect by the deactivation effect of the protonation of $AcrH_2$, in agreement with the experimental results (Figure 24). In addition, the kinetic isotope effect in the presence of dioxygen in Figure 24 ($k_{obs}^H/k_{obs}^D = 7.1$) may be ascribed to that of hydrogen transfer from $AcrH_2^{+\cdot}$ to $CoTPPO_2H^{+\cdot}$. This may be the reason why the observed kinetic isotope effect in the presence of dioxygen (Figure 24) is different from that in the absence of dioxygen where the isotope effect in Table VIII ($k_H/k_D = 4.4$) may be caused by the deprotonation step of $AcrH_2^{+\cdot}$.

Four-Electron Reduction

When iodide ion is used as an electron source, $CoTPP^+$ catalyzes efficiently the overall four-electron reduction of dioxygen by iodide ion in the presence of $HClO_4$ to yield water (Eq. 65).[70] The reduction of $CoTPP^+$ by iodide ion also

$$4I^- \ + \ O_2 \ + \ 4H^+ \ \xrightarrow[\text{CoTPP}^+]{} \ 2I_2 \ + \ 2H_2O \tag{65}$$

occurs rapidly in the absence of dioxygen in MeCN.[70] In the presence of dioxygen and $HClO_4$, CoTPP formed in the reduction of $CoTPP^+$ by I^- can be readily oxidized by dioxygen to produce $CoTPPO_2H^{+\cdot}$ as in Scheme 7. The $CoTPPO_2H^{+\cdot}$ may be reduced by I^- in the presence of $HClO_4$ to yield $CoTPPO_2H_2^{+\cdot}$ which may be further reduced by I^- to yield H_2O. Thus, as shown in Scheme 8,[70] $CoTPP^+$ can catalyze the overall four-electron reduction of dioxygen by I^-.

Iodine formed in the overall four-electron reduction of dioxygen by iodide ion (Eq. 65) is readily reduced by $AcrH_2$ to regenerate iodide ion in MeCN (Eq. 66).[70] Thus, the combination of the $CoTPP^+$-catalyzed oxidation of $AcrH_2$ by

$$AcrH_2 \ + \ I_2 \ \longrightarrow \ AcrH^+ \ + \ H^+ \ + \ 2I^- \tag{66}$$

dioxygen in the presence of $HClO_4$ (Scheme 7) and the catalytic four-electron reduction of dioxygen by I^- (Scheme 8) may result in the overall four-electron reduction of dioxygen by $AcrH_2$. In fact, when iodide ion is added to the catalytic system of the two-electron reduction of dioxygen (Eq. 62), the stoichiometry is changed to the overall four-electron reduction of dioxygen by $AcrH_2$ (Eq. 67).[70] Essentially the same results are obtained when I^- is replaced

$$2AcrH_2 \ + \ O_2 \ + \ 2H^+ \ \xrightarrow[\text{CoTPP}^+/I^-]{} \ 2AcrH^+ \ + \ 2H_2O \tag{67}$$

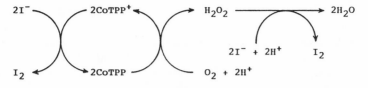

Scheme 8.

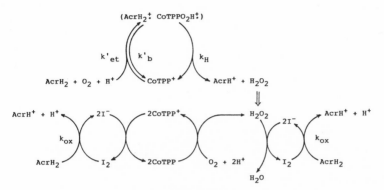

Scheme 9.

by I_2.[70] The mechanism of the catalytic overall four-electron reduction of dioxygen with $AcrH_2$ in the presence of $CoTPP^+$, $HClO_4$, and I^- may be given as shown in Scheme 9 by combining the reduction of I_2 by $AcrH_2$ with Schemes 7 and 8.[70]

5. MECHANISMS OF PHOTOREDUCTION OF SUBSTRATES BY NADH ANALOGUES

The one-electron redox potential of the excited state of an electron donor (D*) is given by Eq. 68, where $E_{0,0}(D-D^*)$ is the zero-zero excitation energy.[10] According to Eqs. 6 and 68, electron transfer of D* becomes energetically much

$$E^0(D^{+\cdot}/D^*) = E^0(D^{+\cdot}/D) - E_{0,0}(D-D^*) \qquad (68)$$

more favorable by the excitation as compared to that of the ground state (D). As such electron transfer from the excited states of NADH analogues to various oxidants occurs efficiently (c.f. Eq. 28). In this Section let us examine mechanisms of photoreduction of substrates by NADH analogues initiated by such photoinduced electron transfer.

5.1.   Photoinduced Radical Chain Mechanisms

On some occasions free radicals produced by photoinduced electron transfer undergo radical chain reactions.[72] For example, hydrogen abstraction of a substrate free radical (SH˙) from NADH, coupled with electron transfer from NAD˙ to the substrate (S) in the presence of proton constitutes a propagation step for two-electron reduction of a substrate (S) by NADH to yield NAD^+ and the reduced substrate (SH_2) as shown in Scheme 10.[10] First we examine such photoinduced radical chain mechanisms of reduction of substrates by NADH analogues.

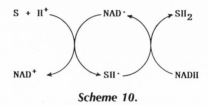

Scheme 10.

Reduction of Dioxygen

The excitation of an MeCN solution of $AcrH_2$ (λ_{max} = 285 nm) results in fluorescence (λ_{max} = 385 nm). The singlet excited state $^1AcrH_2^*$ is efficiently quenched by electron transfer to dioxygen with the diffusion limited rate (1.9×10^{10} M^{-1} s^{-1}).[73] Such photoinduced electron transfer from $^1AcrH_2^*$ to dioxygen initiates the two-electron reduction of dioxygen by $AcrH_2$ in the presence of $HClO_4$ and H_2O (2.6 M) in MeCN (Eq. 69).[73] The presence of H_2O is necessary

$$AcrH_2 \;+\; O_2 \;+\; H^+ \xrightarrow{\;h\nu\;} AcrH^+ \;+\; H_2O_2 \qquad (69)$$

in order to prevent the protonation of $AcrH_2$ by $HClO_4$ in MeCN, which would cause the disappearance of the absorption band due to $AcrH_2$.[34,59] The quantum yield (Φ) for the photooxidation of $AcrH_2$ by dioxygen in the presence of $HClO_4$ (1.0×10^{-3} mol dm^{-3}) in MeCN containing H_2O (2.6 mol dm^{-3}) is proportional to the concentration of $AcrH_2$ with each light intensity as shown in Figure 25,[73] where the quantum yield exceeds unity in the high concentrations of $AcrH_2$. The Φ value is proportional to reciprocal of the square root of light intensity in each concentration of $AcrH_2$. The large quantum yields exceeding unity in Figure 25, combined with the dependence of Φ on the light intensity indicate strongly that the photooxidation of $AcrH_2$ by dioxygen in the presence of $HClO_4$ proceeds via radical chain reactions, initiated by the UV irradiation as shown in Scheme 11.[73] In the initiation step, the excitation of $AcrH_2$ results in the

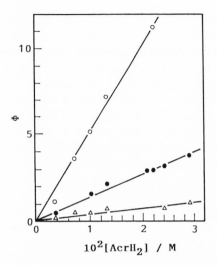

Figure 25. Dependence of the quantum yield (Φ) on the AcrH$_2$ concentration for the photooxidation of AcrH$_2$ by oxygen (2.6 × 10^{-3} M) in the presence of HClO$_4$ (1.0 × 10^{-3} M) and H$_2$O (2.6 M) in MeCN under irradiation of light (220 nm < λ < 440 nm); light intensity (In) 3.4 × 10^{-7} ($\bigcirc$), 5.5 × 10^{-6} ($\bullet$), 3.4 × 10^{-5} ($\triangle$) einstein dm^{-3} s^{-1}.[73]

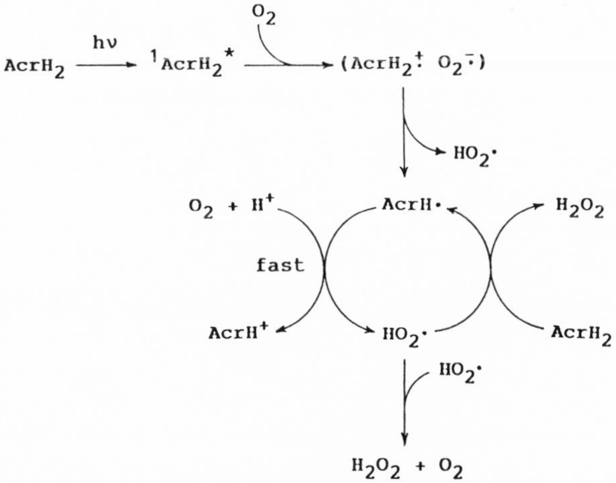

$$AcrH_2 \xrightarrow{h\nu} {}^1AcrH_2^* \xrightarrow{O_2} (AcrH_2^{\cdot+} \; O_2^{\cdot-})$$

Scheme with cycle:

$$\downarrow HO_2\cdot$$

$$O_2 + H^+ \quad AcrH\cdot \quad H_2O_2$$

$$\text{fast}$$

$$AcrH^+ \quad HO_2\cdot \quad AcrH_2$$

$$\downarrow HO_2\cdot$$

$$H_2O_2 + O_2$$

Scheme 11.

formation of the singlet state of $AcrH_2$ ($^1AcrH_2$*), which transfers an electron to O_2 to produce the radical ion pair ($AcrH_2^{+\cdot}O_2^{-\cdot}$) which may dissociate to yield $AcrH^\cdot$ and $HO_2^\cdot$ by the facile proton transfer from $AcrH_2^{+\cdot}$ to $O_2^{-\cdot}$. In the propagation step, $HO_2^\cdot$ abstracts a hydrogen atom from $AcrH_2$ to give H_2O_2 and $AcrH^\cdot$. The electron transfer from $AcrH^\cdot$ to O_2 is endothermic in MeCN, since the oxidation potential of $AcrH^\cdot$ (-0.43 V)[16] is more positive than the reduction potential of O_2 (-0.86 V).[74a] In the presence of $HClO_4$, however, the reduction potential of O_2 may be shifted in the positive direction,[74b] making it possible that $AcrH^\cdot$ transfers an electron to O_2 to yield $AcrH^+$, regenerating $HO_2^\cdot$ (Scheme 10). The termination step is the disproportionation of $HO_2^\cdot$ to yield H_2O_2 and O_2 (Scheme 11).

By applying the steady-state approximation to the radical species ($HO_2^\cdot$ and $AcrH^\cdot$) in Scheme 11, the quantum yield (Φ) given as the function of the light intensity (In) and the concentration of $AcrH_2$ (Eq. 70),[73] where Φ_0 is the quantum

$$\Phi = k_p(\Phi_0/k_t In)^{1/2}[AcrH_2] \tag{70}$$

yield of the initiation step, k_p is the rate constant of the rate-determining propagation step, and k_t is the rate constant of the termination step. Equation 70 agrees well with the experimental results that the Φ value is proportional to the $AcrH_2$ concentration and the reciprocal of the square root of the light intensity ($In^{-1/2}$) as shown in Figure 25.

The primary kinetic isotope effect Φ_H/Φ_D determined by using $AcrD_2$ as the ratio of the rate of formation of $AcrH^+$ to that of $AcrD^+$ is plotted against the logarithm of the concentration of $AcrH_2$ in Figure 26,[73] where the Φ_H/Φ_D value is

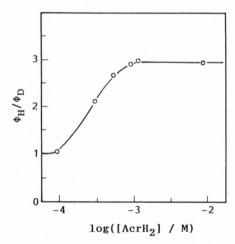

Figure 26. Dependence of the primary kinetic isotope effect (Φ_H/Φ_D) on the $AcrH_2$ concentration for the photooxidation of $AcrH_2$ by dioxygen (2.6×10^{-3} M) in the presence of $HClO_4$ (1.0×10^{-3} M) and H_2O (2.6 M) in MeCN under irradiation of the light (220 nm $< \lambda <$ 440 nm).[73]

approximately unity in the region $[AcrH_2] < 10^{-4}$ M and increases gradually in the region $[AcrH_2] > 10^{-4}$ M to reach a constant value ($\Phi_H/\Phi_D = 3.0$) in the region $[AcrH_2] > 10^{-3}$ M. Such dependence of Φ_H/Φ_D on the $AcrH_2$ concentration suggests that the chain length remains close to unity in the low $AcrH_2$ concentration ($< 10^{-3}$ M) where the rate is mainly determined by the photoinduced electron transfer, while in the high $AcrH_2$ concentration ($> 10^{-3}$ M) the chain length is long enough so that the Φ_H/Φ_D value may be determined mainly by the propagation step where the abstraction of hydrogen from $AcrH_2$ or $AcrD_2$ is involved. In fact, the primary kinetic isotope effect of the hydrogen abstraction of $HO_2^{\cdot}$ from $AcrH_2$ ($K_H/k_D = 3.2 \pm 0.3$), determined in the radical chain decomposition of H_2O_2 by $AcrH_2$ initiated by the Fenton reaction,[73] agrees well with that observed in the photochemical reaction ($\Phi_H/\Phi_D = 3.0 \pm 0.3$). Such agreement confirms that the chain carrier is indeed the $HO_2^{\cdot}$ radical.

The photoreduction of dioxygen by BNAH in an aqueous solution also proceeds by photoinduced radical chain reactions as shown in Scheme 12.[73] In this case BNA$^{\cdot}$ can transfer and electron to O_2 to yield BNA$^+$ and $O_2^{-\cdot}$ in the absence of acid, since the electron transfer from BNA$^{\cdot}$ to dioxygen is highly exergonic based on the one-electron oxidation potential of BNA$^{\cdot}$ (-1.1 V)[16] and the one-electron reduction potential of O_2 (-0.4 V)[74] in a neutral aqueous solution. The hydrogen peroxyl radical $HO_2^{\cdot}$, which exists in equilibrium with $O_2^{-\cdot}$, can abstract hydrogen from BNAH to yield H_2O_2, regenerating BNA$^{\cdot}$ (Scheme 12).

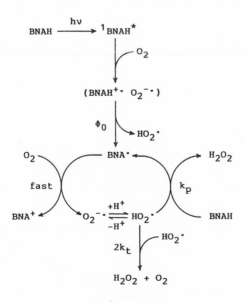

Scheme 12.

Reductive Dehalogenation

The carbon-halogen bond of halogenated compounds (RX) is known to be cleaved readily upon the one-electron reduction to produce alkyl radicals (Eq. 71).[75] The alkyl radical can act as a chain carrier in the radical chain reactions

$$RX \xrightarrow{+e} R\cdot + X^- \qquad (71)$$

in the reductive dehalogenation of RX by NADH analogues. For example, electron transfer from the singlet excited state ^{1}BNAH* to benzyl bromide occurs efficiently ($k_{et} = 4.9 \times 10^9 \, M^{-1} \, s^{-1}$) to produce benzyl radical that can initiate the radical chain reactions as shown in Scheme 13.[76] The benzyl radicals formed in the initiation step abstract hydrogen from BNAH to yield a dehalogenated product PhCH$_3$ and a radical intermediate BNA$\cdot$. Electron transfer from BNA$\cdot$ to PhCH$_2$Br may occur readily to yield BNA$^+$ and PhCH$_2$Br$^{-\cdot}$ which fragments to regenerate benzyl radical (Scheme 13), since benzyl bromide is known to be reduced electrochemically at the oxidation potential of BNA$\cdot$ ($E^0_{ox} = -1.08$ V vs. SCE).[16] As is the case of the photoreduction of dioxygen in Figure 25, the quantum yield increases linearly with an increase in [PhCH$_2$Br], exceeding unity (e.g., $\Phi = 1.61$, when the chain length is 20).[76]

The overall stoichiometry of the photoreduction of PhCH$_2$Br by BNAH in the presence of pyridine in deaerated MeCN is given by Eq. 72.[76] A small amount of the radical coupling product (1,2-diphenylethane) in the termination step (Scheme 13) is also obtained as a byproduct (3–4%).[76] The presence of pyridine

$$BNAH + PhCH_2Br \xrightarrow[\text{MeCN/pyridine}]{h\nu \, (\lambda > 360 \text{ nm})} BNA^+ + Br^- + PhCH_3 \qquad (72)$$

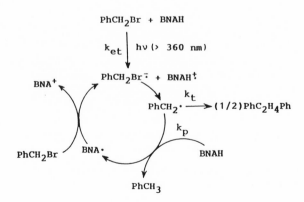

Scheme 13.

seems essential for obtaining a high yield of toluene, since proton that would otherwise be produced from $BNAH^{+\cdot}$ causes the catalytic decomposition of BNAH. In the presence of dioxygen, the chain carrier radicals ($PhCH_2$) are trapped by dioxygen to yield benzylperoxyl radicals (Eq. 73) that undergo a bimolecular reaction to yield equimolar amounts of benzyl alcohol and ben-zaldehyde as well as dioxygen (Eq. 74),[77] when the formation of toluene is

$$2PhCH_2\cdot \ + \ O_2 \ \longrightarrow \ PhCH_2O_2\cdot \tag{73}$$

$$2PhCH_2O_2\cdot \ \longrightarrow PhCH_2OH \ + \ PhCHO \ + \ O_2 \tag{74}$$

completely suppressed.[76] The radical chain character of the reaction is also evident from the strong inhibitory effect of a radical scavenger, isopentyl nitrite as shown in Figure 27.[78]

Essentially the same photoinduced radical chain mechanism is operative for the photoreduction of phenacyl bromide by BNAH as shown in Scheme 14.[79] In the initiation step, electron transfer from $^1BNAH^*$ to $PhCOCH_2Br$ occurs more efficiently with the diffusion limited rate ($k_{et} = 2.3 \times 10^{10}$ M^{-1} s^{-1}) as compared with the case of $PhCH_2Br$.[79] The observation of a large kinetic isotope effect ($\Phi_H/\Phi_D = 4.1$)[79] indicates that the rate-determining step of chain propaga-

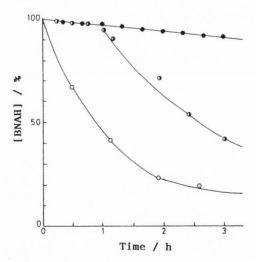

Figure 27. Inhibition of the photoreduction of benzyl bromide (7.60×10^{-1} M) by BNA (4.21×10^{-2} M) in MeCN containing pyridine (1.11×10^{-1} M) with In = 3.55×10^{-6} einstein dm^{-3} s^{-1}; ($\bigcirc$) no inhibitor; ($\bullet$) 6.64×10^{-12} isopentyl nitrite; ($\circledcirc$) 1.34×10^{-3} M isopentyl nitrite.[76]

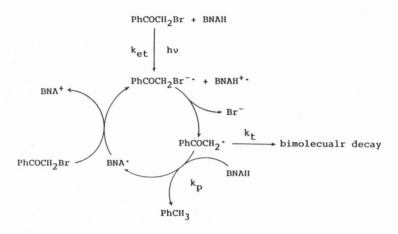

Scheme 14.

tion involves an abstraction of hydrogen atom from BNAH, when the Φ value increases linearly with an increase in [BNAH] to exceed unity (e.g., $\Phi = 4.5$).

By applying the steady-state approximation to the radical species in Scheme 14, the quantum yield may be expressed by Eq. 75, where k_p is the rate constant

$$\Phi = k_p (\Phi_i / 2k_t \mathrm{In})^{1/2} [\mathrm{BNAH}] \tag{75}$$

of the rate-determining propagation step, Φ_i is the quantum yield for the initiation, k_t is the rate constant of the termination step, and In is the light intensity absorbed by BNAH. The initiation quantum yield Φ_i may be given by Eq. 76,

$$\Phi_i = \Phi_\infty K_{et} [\mathrm{PhCOCH_2Br}] / (1 + K_{et} [\mathrm{PhCOCH_2Br}]) \tag{76}$$

where Φ_∞ is the limiting quantum yield to quench all the singlet excited state by $\mathrm{PhCOCH_2Br}$ and $K_{et} = k_{et}\tau^{-1}$ (k_{et} is the rate constant of electron transfer from $^1\mathrm{BNAH^*}$ to phenacyl bromide and τ is the lifetime of $^1\mathrm{BNAH^*}$). Equation 76 agrees well with the experimental dependence of Φ on the BNAH concentration as well as on the light intensity. From Eqs. 75 and 76 is derived Eq. 77, where C

$$\Phi^{-2} = C[1 + (K_{et} [\mathrm{PhCOCH_2Br}])^{-1}] \tag{77}$$

$= 2k_t \mathrm{In}/(\Phi_\infty k_p [\mathrm{BNAH}]^2)$. Linear correlations between Φ^{-2} and $[\mathrm{PhCOCH_2Br}]^{-1}$ for different light intensities in Figure 28 agree well with Eq. 77.[79] From the intercepts and slopes in Figure 28, essentially the same K_{et} values are obtained for different light intensities ($K_{et} = 14$ and 16 for In $= 1.2 \times 10^{-6}$ and $3.9 \times$

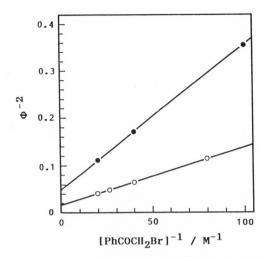

Figure 28. Plots of Φ^{-2} vs light intensity for the photoreduction of phenacyl bromide by BNAH (2.0×10^{-2} M) in MeCN under irradiation of light $\lambda = 370$ nm; [PhCOCH$_2$Br] $= 2.5 \times 10^{-2}$ (○), 5.0×10^{-2} (●) M.[79]

10^{-6} einstein dm^{-3} s^{-1}, respectively).[79] More importantly, the K_{et} values obtained from Figure 28 agree well with that obtained from the fluorescence quenching of ^{1}BNAH* by phenacyl bromide ($K_{et} = 16$ dm^3 mol^{-1}). Such agreements clearly demonstrate that the electron transfer from ^{1}BNAH* to phenacyl bromide is solely responsible for the photoinitiation of the radical chain reaction (Scheme 14).

5.2. Direct Photoreduction by the Excited States

As demonstrated above, HO$_2$ and R· radicals produced by photoinduced electron transfer can initiate radical chain reactions in photoreduction of dioxygen and halogenated compounds (RX) by BNAH. In some cases, however, the direct reduction of substrates by the excited states of NADH analogues is also possible without the contribution of radical chain processes. We examine here the origin of such mechanistic difference by comparing the mechanisms of photoreduction of the same substrate, pheacyl bromide by two different types of NADH model compounds, i.e., BNAH and AcrH$_2$. It should be noted that the most significant difference between BNAH and AcrH$_2$ lies in the difference in the reducing ability of the corresponding neutral radicals BNA· ($E^0_{ox} = -1.08$ V) and AcrH· (-0.43 V).[16]

Irradiation of a deaerated MeCN solution containing AcrH$_2$ and PhCOCH$_2$X (X = Br and Cl) with monochromatized light of $\lambda = 320$ nm which is beyond the absorption maxima of PhCOCH$_2$X results in the conversion of AcrH$_2$ and

$PhCOCH_2X$ into $AcrH^+$ and $PhCOCH_3$, respectively (Eq. 78).[79] When $AcrH_2$ is replaced by the 9,9′-dideuteriated compounds ($AcrD_2$) in the photochemical

$$AcrH_2 + PhCOCH_2X \xrightarrow{h\nu} AcrH^+ + X^- + PhCOCH_3 \qquad (78)$$

reaction with phenacyl bromide in thoroughly dried MeCN, phenacyl bromide is converted to monodeuteriated acetophenone ($PhCOCH_2D$) quantitatively.[79] However, no deuterium is incorporated into the reduced product when H_2O (0.10 M) is added to the $AcrD_2$-phenacyl bromide system. In contrast with the case of BNAH described above, the quantum yields are constant with change of [$AcrH_2$] as shown in Figure 29. In addition, no primary kinetic isotope effect is observed in this case (c.f. $\Phi_H/\Phi_D = 4.1$ in the case of BNAH).[79]

Based on the above results, the mechanism of the photoreduction of $PhCOCH_2X$ by $AcrH_2$ may be given as shown in Scheme 15.[79] First, the photoinduced electron transfer from $^1AcrD_2^*$ to $PhCOCH_2X$ may occur to yield the radical ion pair ($AcrD_2^{+\cdot}\ PhCOCH_2X^{-\cdot}$). Radical anions of phenacyl halides undergo an intramolecular electron transfer to release halide ions.[80] At the same time, the radical anions are readily protonated, and the resulting neutral radicals do not release the halide ions.[81] Thus, there may be the competition between the proton transfer from $AcrD_2^{+\cdot}$ to $PhCOCH_2X^{-\cdot}$ and the intramolecular electron transfer to release the halide ion (Scheme 15). If the proton transfer is much

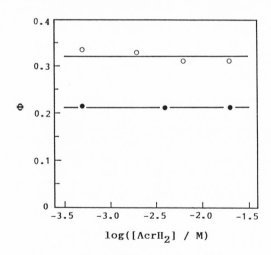

Figure 29. Dependence of the quantum yields Φ on the $AcrH_2$ concentration for the photoreduction of phenacyl bromide ($\bigcirc$) and phenacyl chloride ($\bullet$) by $AcrH_2$ in MeCN under irradiation of light $\lambda = 340$ nm; [$PhCOCH_2X$] $= 1.0 \times 10^{-3}$ M, the light intensity In $= 1.2 \times 10^{-6}$ einstein dm^{-3} s^{-1}.[79]

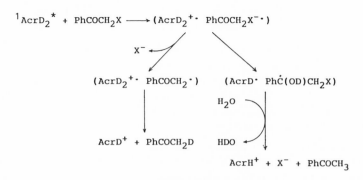

Scheme 15.

faster than the dehalogenation, the deuterium of the resulting $Ph\dot{C}(OD)CH_2X$ radical may be readily exchanged with H_2O to give $Ph\dot{C}(OH)CH_2X$ which yields the final product $PhCOCH_3$ by the subsequent electron transfer from AcrH⁻ (Scheme 15). This may be the reason why no deuterium has been incorporated into acetophenone in the presence of water. Alternatively, if the dehalogenation is much faster than the proton transfer, a hydrogen transfer from $AcrH_2{}^{+\cdot}$ to the dehalogenated radical $PhCOCH_2$ yields $PhCOCH_2D$. In such a case, however, no deuterium exchange with H_2O would be expected.

The mechanistic difference between the NADH analogues, $AcrH_2$ and BNAH, may be ascribed to the difference in pK_a of the corresponding radical cations between $AcrH_2{}^{+\cdot}$ and $BNAH^{+\cdot}$ as well as the difference in the one-electron oxidation potentials between AcrH⁻ and BNA⁻. The smaller pK_a value of $AcrH_2{}^{+\cdot}$ $(2.0)^{16}$ than $BNAH^{+\cdot}$ $(3.6)^{16}$ may be less favorable for the formation of free radicals $PhCOCH_2$, which can initiate the chain reactions (Scheme 14). In addition, the more positive E^0_{ox} value of AcrH⁻ $(-0.43$ V vs. SCE$)^{16}$ than BNA⁻ $(-1.08$ V vs. SCE$)^{16}$ may be less favorable for electron transfer from AcrH⁻ to $PhCOCH_2Br$, which is essential to constitute the radical chain process (Scheme 14). Thus, it may be concluded that an NADH analogue with the smaller pK_a value of the radical cation and the more positive E^0_{ox} value of the deprotonated radical becomes more favorable for the direct photoreduction pathway (Scheme 15), and that the opposite one favors the electron-transfer radical chain pathway (Scheme 14).

5.3. Competition of Dissociative Electron Transfer and Back Electron Transfer

The direct photoreduction of various halogenated compounds (RX; X = I, Br, and Cl) by $AcrH_2$ also occurs in MeCN (Eq. 79) without the contribution of radical chain processes.[82] In this case also electron transfer from AcrH⁻ to RX is energetically unfavorable in contrast with the case of BNAH (c.f. Scheme 13).

$$\text{AcrH}_2 + \text{RX} \xrightarrow{\quad h\nu \quad} \text{AcrH}^+ + \text{RH} + \text{X}^- \qquad (79)$$

Thus, the direct photoreduction may proceed *via* the competition of dissociative photoinduced electron transfer to produce R· and back electron transfer from RX⁻· to AcrH₂⁺· as shown in Scheme 16.[82] The dissociative electron transfer may be followed by facile hydrogen transfer from AcrH₂⁺· to R·, yielding AcrH⁺ and RH (Scheme 16).[82]

By applying the steady-state approximation to the reactive intermediates, ¹AcrH₂* and (AcrH₂⁺· RX⁻·) in Scheme 16, the dependence of Φ on [RX] can be derived as given by Eq. 80, which is rewritten by Eq. 81.[82] In fact, the plots of

$$\Phi = k_{et}\tau k_{br}[\text{RX}]/(1 + k_{et}\tau [\text{RX}])(k_{br} + k_{be}) \qquad (80)$$

$$\Phi^{-1} = k_{br}^{-1}(k_{br} + k_{be})[1 + (k_{et}\tau [\text{RX}])^{-1}] \qquad (81)$$

Φ^{-1} vs. $[\text{RX}]^{-1}$ give linear correlations from which the k_{et} value are obtained.[82] The same k_{et} values are also obtained from the fluorescence quenching of ¹AcrH₂* by RX as listed in Table 9.[82] The absence of primary kinetic isotope effects on k_q (Table 9) suggests that the quenching of ¹AcrH₂* with RX is electron transfer from ¹AcrH₂* to RX. The activation Gibbs energy ($\Delta G_{et}^{\neq}$) of such electron transfer is calculated using the Marcus equation (Eq. 82),[83] where ΔG_{et}^0 is the standard Gibbs energy change of electron transfer and $\Delta G_0^{\neq}$ is $\Delta G_{et}^{\neq}$ at zero driving force ($\Delta G_{et}^0 = 0$). The ΔG_{et}^0 values of electron transfer from ¹AcrH₂* to RX are obtained from the one-electron oxidation potential of the singlet excited state ¹AcrH₂* ($E_{ox}^0 = -3.1$ V vs. SCE)[10,16] and the one-electron

Scheme XVI

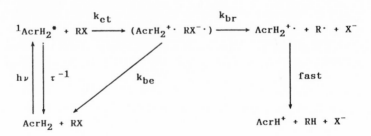

Scheme 16.

Table 9. Observed Rate Constants (k_q) for the Reactions of $^1AcrH_2^*$ and $^1AcrD_2^*$ with RX in MeCN at 298 K, Calculated Rate Constants of Electron Transfer from $^1AcrH_2^*$ to RX, and the Gibbs Energy Change (ΔG_{et}^0) and Intrinsic Barrier ($\Delta G_0^{\neq}$) of the Electron Transfer[82]

RX	$\Delta G^0{}_{et}{}^a$ kcal mol^{-1}	$\Delta G^{\neq}{}_0{}^b$ kcal mol^{-1}	$k_q(AcrH_2)^c$ M^{-1} s^{-1}	$k_q(AcrD_2)^c$ M^{-1} s^{-1}	$k_{et}{}^d$ M^{-1} s^{-1}
PhCl	-7.4^e	5.8^e	6.0 x 10^8	6.2 x 10^8	5 x 10^8
$\underline{p}$-CNC$_6$H$_4$Cl	-21.2^e	5.8^g	2.2 x 10^{10}	2.2 x 10^{10}	2 x 10^{10}
PhBr	-15.2^e	6.3^e	1.2 x 10^9	-	7 x 10^9
PhI	-	-	2.6 x 10^{10}	2.7 x 10^{10}	-
PhCH$_2$Cl	-50.9^f	18.3^h	3.0 x 10^9	2.7 x 10^9	4 x 10^9
CCl$_4$	-52.5^f	11.7^i	3.2 x 10^{10}	-	2 x 10^{10}
CHCl$_3$	-	-	2.0 x 10^{10}	-	-
CH$_2$Cl$_2$	-	-	3.8 x 10^8	3.3 x 10^8	-
C$_3$H$_7$Br	-44.5^f	17.7^j	4.6 x 10^8	4.6 x 10^8	1 x 10^9
C$_2$H$_5$Br	-45.2^f	17.7^j	7.0 x 10^8	6.4 x 10^8	1 x 10^9
PhCH$_2$Br	-55.3^f	17.7^j	2.6 x 10^{10}	-	1 x 10^{10}
C$_4$H$_9$I	-43.6^f	14.5^k	1.7 x 10^{10}	-	9 x 10^9
CH$_3$I	-41.2^f	14.5^l	1.8 x 10^{10}	-	7 x 10^9
C$_2$H$_5$I	-44.7^f	14.5^l	1.8 x 10^{10}	-	1 x 10^{10}

^{a} Obtained from the E_{ox}^0 and E_{red}^0 values of $^1AcrH_2^*$ (refs 10 and 16) and RX by using Eqs. 6 and 68. ^{b} Assumed to be the same as those reported for electron transfer from aromatic radical anions to RX. ^{c} The experimental errors are ± 10%. ^{d} Calculated by using Eqs. 33 and 82. ^{e} The E_{red}^0 values are taken from ref 84. ^{f} The E_{red}^0 values are taken from ref 87. ^{g} Assumed to be the same as that of PhCl. ^{h} Taken from ref 86b. ^{i} Obtained from the data reported in ref 86c by using Eq. 82. ^{j} Assumed to be the same as that of C$_4$H$_9$Br (ref 85), since the simple alkyl halides are known to have similar $\Delta G_0^{\neq}$ values (ref 86a). ^{k} Taken from ref 85. ^{l} Assumed to be the same as that of C$_4$H$_9$I.

reduction potentials of RX (E_{red}^0)[84-87] using Eq. 6. With regard to the intrinsic barrier for the one-electron reduction of RX, the $\Delta G_0^{\neq}$ values of electron transfer from electrogenerated aromatic radical anions to various halogenated compounds have been reported.[84-86] The reported $\Delta G_0^{\neq}$ values may be applied directly to the present case, since the intrinsic barrier for the one-electron oxidation of various aromatic radical anions being constant are similar to that of $AcrH_2$.[10,16] The ΔG_{et}^0 and $\Delta G_0^{\neq}$ values thus obtained are listed in Table 9. On the other hand, the rate constant of photoinduced electron transfer (k_{et}) is known to be given as a function of $\Delta G_{et}^{\neq}$ and ΔG_{et}^0, Eq. 33.[37] The k_{et} values calculated from the ΔG_{et}^0 and $\Delta G_0^{\neq}$ values in Table 9 by using Eqs. 33 and 82 agree well with the experimental values as shown in Table 9.

$$\Delta G^{\neq}{}_{et} = \Delta G^{\neq}{}_0 [1 + (\Delta G^0{}_{et}/4\Delta G^{\neq}{}_0)]^2 \tag{82}$$

According to Eq. 80, the limiting quantum yield Φ_∞ may be given by Eq. 83. The absence of primary kinetic isotope effects on Φ_∞ values in Table 10 also

$$\Phi_\infty = k_{br}/(k_{br} + k_{be}) \tag{83}$$

supports Eq. 83, where no hydrogen transfer process is involved.[82] According to Eq. 83, the Φ_∞ value may be determined by the competition between the bond-breaking process (k_{br}) and the back electron transfer process (k_{be}). The Gibbs energy change of the back electron transfer from $RX^{-\cdot}$ to $AcrH_2^{+\cdot}$ (ΔG_{be}^0) is obtained from the one-electron oxidation potential of $AcrH_2$ ($E_{ox}^0 = 0.80$ V vs. SCE)[16] and the one-electron reduction potentials of RX (E_{red}^0).[84,87] The ΔG_{be}^0 values thus obtained are also listed in Table 10.

Table 10. Limiting Quantum Yields (Φ_∞) of the Photoreduction of Halogenated Compounds (RX) by $AcrH_2$ and $AcrD_2$ in MeCN at 298 K and the Gibbs Energy Change (ΔG_{be}^0) of Back Electron Transfer from $RX^{-\cdot}$ to $AcrH_2$[82]

RX	$\Delta G_{be}^{0\ a}$ kcal mol^{-1}	Φ_∞ ($AcrH_2$)[b]	Φ_∞ ($AcrD_2$)[b]
PhCl	-83	0.12	0.12
$\underline{p}$-CNC$_6$H$_4$Cl	-69	0.17	0.17
PhBr	-76	0.20	-
PhI	-	0.21	0.20
PhCH$_2$Cl	-39	0.21	0.21
CCl$_4$	-37	0.34	-
CHCl$_3$	-	0.27	0.27
CH$_2$Cl$_2$	-	0.17	0.17
C$_3$H$_7$Br	-45	0.20	-
C$_2$H$_5$Br	-45	0.15	0.13
C$_4$H$_9$I	-46	0.32	-
PhCH$_2$Br	-35	0.31	-
CH$_3$I	-49	0.12	-
C$_2$H$_5$I	-45	0.15	-

[a] Obtained from the E_{ox}^0 and E_{red}^0 values of $AcrH_2$ (ref 16) and RX (refs 84 and 87) using Eq. 6. [b] The experimental errors are $\pm 10\%$.

It has been reported that the lifetime of radical anions of aromatic halides (k_{br}^{-1}) increases generally with the positive shift of the one-electron reduction potentials of aromatic halides.[85b] Unlike the case of aromatic halides, radical anions of alkyl halides are generally believed to have no detectable lifetime.[85,88] In this case as well the lifetime may increase with the positive shift of the one-electron reduction potentials of alkyl halides, since the discreet radical anions of alkyl halides with electron withdrawing substitutents such as $CCl_4^{-\cdot}$ and $CF_3X^{-\cdot}$ are known to exist.[89,90] Thus, the k_{br} values of radical anions of halogenated compounds in Table 9, where the Gibbs energy change of back electron transfer from $RX^{-\cdot}$ to $AcrH_2^{+\cdot}$ (ΔG_{be}^0) spanning a wide range are expected to vary significantly. In this context, the rather constant Φ_∞ values in Table 10 (0.12 − 0.32) may at first sight seem surprising. However, the k_{be} value may also vary in parallel with the k_{br} value. This possibility is indicated in Figure 30, which displays the plausible energy surface profiles of photoinduced electron transfer from $^1AcrH_2^*$ to RX schematically. Initially, excitation of $AcrH_2$ brings the reactant system to an excited-state energy surface where thermal equilibration into a lower vibration state is rapidly established. Following electron transfer,

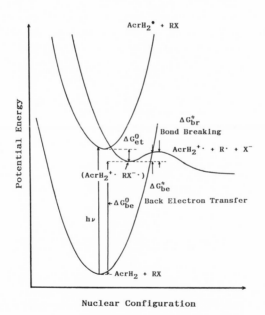

Figure 30. Qualitative potential energy curves for photoinduced electron transfer from $^1AcrH_2^*$ to RX emphasizing the similarity of the energetic barrier of back electron transfer from $RX^{-\cdot}$ to $AcrH_2^{+\cdot}$ and that of C-X bond breaking of $RX^{-\cdot}$.[82]

nuclear relaxation rapidly established the thermally equilibrated radical ion pair $(AcrH_2^{+\cdot} RX^{-\cdot})$. The stretching of $R - X$ bond of $RX^{-\cdot}$ by surmounting the bond breaking barrier $(\Delta G_{br}^{\neq})$ yields the products $(AcrH_2^{+\cdot}, R^{\cdot},$ and $X^-)$. When the back electron transfer from $RX^{-\cdot}$ to $AcrH_2^{+\cdot}$ is highly exergonic $(\Delta G_{be}^0 \ll 0)$ as shown in Table 10, the activation Gibbs energy of back electron transfer $(\Delta G_{be}^{\neq})$ may be close to that of bond breaking process $(\Delta G_{br}^{\neq})$ as shown in Figure 30. Thus, irrespective of the magnitude of $\Delta G_{br}^{\neq}$ (or lifetime of $RX^{-\cdot}$) the approximate relation $\Delta G_{br}^{\neq} \cong \Delta G_{be}^{\neq}$ $(k_{br} \cong k_{be})$ may always hold, when the Φ_∞ value $[= k_{br}/(k_{br} + k_{be})]$ is approximately constant being close to 0.5 as observed in Table 10 $(0.12 - 0.32)$.

5.4. Photosensitized Reactions

The photoreduction of substrates by the excited states of NADH analogues require UV or near-UV irradiation because of the high-lying excited states $(\lambda_{max} = 285$ and 350 nm for $AcrH_2$ and BNAH, respectively).[10] However, the use of a photosensitizer, $[Ru(bpy)_3]^{2+}$, makes it possible to utilize visible light to initiate the reaction.[10] Thus, the addition of $[Ru(bpy)_3]^{2+}$ to the BNAH-PhCH$_2$Br system and selective irradiation of the absorption band due to $[Ru(bpy)_3]^{2+}$ $(\lambda_{max} = 452$ nm) also results in the net photoreduction of PhCH$_2$Br by BNAH.[91] However, the photosensitized reaction yields the one-electron reduced product, 1,2-diphenylethane (Eq. 84)[91] instead of the two-electron reduced product, toluene obtained in the absence of $[Ru(bpy)_3]^{2+}$ (c.f. Eq. 72).[76] The dependence of Φ on

$$\text{BNAH} + 2\text{PhCH}_2\text{Br} \xrightarrow[\text{[Ru(bpy)}_3]^{2+}]{h\nu\ (\lambda > 400\ \text{nm})} \text{BNA}^+ + \text{PhC}_2\text{H}_4\text{Ph} + \text{Br}^- + \text{HBr} \quad (84)$$

[BNAH] is also changed from the linear dependence exceeding unity, which is characteristic of the radical chain process, in the absence of $[Ru(bpy)_3]^{2+}$ (Eq. 72) to that given by Eq. 85,[91] where the limiting quantum yield Φ_∞ is 0.83. The

$$\Phi^{-1} = \Phi_\infty^{-1}[1 + (k_q\tau\ [\text{BNAH}])^{-1}] \quad (85)$$

Φ_∞ value agrees well with the quantum yield of the formation of $[Ru(bpy)_3]^{2+*}$, and the $k_q\tau$ value $(4.2 \times 10^2\ M^{-1})$ obtained from the ratio of the intercept to the slope of the plot of Φ^{-1} and $[BNAH]^{-1}$ and the τ value (850 ns) agrees well with that determined from the quenching of $[Ru(bpy)_3]^{2+*}$ emission by BNAH $(3.5 \times 10^2\ M^{-1})$.[91] Thus, the observed quantum yield is determined solely by the efficacy of the electron transfer quenching of $[Ru(bpy)_3]^{2+*}$ with BNAH. Moreover, the addition of a radical scavenger, isopentyl nitrite shows essential-

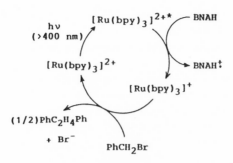

Scheme 17.

ly no effect on the reaction rate, in contrast with the case in the absence of [Ru (bpy)$_3$]$^{2+}$ (c.f. Figure 27).

The drastic change in the product and kinetics in the presence of [Ru(bpy)$_3$]$^{2+}$ may be caused by the presence of a strong reductant [Ru(bpy)$_3$]$^+$ produced by electron transfer from BNAH to [Ru(bpy)$_3$]$^{2+*}$ (*vide infra*). It is known that a strong reductant such as sodium naphthalenide can reduce benzyl halide by successive two-electron transfer from the reductant to benzyl halide, resulting in the formation of the carbanion PhCH$_2^-$.[92] The electrochemical reduction of benzyl bromide at -1.2 V vs. SCE is also known to produce the carbanion.[93] Thus, in the presence of a strong reductant [Ru(bpy)$_3$]$^+$ ($E^0_{ox} = -1.33$ V vs. SCE),[94] the reduction of benzyl bromide may proceed via the successive two-electron reduction of benzyl bromide by [Ru(bpy)$_3$]$^+$ as shown in Scheme 17, where the benzyl radical formed by the electron transfer from [Ru(bpy)$_3$]$^+$ to benzyl bromide is further reduced by [Ru(bpy)$_3$]$^+$ before abstracting hydrogen from BNAH (c.f. Scheme 13). The carbanion may react with benzyl bromide in a nucleophilic fashion to yield 1,2-diphenylethane (Scheme 13). As such, a drastic change in the product in the presence and absence of [Ru(bpy)$_3$]$^{2+}$ is caused by the presence of a strong reductant [Ru(bpy)$_3$]$^+$ which reduces benzyl radical to the carbanion. Thus, the occurrence of a radical chain process which yield toluene (Scheme 13) is suppressed.

5.5.   Acid Catalysis in Photosensitized Reactions

The [Ru(bpy)$_3$]$^{2+}$ functions also as a photosensitizer in the photoreduction of phenacyl bromide by AcrH$_2$ in MeCN, yielding the same products as the case of the direct excitation of the absorption band due to AcrH$_2$, Eq. 86 (c.f. Eq. 78).[33] The addition of HClO$_4$ to this system results in significant change in the quantum

$$\text{AcrH}_2 + \text{PhCOCH}_2\text{Br} \xrightarrow[\text{[Ru(bpy)}_3]^{2+}]{h\nu\ (\lambda > 400\ \text{nm})} \text{AcrH}^+ + \text{Br}^- + \text{PhCOCH}_3 \quad (86)$$

yield as shown in Figure 31, where the Φ value increases with an increase in the $HClO_4$ concentration, but decreases through a maximum with a further increase in the $HClO_4$ concentration.[33] In the high $HClO_4$ concentrations (see the logarithm scale in Figure 31), the Φ value increases again with an increase of the $HClO_4$ concentration. The complexed dependence of Φ on the $HClO_4$ concentration (Figure 31) can be explained by acid-catalysis in electron transfer reactions involved in the photosensitized reaction as follows.

In the absence of $HClO_4$, the reductive quenching of $[Ru(bpy)_3]^{2+}*$ by $AcrH_2$ occurs efficiently by electron transfer from $AcrH_2$ to $[Ru(bpy)_3]^{2+}*$ to produce $AcrH_2^{+\cdot}$ and $[Ru(bpy)_3]^+$ (c.f. Eq. 27).[33] Since the $[Ru(bpy)_3]^+$ is a strong reductant (*vide supra*), phenacyl bromide and para-substituted phenacyl bromides can be readily reduced by $[Ru(bpy)_3]^+$ to yield the corresponding acetophenone derivatives. However, phenacyl chloride which is a weaker oxidant than phenacyl bromide cannot be reduced by $[Ru(bpy)_3]^+$ and thus no $[Ru(bpy)_3]^{2+}$-sensitized reduction of phenacyl chloride occurs in the absence of $HClO_4$.[33] In the presence of $HClO_4$ the reductive quenching of $[Ru(bpy)_3]^{2+}*$ by $AcrH_2$ may be followed by acid-catalyzed electron transfer from $[Ru(bpy)_3]^+$ to $PhCOCH_2X$ to give $Ph\overset{\cdot}{C}(OH)CH_2X$, accompanied by regeneration of

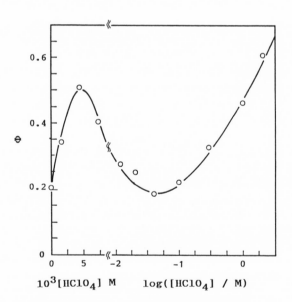

Figure 31. Plot of the quantum yield Φ vs the $HClO_4$ concentration for the [Ru (bpy)$_3$]$^{2+}$-photosensitized reduction of phenacyl bromide (1.0×10^{-2} M) by AcrH$_2$ (1.0×10^{-2} M) in MeCN under irradiation of the visible light $\lambda = 452$ nm; [Ru (bpy)$_3$]$^{2+}$: 2.5×10^{-5} M, light intensity: 1.85×10^{-6} einstein dm^{-3} s^{-1}.[33]

$[Ru(bpy)_3]^{2+}$, in competition with the back electron transfer from $[Ru(bpy)_3]^+$ to $AcrH_2^{+\cdot}$ as shown in Scheme 18.[33] The $AcrH_2^{+\cdot}$ radical may be deprotonated to give AcrH· which can reduce $Ph\dot{C}(OH)CH_2X$ to yield $AcrH^+$ and $PhCOCH_3$ (Scheme 18). According to Scheme 18, the hydrogen in the reduced acetophenone comes from proton and thereby replacement of $AcrH_2$ by $AcrD_2$ or $AcrH_2$-CD_3 results in no incorporation of deuterium into acetophenone.[33] No kinetic isotope effect is observed, either, since the rate-determining step involves only an electron transfer process, the reductive quenching of $[Ru(bpy)_3]^{2+}*$ by $AcrH_2$ or electron transfer from $[Ru(bpy)_3]^+$ to $PhCOCH_2X$.[33] The latter may be the rate-determining step, since the quantum yield Φ in the absence of $HClO_4$ decreases with a decrease in the donor ability of phenacyl halides as shown in Table 11. The Φ value of phenacyl bromide in the presence of $HClO_4$ increases with an increase in the $HClO_4$ concentration ($0 - 5.0 \times 10^{-3}$ M in Figure 31), when $HClO_4$ may accelerate electron transfer from $[Ru(bpy)_3]^+$ to $PhCOCH_2X$ but inhibits electron transfer from $AcrH_2$ to $[Ru(bpy)_3]^{2+}*$ (Figure 7). Thus, the inhibitory effect of $HClO_4$ may be ascribed to the protonation on $AcrH_2$ (Eq. 29).

With an increase in the $HClO_4$ concentration, the rate of reductive quenching of $[Ru(bpy)_3]^{2+}*$ by $AcrH_2$ decreases as shown in Figure 7, while the rate of reduction of $PhCOCH_2X$ by $[Ru(bpy)_3]^+$ may increase. In such a case, the rate-determining step may be changed from the reduction of $PhCOCH_2X$ by

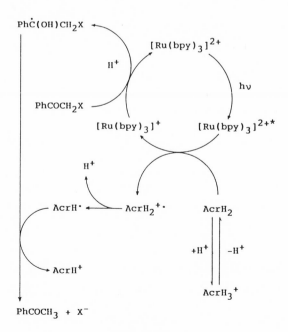

Scheme 18.

Table 11. Quantum Yields Φ for the $[Ru(bpy)_3]^{2+}$ (2.5×10^{-5} M)– Sensitized Photoreduction of Phenacyl Halides (1.0×10^{-2} M) by a NADH Analogue (1.0×10^{-2} M) in the Absence and Presence of $HClO_4$ under Irradiation with Visible Light (λ 452 nm)[33]

NADH analogue	substrate	Φ^a	
		$[HClO_4]$, 0 M	$[HClO_4]$, 2.0 M
$AcrH_2$	$p\text{-}CNC_6H_4COCH_2Br$	0.37	0.18
$AcrH_2$	$p\text{-}BrC_6H_4COCH_2Br$	0.39	0.24
$AcrH_2$	$PhCOCH_2Br$	0.21	0.61
$AcrD_2$	$PhCOCH_2Br$	0.21	0.61
$AcrH_2\text{-}CD_3$	$PhCOCH_2Br$	0.21	0.61
$AcrH_2$	$p\text{-}MeC_6H_4COCH_2Br$	0.22	0.62
$AcrH_2$	$p\text{-}MeOC_6H_4COCH_2Br$	0.12	0.53
$AcrH_2$	$PhCOCH_2Cl$	0	0.43

[a] The experimental errrors are within $\pm 10\%$.

$[Ru(bpy)_3]^+$ to the reductive quenching of $[Ru(bpy)_3]^{2+*}$ by $AcrH_2$. This may be the reason why the quantum yield decreases with an increase in the $HClO_4$ concentration ($5.0 \times 10^{-3} - 4.0 \times 10^{-2}$ M in Figure 31).

In the high concentrations of $HClO_4$, the $[Ru(bpy)_3]^{2+}$-sensitized reactions may be initiated by the oxidative quenching of $[Ru(bpy)_3]^{2+*}$, instead of the reductive quenching by $AcrH_2$, as shown in Scheme 19.[33] No oxidative quenching of $[Ru(bpy)_3]^{2+*}$ by $PhCOCH_2X$ occurs in the absence of $HClO_4$ in MeCN.[33] However, the oxidative quenching occurs in the presence of $HClO_4$, and the rate constant increases linearly with an increase in the $HClO_4$ concentration (c.f. Eq. 41).[33] Since the rate constant of the reductive quenching of $[Ru(bpy)_3]^{2+*}$ by $AcrH_2$ decreases with an increase in the $HClO_4$ concentration (Figure 7), the oxidative quenching of $[Ru(bpy)_3]^{2+*}$ by phenacyl halides ($PhCOCH_2X$) may become a predominant pathway at the high $HClO_4$ concentration. This may be the reason why the Φ value increases again in the high concentrations of $HClO_4$ (Figure 31). The oxidative quenching of $[Ru(bpy)_3]^{2+*}$ by $PhCOCH_2X$ in the presence of high concentrations of $HClO_4$ produces $Ph\dot{C}(OH)CH_2X$ and $[Ru(bpy)_3]^{3+}$, the latter of which is known to be a very strong oxidant (the reduction potential is 1.3 V vs. SCE).[94] Thus, $[Ru(bpy)_3]^{3+}$ can oxidize $AcrH_2$ even in the presence of $HClO_4$ to produce $AcrH_2^{+\cdot}$, accompanied by regeneration of $[Ru(bpy)_3]^{2+}$. The $AcrH_2^{+\cdot}$ may react with $Ph\dot{C}(OH)CH_2X$ after depro-

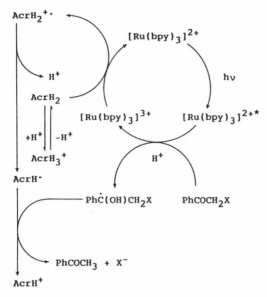

Scheme 19.

tonation to yield the same products as the case in Scheme 18. In Scheme 19 as well, the electron transfer step, the acid-catalyzed oxidative quenching of $[Ru(bpy)_3]^{2+*}$ by $PhCOCH_2X$, is rate-determining, and thus no kinetic isotope effect has been observed in the $[Ru(bpy)_3]^{2+}$-sensitized reduction of phenacyl bromide by $AcrH_2$ in the presence of a high concentration of $HClO_4$ (2.0 M).[33]

6. REDUCTION OF NAD⁺ ANALOGUES

We have so far focussed on mechanisms and catalysis in electron transfer pathways in thermal and photoinduced reduction of various substrates by NADH analogues. In this Section we focus on mechanisms of both one-electron and two-electron reduction of NAD^+ analogues, since enzymatic redox reactions involving NADH/NAD⁺ coenzymes are reversible and undergo both directions, oxidation of NADH and reduction of NAD^+ (Eq. 1).

6.1. One-Electron Reduction

Radical Chain Pathways

One-electron reduction of NAD^+ analogues such as pyridinium ions is usually made possible by electrochemical methods or by electron transfer from one-electron reductants to Py^+, followed by the dimerization of the resulting radicals

(Py·) to yield the corresponding dimer (Py − Py), Eq. 87.[95] On the other hand, the reduction of Py^+ by two-electron reductants generally results in the two-

$$Py^+ \xrightarrow{+e} Py· \longrightarrow 1/2(Py-Py) \qquad (87)$$

electron reduction of Py^+. However, group 14 dimetals, which are known as two-electron σ-donors,[27,96] can reduce an NAD^+ analogue, 10-methylacridinium ion ($AcrH^+$) to yield the one-electron reduced product, i.e., 10,10'-dimethyl-9,9'-biacridine [$(AcrH)_2$] selectively (Eq. 88).[97] The group 14 dimetals

$$Me_3SnMMe_3 + 2 \, (AcrH^+) \longrightarrow Me_3Sn^+ + Me_3M^+ + (AcrH)_2 \qquad (88)$$
$$(M = Sn, Ge, Si)$$

containing Sn, ($Me_3SnSnMe_3$, $Me_3SnGeMe_3$, and $Me_3SnSiMe_3$) are reactive towards $AcrH^+$, but other compounds ($Me_3GeGeMe_3$, $Me_3SiGeMe_3$, and $Me_3$$SiSiMe_3$), which have higher ionization potentials as compared with those involving Sn,[98] show no reactivity towards $AcrH^+$ in deaerated acetonitrile (MeCN) in the dark.[97] Since the dimer $(AcrH)_2$ is sparingly soluble in MeCN, it can be readily isolated quantitatively. When $AcrH^+$ is replaced by a common NAD^+ analog, 1-benzylnicotinamidium ion (BNA^+), which is a much weaker oxidant than $AcrH^+$,[16] however, no reduction of BNA^+ by Me_3SnMMe_3 occurs in deaerated MeCN at 333 K.[97] On the other hand, the reduction of $AcrH^+$ by Me_3SnMMe_3 (Eq. 88) is strongly inhibited by the presence of dioxygen. As such, essentially no reaction proceeds in aerated MeCN at 333 K.[97]

The strong inhibitory effect of dioxygen indicates that the one-electron reduction of $AcrH^+$ by Me_3SnMMe_3 proceeds via electron transfer radical chain processes as shown in Scheme 20.[97] The reaction may be initiated by electron transfer (k_i) from Me_3SnMMe_3 to $AcrH^+$ to produce $Me_3SnMMe_3^{+·}$ and AcrH·. The Sn-M bond of $Me_3SnMMe_3^{+·}$ (M = Sn, Ge, Si) is known to be readily cleaved to give mainly $Me_3Sn·$ and $Me_3M^{+·}$.[98,99] Then, electron transfer from $Me_3Sn·$ to $AcrH^+$ may occur to give acridinyl radical AcrH· which may react with $AcrH^+$ to form the dimer radical cation $(AcrH)_2^{+·}$. The electron transfer from Me_3SnMMe_3 to $(AcrH)_2^{+·}$ (k_p) may be the rate-determining step to yield $(AcrH)_2$, accompanied by regeneration of $Me_3SnMMe_3^{+·}$ (Scheme 20). The chain carrier radical AcrH· may be coupled in the termination step (k_t) to yield $(AcrH)_2$.

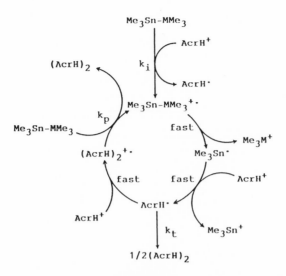

Scheme 20.

By applying the steady-state approximation to the reactive intermediates in Scheme 20 is derived the kinetic formulation (Eq. 89), where k_{obs} corresponds

$$-d[AcrH^+]/dt = k_{obs}[Me_3SnMMe_3]^{3/2}[AcrH^+]^{1/2} \qquad (89)$$

to $k_p(k_i/k_t)^{1/2}$. In fact, the rates obey the pseudo-one-half-order kinetics, when $[AcrH^+]^{1/2}$ decreases linearly with an increase in the reaction time.[97] The observed pseudo-one-half-order rate constants are proportional to $[Me_3SnMMe_3]^{3/2}$, in agreement with Eq. 89.[97] The observed over-all second-order rate constants (k_{obs}) in deaerated MeCN at 333 K·are listed in Table 12,[97] together with the ionization potentials of $Me_3MM'Me_3$.[98] The k_{obs} value decreases in the order $Me_3SnSnMe_3 > Me_3SnGeMe_3 > Me_3SnSiMe_3$, when the donor ability of $Me_3MM'Me_3$ decreases as indicated by the increase in the I_D (ionization potential) value (Table 12). The unreactivity of the group 14 dimetals $Me_3MM'Me_3$ (M, M' = Ge, Si) which do not contain Sn may be ascribed to the much less reducing ability of $Me_3Ge·$ or $Me_3Si·$ in the propagation step (k_p) as compared with $Me_3Sn·$, combined with the less reducing ability of $Me_3MM'Me_3$ than that of Me_3SnMMe_3 (M = Sn, Ge, Si) in the initiation step (k_i) as indicated by the I_D values in Table 12. By the same token, BNA^+, which is a much weaker oxidant than $AcrH^+$,[16] has no ability to start or to continue the chain reactions with Me_3SnMMe_3. The strong inhibitory effect of dioxygen, which may be ascribed to the efficient trap of the chain carrier radical $AcrH·$ by dioxygen,[10,73] indicates a long chain length of the radical chain reactions. Such a long chain length causes

Table 12. Observed Second-Order Rate Constants (k_{obs}) for the One-Electron Reduction of AcrH$^+$ by Group 14 Dimetals Me$_3$MM'Me$_3$ (M, M' = Sn, Ge, Sn) in Deaerated MeCN at 333 K, and the Ionization potentials (I_D) of Me$_3$MM'Me$_3$[97]

Me$_3$MM'Me$_3$	I_D,[a] eV	k_{obs},[b] M^{-1} s^{-1}
Me$_3$SnSnMe$_3$	8.20	5.6 x 10^{-2}
Me$_3$SnGeMe$_3$	8.36	4.6 x 10^{-2}
Me$_3$SnSiMe$_3$	8.39	3.6 x 10^{-2}
Me$_3$GeGeMe$_3$	8.60	c
Me$_3$GeSiMe$_3$	8.62	c
Me$_3$SiSiMe$_3$	8.68	c

[a] Ref 98. [b] The experimental errors are ± 5%. [c] No reaction.

the highly selective formation of the dimer (AcrH)$_2$, in contrast with usual radical reactions.

Photoinduced Electron Transfer Pathway

Although no thermal reduction of AcrH$^+$ by Me$_3$GeGeMe$_3$ occurs in MeCN at 333 K (*vide supra*), the one-electron reduction undergoes efficiently under irradiation of visible light ($\lambda > 360$ nm) to yield the dimer [(AcrH)$_2$] (Eq. 90).[100]

$$\text{Me}_3\text{GeGeMe}_3 + 2\text{AcrH}^+ \xrightarrow{\quad h\nu\ (\lambda > 360\ \text{nm})\quad} 2\text{Me}_3\text{Ge}^+ + (\text{AcrH})_2 \qquad (90)$$

The photoinduced one-electron reduction of AcrH$^+$ occurs also by other group 14 dimetals (Me$_3$GeSiMe$_3$, Me$_3$SnSiMe$_3$, Me$_3$SnSnMe$_3$)[100] except for Me$_3$SiSiMe$_3$ by which photoinduced two-electron reduction of AcrH$^+$ occurs as described later.[101]

The dependence of the quantum yield Φ with 358 nm irradiation on [Me$_3$MM'Me$_3$] is given by Eq. 91, where k_{obs} is the quenching constant of the

$$\Phi^{-1} = \Phi_\infty^{-1}[1 + (k_{obs}\tau\,[\text{Me}_3\text{MM'Me}_3])^{-1}] \qquad (91)$$

excited state of AcrH$^+$ in the photoreduction of AcrH$^+$ and τ is the lifetime of the singlet excited state (τ 31 ns).[10,102] From the linear plots of Φ^{-1} vs.

$[Me_3MM'Me_3]^{-1}$ are obtained the ϕ_∞ and k_{obs} values, which are listed in Table 13, together with the one-electron oxidation potentials of $Me_3MM'Me_3$ (E^0_{ox}).[103]

10-Methylacridinium perchlorate (green color) has the absorption maximum at $\lambda_{max} = 417$ nm and the irradiation of the absorption band results in the occurrence of fluorescence at $\lambda_{max} = 490$ nm in acetonitrile (MeCN). The fluorescence of $AcrH^+$ $(\lambda_{max} = 490$ nm) is quenched by $Me_3MM'Me_3$ in MeCN at 298 K. The quenching rate constants k_q determined from the slopes of the Stern-Volmer plots and the lifetime of the singlet excited state $^1AcrH^{+*}$ $(\tau\ 31$ ns) are also listed in Table 13,[100] where k_{obs} values agree well with the corresponding k_q values. The k_{obs} and k_q values agree also with the calculated rate constants (k_{et}) of electron transfer from $Me_3MM'Me_3$ to $^1AcrH^{+*}$ from the E^0_{ox} values, the one-electron reduction potential of $^1AcrH^{+*}$ $(E^0_{red} = 2.3$ V vs. SCE)[10] and the reorganization energy $(\lambda = 38$ kcal mol$^{-1})$[103] by using the Marcus theory (Table 13).[83] Such agreements indicate that the photoinduced one-electron reduction of $AcrH^+$ by $Me_3MM'Me_3$ is initiated by electron transfer from $Me_3MM'Me_3$ to the single excited state $^1AcrH^{+*}$ as shown in Scheme 21. Since the one-electron oxidation of $Me_3MM'Me_3$ is known to result in the facile cleavage of metal-metal bonds,[99] electron transfer from $Me_3MM'Me_3$ to $^1AcrH^{+*}$ may yield the metal centered radical $Me_3H^.$ which has strong reducing ability. Then, another $AcrH^+$ molecule may be reduced by $Me_3H^.$ to produce $AcrH^.$ which dimerizes to yield the one-electron reduced product $(AcrH)_2$.

According to Scheme 21, the limiting quantum yield (Φ_∞) may be determined by the competition between the back electron transfer from $AcrH^.$ to $Me_3MM'Me_3^{+\cdot}$ (k_b) and the cleavage of metal-metal bonds of $Me_3MM'Me_3^{+\cdot}$ (k_c) as given by Eq. 92. The k_b values can also be calculated from the E^0_{ox} values,

$$\Phi_\infty = k_c/(k_c + k_b) \qquad (92)$$

the one-electron reduction potential of $AcrH^+$ $(E^0_{red} = -0.43$ V),[16] and the λ values by using the Marcus theory.[83,100] Then, the $k_c/(k_c + k_b)$ values are estimated from the k_b values by using Eq. 92 in which the k_c values are assumed

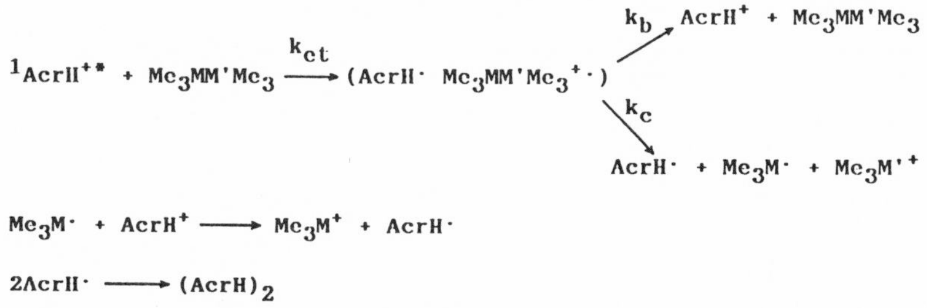

$$^1AcrH^{+*} + Me_3MM'Me_3 \xrightarrow{k_{et}} (AcrH^. \ Me_3MM'Me_3^{+\cdot}) \nearrow^{k_b} AcrH^+ + Me_3MM'Me_3$$
$$\searrow^{k_c} AcrH^. + Me_3M^. + Me_3M'^{+}$$

$$Me_3M^. + AcrH^+ \longrightarrow Me_3M^+ + AcrH^.$$

$$2AcrH^. \longrightarrow (AcrH)_2$$

Scheme 21.

Table 13. Limiting Quantum Yields (Φ_∞), Rate Constants k_{obs}, k_q, k_{et} ($M^{-1} s^{-1}$), One-Electron Oxidation Potentials E^0_{ox} vs. SCE) of $Me_3MM'Me_3$, and the Estimated Ratio of the Rate Constants, $k_c/(k_c + k_b)$, for the Photoinduced Reduction of $AcrH^+$ by $Me_3MM'Me_3$

$Me_3MM'Me_3$	Φ_∞	E^0_{ox},[a] V	k_{obs}, $M^{-1} s^{-1}$	k_q, $M^{-1} s^{-1}$	k_{et},[b] $M^{-1} s^{-1}$	$k_c/(k_c+k_b)$[c]
$Me_3SiSiMe_3$	0.038	0.92	7.1×10^9	7.1×10^9	8.7×10^9	0.042
$Me_3GeSiMe_3$	0.043	0.88	8.7×10^9	9.1×10^9	8.9×10^9	0.048
$Me_3GeGeMe_3$	0.039	0.84	9.0×10^9	9.3×10^9	9.2×10^9	0.057
$Me_3SnSiMe_3$	0.11	0.82	9.6×10^9	9.8×10^9	9.3×10^9	0.062
$Me_3SnSnMe_3$	0.13	0.68	1.2×10^{10}	1.2×10^{10}	9.6×10^9	0.13

[a] The E^0_{ox} values have been determined by the analysis of cyclic voltammograms. [b] Calculated by applying the Marcus theory (Eq. 82). [c] The k_b values are also calculated by applying the Marcus theory (Eq. 82).

to be the same ($1.6 \times 10^{11} s^{-1}$). The $k_c/(k_c + k_b)$ values agree reasonably well with the observed variation of Φ_∞ values depending on $Me_3MM'Me_3$ (Table 13), demonstrating the validity of Scheme 21.

6.2. Two-Electron Reduction

In contrast with the case of Me_3SnMMe_3 (Eq. 88) or $Me_3GeGeMe_3$ (Eq. 90), the photoreduction of $AcrH^+$ by $Me_3SiSiMe_3$ results in the two-electron reduction of $AcrH^+$.[101] The product is identified as 9,10-dihydro-9-trimethylsilyl-10-methylacridine [$AcrH(SiMe_3)$] after visible light irradiation ($\lambda > 360$ nm) of a dehydrated $CD_3CN/CDCl_3$ (1:1 v/v) solution containing $AcrH^+$ and $Me_3SiSiMe_3$.[101] The addition of water to the resulting solution yields $AcrH_2$ as shown in Scheme 22.[101] When the photochemical reaction of $AcrH^+$ with $Me_3SiSiMe_3$ is carried out in MeCN containing H_2O initially, the overall hydride reduction of $AcrH^+$ occurs to yield $AcrH_2$ selectively (Scheme 22).[101] Such photoinduced hydride reduction of $AcrH^+$ occurs also with $Me(SiMe_2)_3Me$ and $(Me_2Si)_6$ which act as two-electron donors and a proton is provided separately from H_2O.[101]

The photoreduction of $AcrH^+$ is initiated by electron transfer from permethylpolysilanes (e.g., $Me_3SiSiMe_3$) to the singlet excited state, $^1AcrH^{+*}$, since the k_{obs} values obtained from the dependence of Φ on the concentrations of polysilanes (Eq. 91) agree well with those of the k_q values of the fluorescence quenching of $^1AcrH^{+*}$ as well as the calculated k_{et} values of electron transfer

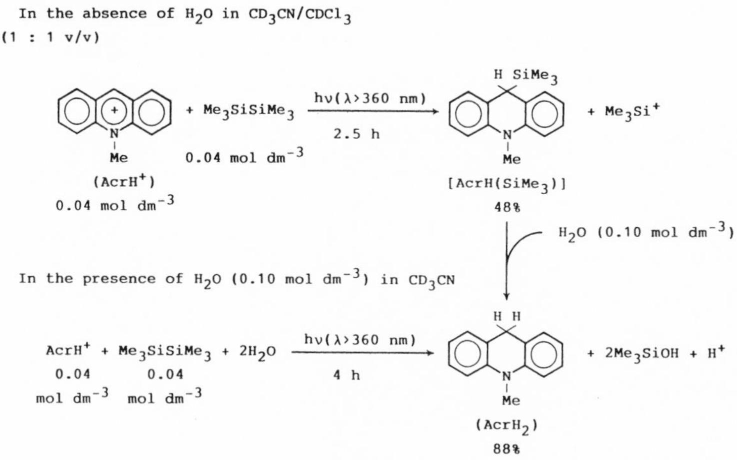

In the absence of H_2O in $CD_3CN/CDCl_3$
(1 : 1 v/v)

$Me_3SiSiMe_3$ + $^1AcrH^{+*}$ $^1(Me_3SiSiMe_3^{+\cdot} \ AcrH^{\cdot})$

Scheme 22.

(Table 13). The facile cleavage of the Si-Si bond may be followed to give the singlet radical pair, AcrH and Me_3Si, and subsequent radical coupling yields $AcrH(SiMe_3)$ selectively (Eq. 93). In the case of the other group 14 dimetals, electron transfer from Me_3Sn (or Me_3Ge), that is much stronger reductant than Me_3Si, to $AcrH^+$ occurs instead of the radical coupling (Scheme 21).[100] In the presence of H_2O, the hydrolysis of Me_3SiClO_4 occurs to yield the silanol and perchloric acid (Eq. 94), followed by the acid cleavage of the Si-C bond of $AcrH(SiMe_3)$ to yield $AcrH_2$ (Eq. 95). The stoichiometry of such overall photo-induced hydride reduction of $AcrH^+$ by $Me_3SiSiMe_3$ agrees with that in Scheme 22. Thus, permethylpolysilanes can be used as unique sources of a hydride ion, consisting of two electrons and a proton, which are provided separately by permethylpolysilanes and water, respectively (Eqs. 93–95).[104]

The metal-carbon bond of alkylmetals (RM) such as tetraalkyltin compounds and dialkylmercury is also readily cleaved by the one-electron oxidation (electron transfer) as shown in Eq. 96.[27,105] The fluorescence of $AcrH^+$ is quenched

$$Me_3SiSiMe_3 + {}^1AcrH^{+*} \longrightarrow {}^1(Me_3SiSiMe_3^{+\cdot} \ AcrH^{\cdot})$$

$$\longrightarrow {}^1(Me_3Si^+ \ Me_3Si^{\cdot} \ AcrH^{\cdot}) \longrightarrow Me_3Si^+ + AcrH(SiMe_3) \quad (93)$$

$$Me_3SiClO_4 + H_2O \longrightarrow Me_3SiOH + HClO_4 \quad (94)$$

$$AcrH(SiMe_3) + HClO_4 \longrightarrow AcrH_2 + Me_3SiClO_4 \quad (95)$$

$$RM \xrightarrow{\quad -e \quad} RM^{+\cdot} \longrightarrow R^{\cdot} + M^{+} \qquad (96)$$

efficiently by group 14 monometals (tetraalkyltin compounds R_4Sn (R = Me, Et, Bu^n, and Pr^j) as well as diethylmercury in MeCN at 298 K.[106] Little quenching of the fluorescence of $AcrH^+$ is observed by Et_4Si, however.[106] The quenching rate constants k_q increase with increasing donor ability of R_4Sn as the E^0_{ox} value is shifted in the negative direction to reach the diffusion rate constant, 2.0×10^{10} M^{-1} s^{-1} in MeCN as shown in Table 14. The calculated k_{et} values by applying the Marcus theory of electron transfer[83] are in reasonable agreements with the k_q values (Table 14).[106] Thus, the fluorescence quenching of $^1AcrH^{+*}$ by group 14 organometallic compounds (RM) may occur by electron transfer from RM to $^1AcrH^{+*}$. Thus, photoinduced electron transfer from RM to $^1AcrH^{+*}$ initiates the reductive alkylation of $AcrH^+$ (two-electron reduction) as shown in Scheme 23.

The reductive alkylation of $AcrH^+$ also occurs by the photoreduction of $AcrH^+$ by fatty acids in the presence of a base ($RCOO^-$) under irradiation of visible light (Eq. 97).[107] The formation of AcrHR is highly selective as is evident from the change of the absorption spectra with a clean isosbestic point as shown in Figure 32, and the AcrHR derived from various fatty acids (R = H, Me, Et, Pr^j, Bu^t, $C_{11}H_{23}$, $C_{15}H_{31}$) can be isolated quantitatively.[107]

$$AcrH^+ + RCOO^- \xrightarrow{\quad h\nu \quad} AcrHR + CO_2 \qquad (97)$$

Table 14. Rate Constants k_q (M^{-1} s^{-1}) of the Fluorescence Quenching of $^1AcrH^{+*}$ by Alkylmetals and the Calculated Rate Constants k_{et} (M^{-1} s^{-1}) of the Electron Transfer Reactions from Alkylmetals to $^1AcrH^{+*}$ in MeCN at 298 K[106]

alkylmetal	$\log k_q{}^a$	$\log k_{et}{}^b$
Et_4Si	c	
Me_4Sn	8.34	8.46
Et_4Sn	10.00	9.91
$Bu^n{}_4Sn$	10.08	10.01
$Pr^i{}_4Sn$	10.32	10.14
Et_2Hg	10.30	10.14

[a] The experimental errors are within ± 10%. [b] Calculated by applying the Marcus theory (Eq. 82). [c] Too small to be determined accurately.

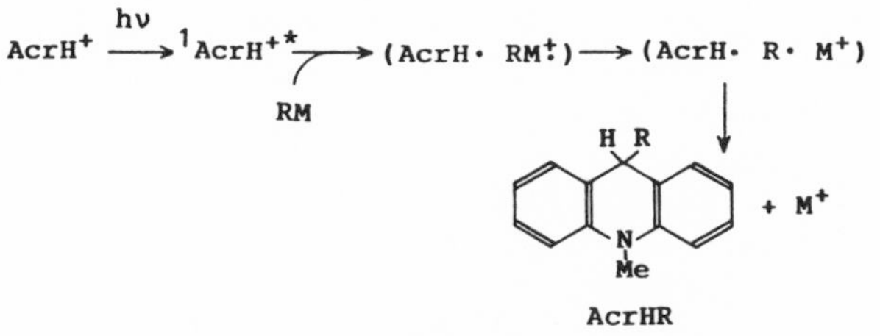

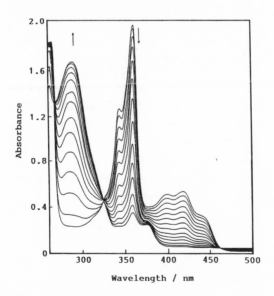

Scheme 23.

The anodic oxidation of $RCOO^-$ at about 2 V (vs. SCE), known as the Kolbe reaction, produces the radical coupling products of the alkyl groups of $RCOO^-$, R-R, and CO_2.[108] The one-electron reduction potential of the singlet excited state $^1AcrH^{+*}$ is 2.3 V (vs. SCE),[10] which is positive enough to oxidize $RCOO^-$. In fact, the fluorescence of $^1AcrH^{+*}$ (λ_{max} 490 nm) is readily quenched by photoinduced electron transfer from $RCOO^-$ to $^1AcrH^{+*}$. The photoinduced electron transfer may generate a singlet radical pair $^1(AcrH^{\cdot}\ RCOO^{\cdot})$ in which $RCOO^{\cdot}$ is known to undergo facile decarboxylation,[108] followed by the radical coupling in the singlet radical pair $^1(AcrH^{\cdot}\ R^{\cdot})$ to yield 9,10-dihydro-9-alkyl-10-methylacridine (AcrHR) selectively as shown in Scheme 24.[107]

Figure 32. Electronic spectra observed in photoreduction of $AcrH^+$ (1.0×10^{-4} M) by $(CH_3)_2CHCOOH$ (0.10 M) in the presence of NaOH (3.0×10^{-2} M) in deaerated $MeCN/H_2O$ (1:1 v/v) at 298 K.[107]

Scheme XXIV

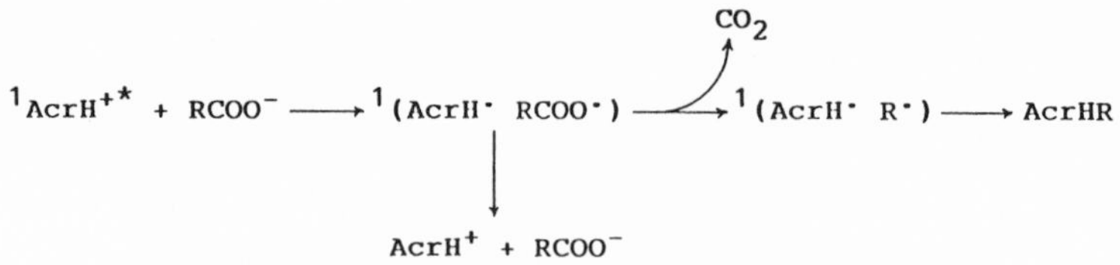

$$^1\text{AcrH}^{+*} + \text{RCOO}^- \longrightarrow {}^1(\text{AcrH}\cdot\ \text{RCOO}\cdot) \xrightarrow{\quad\text{CO}_2\quad} {}^1(\text{AcrH}\cdot\ \text{R}\cdot) \longrightarrow \text{AcrHR}$$

$$\downarrow$$

$$\text{AcrH}^+ + \text{RCOO}^-$$

Scheme 24.

6.3. Reversible Transformation between NAD^+ and NADH Analogues

The reverse reaction of the reduction of aldehydes by an NADH analogue, i.e., the oxidation of the corresponding alcohol by an NAD^+ analogue is made possible to occur by using the strong oxidizing ability of the singlet excited state, $^1\text{AcrH}^{+*}$ (*vide supra*). For example, irradiation of the absorption band due to 10-methylacridinium ion (AcrH^+) in deaerated MeCN containing benzyl alcohol derivatives ($\text{X-C}_6\text{H}_4\text{CH}_2\text{OH}$) results in the reduction of AcrH^+ to yield AcrH_2 and the corresponding aldehydes (Eq. 98).[109] Since proton is produced in the photoreduction of AcrH^+ (Eq. 98), the oxidization of AcrH_2 by $\text{X-C}_6\text{H}_4\text{CHO}$ may occur thermally (Eq. 99, c.f. Eq. 42). In fact, the photo-reduction of AcrH^+ by p-chlorobenzyl alcohol in MeCN under irradiation of visible light of $\lambda > 360$ nm is followed by the thermal oxidization of AcrH_2 by the photo-product, p-chlorobenzaldehyde at 333 K in the dark, although the prolonged reaction time is required to complete the reaction.[110] This reversible transformation between AcrH^+ and AcrH_2 can be repeated as shown in Figure 33, where the decrease and increase in the AcrH^+ concentration in the redox cycle are plotted against the photochemical and thermal reaction time, respectively.[110] Such reversible transformation between AcrH^+ and AcrH_2 is also observed for the photooxidation of benzl alcohol and p-methylbenzyl alcohol and the thermal reduction of the corresponding aldehydes.[110]

$$\text{AcrH}^+ + \text{X-C}_6\text{H}_4\text{CH}_2\text{OH} \xrightarrow[\lambda > 360\ \text{nm}]{h\nu} \text{AcrH}_2 + \text{X-C}_6\text{H}_4\text{CHO} + \text{H}^+ \qquad (98)$$

$$\text{AcrH}_2 + \text{X-C}_6\text{H}_4\text{CHO} + \text{H}^+ \longrightarrow \text{AcrH}^+ + \text{X-C}_6\text{H}_4\text{CH}_2\text{OH} \qquad (99)$$

6.4. Photocatalytic Systems

When the photochemical reaction of AcrH^+ with $\text{X-C}_6\text{H}_4\text{CH}_2\text{OH}$ (Eq. 98) is carried out in the presence of dioxygen, dehydrogenation of $\text{X-C}_6\text{H}_4\text{CHO}$ by dioxygen occurs efficiently (Eq. 100), when the concentration of AcrH^+ remains

$$\underset{\text{AcrH}^+}{\overset{h\nu}{\text{X-C}_6\text{H}_4\text{CH}_2\text{OH} + \text{O}_2 \longrightarrow \text{X-C}_6\text{H}_4\text{CHO} + \text{H}_2\text{O}_2}} \qquad (100)$$

unchanged.[109] Thus, AcrH^+ acts as an efficient and stable photocatalyst in the photooxidation of $\text{X-C}_6\text{H}_4\text{CH}_2\text{OH}$ with dioxygen. The quantum yields at a constant $\text{X-C}_6\text{H}_4\text{CH}_2\text{OH}$ concentration are shown in Table 15.[109] The maximum quantum yield is achieved when $X = p\text{-Pr}^i$, whereas no photooxidation is observed with strongly electron-donating ($X = p\text{-HO}$ or $p\text{-MeO}$) or -withdrawing ($X = p\text{-NC}$ or $p\text{-NO}_2$) substitutents (Table 15). The rate constants k_{et} of photoinduced electron transfer from $\text{X-C}_6\text{H}_4\text{CH}_2\text{OH}$ to $^1\text{AcrH}^{+*}$ are also listed in Table 15, where the k_{et} values agree well with those derived from the dependence of Φ on $[\text{X-C}_6\text{H}_4\text{CH}_2\text{OH}]$.[109]

Thus, the substrate-selective photocatalytic oxidation of $\text{X-C}_6\text{H}_4\text{CH}_2\text{OH}$ may be initiated by electron transfer from $\text{X-C}_6\text{H}_4\text{CH}_2\text{OH}$ to $^1\text{AcrH}^{+*}$ produces $\text{X-C}_6\text{H}_4\text{CH}_2\text{OH}^{+\cdot}$ and $\text{AcrH}^\cdot$ as shown in Scheme 25. In the absence of dioxygen, the subsequent transfer of hydrogen (proton and electron) from $\text{X-C}_6\text{H}_4\text{CH}_2\text{OH}^{+\cdot}$ to $\text{AcrH}^\cdot$ yields AcrH_2, $\text{X-C}_6\text{H}_4\text{CHO}$, and proton (Eq. 98). Once AcrH^+ is fully reduced to AcrH_2, no oxidation of AcrH_2 by dioxygen occurs to regenerate AcrH^+. In the presence of dioxygen, however, a half-reduced radical $\text{AcrH}^\cdot$ is efficiently quenched by dioxygen to give $\text{AcrHO}_2^\cdot$,[73] and subsequent proton transfer from $\text{X-C}_6\text{H}_4\text{CH}_2\text{OH}^{+\cdot}$ to $\text{AcrHO}_2^\cdot$ occurs, followed by electron and proton transfer in

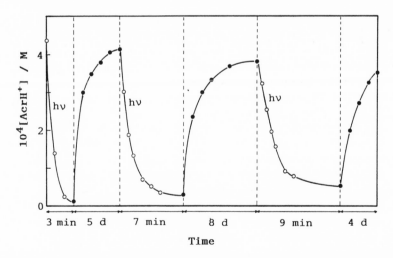

Figure 33. Repeated cycles for the decrease (○) and increase (●) in the AcrH^+ concentration in the photoreduction of AcrH^+ (4.4×10^{-4} M) by p-chlorobenzyl alcohol (5.0×10^{-2} M) in MeCN at 298 K under irradiation of visible light of $h\nu$ ($\lambda >$ 360 nm) and the thermal oxidation of AcrH_2 by the corresponding aldehyde at 333 K, respectively.[110]

Table 15. Quantum Yields Φ of Photocatalytic Oxidation of Benzyl Alcohol Derivatives $X-C_6H_4CH_2OH$ (5.0×10^{-2} M) with Dioxygen, Catalyzed by AcrH$^+$, and Rate Constants of Photoinduced Electron Transfer Reactions from $X-C_6H_4CH_2OH$ to ^{1}AcrH^{+*} in MeCN at 298 K[109]

$X-C_6H_4CH_2OH$ X	Φ	log $k_{et}{}^a$	log $k_{et}{}^b$
p-HO	0		10.0
p-MeO	0		10.2
p-Pr^i	0.17	9.9	10.0
p-Me	0.09	9.9	10.1
p-Cl	0.14	8.0	8.3
H	0.07	7.6	7.8
p-NC	0	c	c
p-NO$_2$	0	c	c

^{a} Determined from plots of Φ^{-1} vs. $[X-C_6H_4CH_2OH]^{-1}$. ^{b} Determined from the fluorescence quenching of ^{1}AcrH^{+*} by $X-C_6H_4CH_2OH$. ^{c} Too small to be determined accurately.

the cage to yield $X-C_6H_4CHO$ and H_2O_2, regenerating AcrH$^+$. The strongly electron-withdrawing substitutents on benzyl alcohol disfavor the electron transfer process from $X-C_6H_4CH_2OH$ to ^{1}AcrH^{+*}. In contrast, strongly electron-donating substituents favor the electron transfer process, but disfavor the proton transfer process from $X-C_6H_4CH_2OH^{+\cdot}$ to AcrHO$_2^\cdot$, since it is known that an increase in the electron-donor ability of substituents leads to a decrease in the proton-donor ability of the oxidized species.[111] Thus, in order to achieve efficient photocatalytic oxidation, both the electron- and proton-transfer processes should be fast enough to compete with the decay of ^{1}AcrH^{+*} and the back electron transfer reactions from AcrHO$_2^\cdot$ to $X-C_6H_4CH_2OH^{+\cdot}$, respectively (Scheme 25). As such, a sensitive balance between the electron- and proton-transfer processes to control the electron- and proton-donor abilities of $X-C_6H_4CH_2OH$ is required by choosing appropriate substituents X.

The reducing power of AcrH$_2$ is weak as recognized by the slow rate of the thermal oxidation of AcrH$_2$ by p-chlorobenzaldehyde (Figure 33). However, the singlet excited state ^{1}AcrH$_2^*$ is a much stronger reductant than the ground state as described in Section 5. Thus, the photooxidation of AcrH$_2$ by an appropriate substrate under irradiation of the absorption band due to AcrH$_2$ (λ_{max} 285 nm) may occur to regenerate AcrH$^+$. In such a case, AcrH$^+$ may act as a photo-

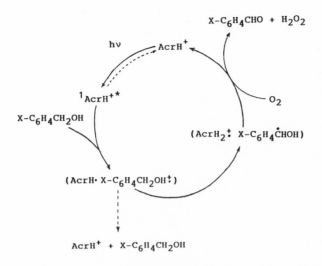

X-C$_6$H$_4$CHO + H$_2$O$_2$

^{1}AcrH^{+*}

X-C$_6$H$_4$CH$_2$OH

O$_2$

(AcrH$_2$$\overset{\cdot}{\cdot}$ X-C$_6$H$_4$$\overset{\cdot}{C}$HOH)

(AcrH· X-C$_6$H$_4$CH$_2$OH$\overset{\cdot}{\cdot}$)

AcrH$^+$ + X-C$_6$H$_4$CH$_2$OH

Scheme 25.

catalyst for the oxidation of *p*-chlorobenzyl alcohol by the substrate. In fact, irradiation of an MeCN solution containing AcrH$^+$, *p*-chlorobenzyl alcohol and dibenzyl disulfide with visible light of λ > 360 nm results in the reduction of AcrH$^+$ by *p*-chlorobenzyl alcohol to yield AcrH$_2$ and *p*-chlorobenzaldehyde (Eq. 98), and the subsequent irradiation of the reaction mixture with light of λ 285 nm which corresponds to the absorption maximum of AcrH$_2$ results in the regeneration of AcrH$^+$ by the photooxidation of AcrH$_2$ with dibenzyl disulfide to yield α-toluenethiol (Eq. 101).[110] This redox cycle can be repeated as shown in Figure

$$\text{AcrH}_2 + (\text{PhCH}_2\text{S})_2 + \text{H}^+ \xrightarrow[\lambda\ =\ 285\ \text{nm}]{h\nu} \text{AcrH}^+ + 2\text{PhCH}_2\text{SH} \qquad (101)$$

34.[110] Thus, the appropriate choice of irradiation wavelengths makes it possible to control the direction of the redox reactions, Eq. 98 or Eq. 101. The combination of the reactions (Eqs. 98 and 101) under irradiation of light that can irradiate both AcrH$_2$ and AcrH$^+$ results in the overall photoinduced reduction of (PhCH

$$\underline{p}\text{-ClC}_6\text{H}_4\text{CH}_2\text{OH} + (\text{PhCH}_2\text{S})_2 \xrightarrow[\text{AcrH}^+/\text{AcrH}_2]{h\nu} \underline{p}\text{-ClC}_6\text{H}_4\text{CHO} + 2\text{PhCH}_2\text{SH} \qquad (102)$$

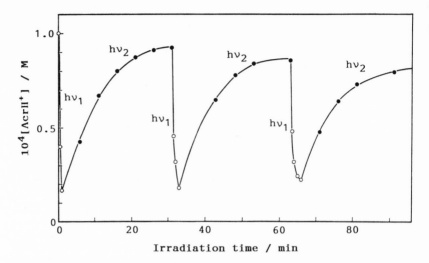

Figure 34. Repeated cycles for the decrease (○) and increase (●) in the AcrH$^+$ concentration in the photoreduction of AcrH$^+$ (1.0 × 10^{-4} M) by p-chlorobenzyl alcohol (5.0 × 10^{-2} M) in MeCN containing dibenzyl disulfide (1.0 × 10^{-3} M) and the photooxidation of AcrH$_2$ by dibenzyl disulfide at 298 K under irradiation of light of hν_1 (λ > 360 nm) and hν_2 (λ 285 nm), respectively.

$_2$S)$_2$ by p-ClC$_6$H$_4$CH$_2$OH (Eq. 102), in which the AcrH$^+$/AcrH$_2$ redox pair acts as an efficient photocatalyst as shown in Scheme 26.[110]

In Scheme 26 both the excited states of ^{1}AcrH$_2$* and ^{1}AcrH$^+$* that are strong reductant and oxidant, respectively, are involved in the photocatalytic function. Alternatively, the reduction of substrates by ^{1}AcrH$_2$* may be combined with the thermal reduction of AcrH$^+$ by appropriate reductants. In fact, AcrH$_2$ acts as an efficient photocatalyst for reductive dechlorination of p-chlorobiphenyl (ClBP), which is known to be most difficult to be reduced among PCBs,[112] with

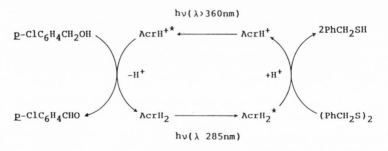

Scheme 26.

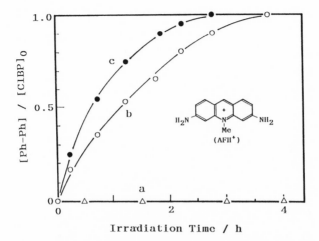

Irradiation Time / h

Figure 35. Photodechlorination of ClBP (0.10 M) with NaBH$_4$ (1.0 M) (**a**) in the absence of catalyst (△), (**b**) in the presence of AcrH$_2$ (2.0 × 10^{-2} M) (○), and (**c**) AFH$^+$ (2.0 × 10^{-2} M) (●) in MeCN/H$_2$O (9:1 v/v) at 298 K under irradiation of light from a xenon lamp. Plots of ratio of the product concentration [Ph-Ph] to the initial ClBP concentration [ClBP]$_0$ vs. irradiation time.

NaBH$_4$ in a mixture of acetonitrile and H$_2$O (MeCN/H$_2$O, 9:1 v/v) to yield biphenyl as shown in Figure 35b.[82,113] No appreciable photoreduction of ClBP by NaBH$_4$ occurs in the absence of photocatalyst under otherwise the same conditions (Figure 35a). When AcrH$_2$ is replaced by the oxidized form, AcrH$^+$ClO$_4^-$, essentially the same result is obtained, since AcrH$^+$ is readily reduced by NaBH$_4$ to yield AcrH$_2$ selectively.[114] Similarly acriflavine (AFH$^+$) can act as an efficient photocatalyst in reductive dechlorination of ClBP (Figure 35c). No appreciable photodegradation of the catalysts has been observed during the photocatalytic reaction. Thus, both AcrH$_2$/AcrH$^+$ and AFH$_2$/AFH$^+$ redox pairs act as not only efficient but also stable photocatalysts for dechlorination of ClBP with NaBH$_4$. Since the quantum yields (e.g., Φ_∞ = 0.63 in the case of AFH$^+$ under irradiation of light of λ = 350 nm) of the photocatalytic reactions are essentially the same as those in the stoichiometric photoreduction of ClBP by AcrH$_2$ (or AFH$_2$) in the absence of NaBH$_4$, the photocatalytic dechlorination of ClBP by NaBH$_4$ proceeds via the rate-determining reductive dechlorination of ClBP by the singlet excited states ^{1}AcrH$_2$* (or ^{1}AFH$_2$*), followed by the facile thermal reduction of AcrH$^+$ (or AFH$^+$) with NaBH$_4$ to regenerate AcrH$_2$ (or AFH$_2$) as shown in Scheme 27.[82,113] The photoinduced reductive dechlorination proceeds *via* electron transfer from ^{1}AcrH$_2$* (or ^{1}AFH$_2$*) to CLBP as shown in Scheme 16.[82]

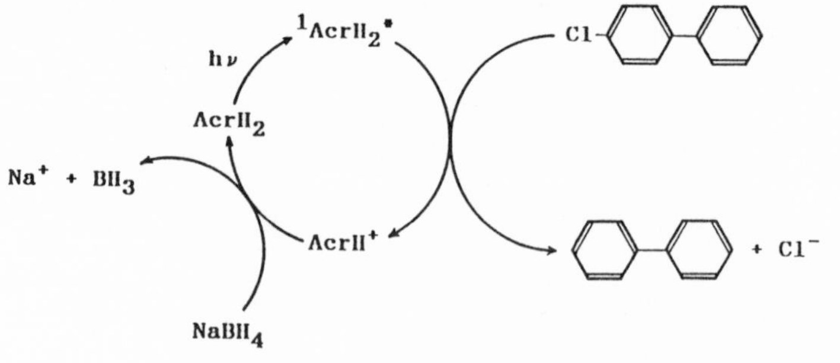

Scheme 27.

7. ELECTRON TRANSFER AND CATALYSIS OF FLAVINS AND ANALOGUES

The other major redox coenzymes other than NAD(P)H in the biological redox reactions are flavin adenine dinucleotide and flavin mononucleotide. The abbreviations that we use here for the oxidized and reduced forms of the flavin coenzymes and analogues are Fl and FlH$_2$, respectively. The reactive part of Fl is its alloxazine ring which can accept two electrons and two protons to give the reduced form FlH$_2$ (Eq. 2). In contrast with the case of NAD(P)H coenzymes that are inert to dioxygen without an appropriate enzyme (or catalyst), FlH$_2$ can be directly oxidized by dioxygen to yield the oxidized form Fl (Eq. 103). In

$$FlH_2 + O_2 \longrightarrow Fl + H_2O_2 \tag{103}$$

addition, the radical intermediates (half-reduced Fl or half-oxidized FlH$_2$) are much more stable than those of NAD(P)H coenzymes. In this context, electron transfer reactions of Fl and FlH$_2$ are more versatile than those of NAD(P)H and NAD(P)$^+$. In this Section, we examine electron transfer chemistry and the catalytic function of flavins and analogues in both the dehydrogenation and dioxygenation of substrates.

7.1.   Dehydrogenation

Flavin-Metal Ion Complexes Acting as Photocatalysts

Dehydrogenation of substrates catalyzed by flavin analogues has merited considerable interest in relation to flavoenzyme-catalyzed dehydrogenation reactions, although thermally oxidizable substrates under mild conditions have been limited to rather strong reductants such as alcoholate anions.[115] On the other hand, photochemical activation of flavin analogues may make it possible to oxidize substrates that cannot be oxidized thermally. In order to use flavin analogues as efficient photocatalysts, however, there are two difficult problems to be solved: one is the photodegradation of flavin analogues themselves[116] resulting in facile deactivation of the catalyst system and the other is that oxidizing ability of the excited states of flavin analogues is still insufficient to oxidize neutral alcohols because of the predominant photodegradation of flavin analogues. These two difficult problems can be resolved altogether by using flavin analogues-metal ion complexes as photocatalysts which have much stronger oxidizing ability as well as much improved stability against the visible light than free flavin analogues.[117]

As is the case of NADH analogues (Eq. 29), Mg^{2+} (or Zn^{2+}) ion forms complexes with flavin analogues **1** and **2a–c** with a 1:1 stoichiometry in dry

$$Fl + Mg^{2+} \xrightleftharpoons{K} (Fl\ Mg^{2+}) \tag{104}$$

MeCN at 298 K (Eq. 104).[117] The formation constants K are listed in Table 16.[117] The removal of H_2O from solvent is essential to obtain large formation constants.

Table 16. Formation Constants K of the Mg^{2+} or Zn^{2+} Complexes with Flavin Analogues in MeCN at 298 K

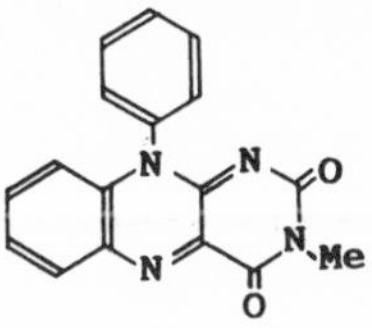

1

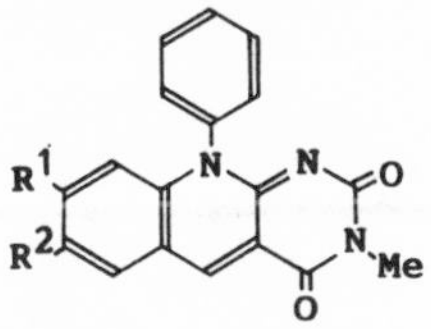

2a: $R^1 = R^2 = H$
2b: $R^1 = Cl$, $R^2 = H$
2c: $R^1 = H$, $R^2 = NO_2$

flavin analogue	K, M^{-1}	
	Mg^{2+}	Zn^{2+}
1	1.7×10^2	4.8×10
2a	1.1×10^3	1.5×10^2
2b	6.4×10^2	9.9×10
2c	1.8×10^2	7.7×10

As such, the addition of small concentrations of H_2O to the Fl-Mg^{2+} system causes a significant decrease in the K value; the K values (1.5×10^2 and 6.5×10 M^{-1} in the presence of 2.8×10^{-2} and 8.3×10^{-2} M H_2O, respectively) become much smaller than that (1.7×10^2 M^{-1}) in dry MeCN where the H_2O concentration is less than 1×10^{-3} M.[117] In fact, no complex formation of 1 with Mg^{2+} is observed in H_2O.[117] The metal ion interacts with the C^2-carbonyl group of Fl as is evident from the significant red shift of only the $C = O$ stretching bands due to the C^2-carbonyl group of 1 and 2a–c in the Mg^{2+} complexes.[117]

The complex formation of Mg^{2+} with NADH analogues being reductants (Eq. 30) result in a significant decrease of the reducing ability.[35] In contrast, the complex formation of Mg^{2+} with flavins being oxidants may cause enhancement of the oxidizing ability. In fact, significant enhancement of the oxidizing ability of the singlet excited states of flavin analogues by the complex formation with metal ions is demonstrated in Figure 36, where the logarithms of the quenching rate constants k_q of $^1Fl^*$ and $^1Fl^*$-Mg^{2+} (or $^1Fl^*$-Zn^{2+}) by various aromatic

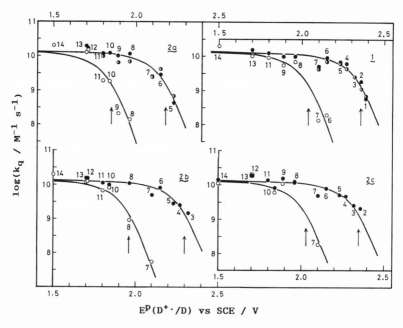

Figure 36. Plots of the logarithm of the quenching rate constants k_q vs the oxidation peak potential of quenchers $E^P(D^+/D)$ for the fluorescence quenching of flavin analogues (1, 2a–c) by methyl- and methoxy-substituted benzenes in the absence (◯) and presence of 0.10 M Mg^{2+} ion (●) or Zn^{2+} ion (◖) in MeCN.[117] Numbers refer to the quenchers (e.g., $1 = MeC_6H_5$, $14 = p - (MeO)_2C_6H_4$). The solid lines are drawn by the simulation based on Eqs. 33–35. The arrows indicate the $E^P(D^+/D)$ values when $\Delta G_{23} = 0$.

electron donors are plotted against the oxidation peak potentials of the donors $E^p(D^{+\cdot}/D)$ as shown by the open and closed or half-closed circles, respectively. The dependence of k_q on $E^p(D^{+\cdot}/D)$ in Figure 36 are typical for photoinduced electron transfer reactions (c.f. Figure 8a–c). Thus, they are well analyzed in the context of Rehm-Weller relation (Eq. 34) as shown by the calculated dependence (solid lines) in Figure 36. The k_q values of the Fl-metal ion complexes are much larger than those of free Fl. The increase of the oxidizing ability of the singlet excited states of Fl by the complex formation with Mg^{2+} or Zn^{2+} is evaluated quantitatively as the positive shifts of $E^0(^1Fl^*/Fl^{-\cdot})$, that correspond to the positive shift in the direction of the abscissa $E^p(D^{+\cdot}/D)$ in Figure 36. The magnitude of the shift is approximately constant (0.33 ± 0.01 V) for different Fl-metal ion complexes.[117]

The complex formation with metal ions not only increases the oxidizing ability of the ground and excited states of Fl but also stabilizes Fl against irradiation of the visible light to prevent the photodegradation. For example, the quantum yield Φ_d of photodegradation of $1\text{-}Mg^{2+}$ complex in deaerated MeCN is 6.2×10^{-4} which is negligibly small as compared with that of a free flavin 1 ($\Phi_d = 1.6 \times 10^{-2}$).[117] Taken together, irradiation of the absorption band of a $1\text{-}Mg^{2+}$ complex makes it possible to oxidize *p*-methylbenzyl alcohol to *p*-methylbenz-aldehyde, while irradiation of that of a free flavin 1 results in no dehydrogenation of *p*-methylbenzyl alcohol, but instead, only the predominant photodegradation occurs.[117,118]

The reduced flavin-Mg^{2+} complex, $FlH_2\text{-}Mg^{2+}$ produced in the photooxidation of *p*-methylbenzyl alcohol by $Fl\text{-}Mg^{2+}$ is readily oxidized by dioxygen to regenerate the oxidized form $Fl\text{-}Mg^{2+}$ (c.f. Eq. 103).[117,118] Thus, flavin-metal ion complexes act as efficient photocatalysts for the dehydrogenation of *p*-methylbenzyl alcohol as shown in Scheme 28. The photocatalytic dehydrogenation of *p*-methylbenzyl alcohol may be initiated by electron transfer from *p*-methylbenzyl alcohol to the singlet excited state $^1Fl^*\text{-}Mg^{2+}$, since the rate constant obtained from the Φ dependence on the concentration of *p*-methylbenzyl alcohol agrees well with that obtained independently from the fluorescence quenching of $^1Fl^*\text{-}Mg^{2+}$.[117]

Protonated Flavin and Pteridine Analogues

Pterin coenzymes such as folic aid (pteroylglutamic acid) and biopterin which contain a dicylic pteridine ring, a part of the skeleton of flavins, are also known to play versatile roles in biological redox reactions.[1] In contrast with the flavin photochemistry, little is known of the excited state chemistry of pteridine analogues.[119] In addition, pteridine analogues as well as flavins are known to be subjected to the photodegradation and thus, they cannot be used as efficient photocatalysts by themselves.[117,120] As described above, flavin analogues can be used as photocatalysts for the oxidation of *p*-methylbenzyl alcohol when they are

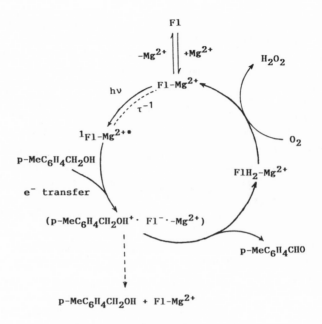

Scheme 28.

complexed with metal ions.[117,118] We show here that protonated pteridine derivatives, aminopterin (4-aminofolic acid) and lumazine (2,4-pteridinediol), as well
as a protonated flavin analogue (riboflavin-2′,3′,4′,5′-tetraacetate) can be used
as much more efficient and stabler photocatalysts for the substrate-selective
oxidation of benzyl alcohol derivatives by dioxygen than the flavin-metal ion
complex.[121] By examining the photocatalytic reactions, we can compare the
photocatalytic activity of pteridine analogues of biologically important redox
coenzymes, folic acid and biopterin, with that of a structurally related flavin
coenzyme analogue.

No appreciable photooxidation of benzyl alcohol by dioxygen occurs when
aminopterin (AP), lumazine (Lu), or riboflavin-2′,3′,4′,5′-tetraacetate (Fl) is
used as a photocatalyst in the absence of acid in acetonitrile (MeCN).[121] When
perchloric acid was added to this system, the flavin and pteridine derivatives are
protonated (λ_{max} 334, 350, and 392 nm for APH$^+$, LuH$^+$, and FlH$^+$, respectively).[122,123] Each protonated species (catH$^+$) can act as an efficient photocatalyst
for the oxidation of benzyl alcohol derivatives (X-C$_6$H$_4$CH$_2$OH) by dioxygen
(Eq. 105) when no appreciable photodegradation of each catalyst occurs. The
quantum yield Φ increases with an increase in the HClO$_4$ concentration to reach

$$X\text{-}C_6H_4CH_2OH + O_2 \xrightarrow[\text{catH}^+]{h\nu} X\text{-}C_6H_4CHO + H_2O_2 \qquad (105)$$

a constant value ($> 1.0 \times 10^{-2}$ M) when all the photocatalyst molecules are protonated. The Φ values at a constant X-C$_6$H$_4$CH$_2$OH concentration (2.9 $\times$ 10^{-2} M) as well as the limiting quantum yields Φ_∞ in the presence of HClO$_4$ (1.4 $\times$ 10^{-2} M) are listed in Table 17. The Φ value (0.30) for FlH$^+$ at 2.9×10^{-2} M p-MeC$_6$H$_4$CH$_2$OH is 13-fold larger than the reported Φ value for a flavin-Mg^{2+} complex.[117] Such large Φ values are obtained for each photocatalyst when the substituents X are moderately electron-donating or electron-withdrawing (X = o-Br, p-Cl, H, p-Me, p-Pr^i). Thus, protonated flavin and pteridine analogues act as much more efficient and stabler photocatalysts than a flavin-metal ion complex. However, no appreciable photooxidation of X-C$_6$H$_4$CH$_2$OH by dioxygen was observed with strongly electron-donating (X = p-OH, p-MeO) or

Table 17. Quantum Yields Φ of Photocatalytic Oxidation of Benzyl Alcohol Derivatives X$-$C$_6$H$_4$CH$_2$OH with Dioxygen, Catalyzed by APH$^+$, LuH$^+$, and FlH$^+$ in the Presence of HClO$_4$ (1.4 $\times$ 10^{-2} in MeCN at 298 K[121]

AP   Lu   Fl

R=CH$_2$NHC$_6$H$_4$CONHCH(COOH)C$_2$H$_4$COOH   R'=CH$_2$(CHOAc)$_3$CH$_2$OAc

X-C$_6$H$_4$CH$_2$OH X	APH$^+$ Φ^a	LuH$^+$ Φ^a	LuH$^+$ $\Phi_\infty{}^b$	FlH$^+$ Φ^a	FlH$^+$ $\Phi_\infty{}^{b,c}$
p-NO$_2$	d	d	d	d	e (0.18)
o-Br	0.084	0.020	0.10	0.089	0.17 (0.17)
p-Cl	0.16	0.088	0.17	0.22	0.28 (0.28)
H	0.15	0.17	0.38^f	0.094	0.23 (0.25)
p-Me	0.13	0.18	0.30	0.21	0.29 (0.30)
p-Pr^i	0.17	0.18	0.23	0.19	0.28 (0.31)
p-MeO	0.020	d	d	d	e (0.0016)
p-HO	d	d	d	d	d d

^{a} [X$-$C$_6$H$_4$CH$_2$OH] 2.9 $\times$ 10^{-2} M. ^{b} Limiting quantum yields Φ_∞ were obtained from the intercepts in the linear plots between Φ^{-1} and [X$-$C$_6$H$_4$CH$_2$OH]$^{-1}$. ^{c} The values in parentheses are those for the formation of FlH$_2{}^{+\cdot}$ in the absence of dioxygen. ^{d} Values $< 1 \times 10^{-3}$. ^{e} Value could not be determined accurately. ^{f} The Φ_∞ value in the absence of oxygen is 0.40.

-withdrawing ($X = p\text{-}NO_2$) substituents. Such substrate selectivities and the magnitude of quantum yields are similar among the photocatalysts irrespective of dicyclic pteridine analogues (APH^+ and LuH^+) or a tricyclic flavin (FlH^+) as shown in Table 17.[121] The similar photocatalytic activities may be ascribed to the cancellation effect of the difference in the ground state oxidizing ability, which is in the order $FlH^+ > LuH^+ > APH^+$,[123] by that in the excitation energy, which is in the opposite order $FlH^+ < LuH^+ < APH^+$.

In the absence of dioxygen, FlH^+ can be reduced by $X\text{-}C_6H_4CH_2OH$ under irradiation of the absorption band due to FlH^+ (λ_{max} 392 nm) to yield the dihydroflavin radical cation $FlH_2^{+\cdot}$ (λ_{max} 416 nm) and $X\text{-}C_6H_4CHO$, Eq. 106.[124]

$$2RFlH^+ + X\text{-}C_6H_4CH_2OH \xrightarrow{h\nu} 2RFlH_2^{+\cdot} + X\text{-}C_6H_4CHO \qquad (106)$$

The radical cation $FlH_2^{+\cdot}$ is stable at 298 K, and it takes about 10 hr for $FlH_2^{+\cdot}$ to disappear even in the presence of dioxygen. Similarly, irradiation of the absorption band due to LuH^+ (λ_{max} 350 nm) in deaerated MeCN containing benzyl alcohol results in the formation of the dihydrolumazine radical cation ($LuH_2^{+\cdot}$: λ_{max} 416 nm). The ESR spectra of $FlH_2^{+\cdot}$ and $LuH_2^{+\cdot}$ produced in the photoreduction of FLH^+ and LuH^+ by p-methylbenzyl alcohol in the presence of $HClO_4$ in deaerated MeCN are shown in Figure 37a and 37b, together with the corresponding computer simulation spectra, respectively.[124] The hyperfine splitting (hfs) values of $FlH_2^{+\cdot}$ agree well with those of other dihydroflavin radical cations.[125] In both $FlH_2^{+\cdot}$ and $LuH_2^{+\cdot}$ no appreciable hfs on the pyrimidine ring is observed and thus, spin distribution is similar to each other, although the hfs values due to N(5) and N(8) of $LuH_2^{+\cdot}$ are somewhat larger than those due to N(5) and N(10) of $FlH_2^{+\cdot}$.

The limiting quantum yields Φ_∞ for the formation of $FlH_2^{+\cdot}$ are also listed in Table 27. The Φ_∞ values in the absence of dioxygen agree well with those of the FlH^+-catalyzed photooxidation of $X\text{-}C_6H_4CH_2OH$ by dioxygen (Table 17).[121] Such an agreement of the Φ_∞ values between the absence and presence of dioxygen is confirmed also in the case of LuH^+ (Table 17). In addition, the reduced flavin and pteridine analogues are known to be readily oxidized by dioxygen to yield hydrogen peroxide.[7,115] Thus, the photocatalytic oxidation of $X\text{-}C_6H_4CH_2OH$ by dioxygen may proceed via the rate-determining photoreduction of the catalyst ($catH^+$), followed by the facile thermal oxidation of the reduced catalyst ($catH_3^+$) by dioxygen to yield H_2O_2, accompanied by the regeneration of $catH^+$, as shown in Scheme 29.[121]

The mechanism of photoreduction of the catalyst by $X\text{-}C_6H_4CH_2OH$ that can account for the substrate selectivities in Table 17 is given in Scheme 30 (shown in the case of FlH^+), where photoinduced electron transfer from $X\text{-}C_6H_4CH_2OH$ to the excited state FlH^{+*} generates the radical pair ($X\text{-}C_6H_4CH_2OH^{+\cdot}$ $FlH\cdot$)

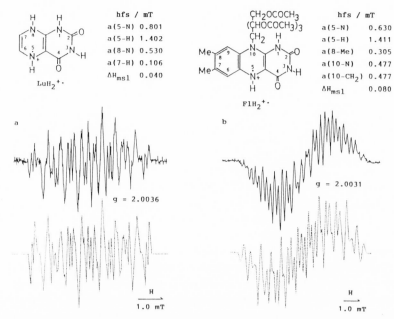

hfs / mT

LuH$_2$$^{+\cdot}$

a(5-N)	0.801
a(5-H)	1.402
a(8-N)	0.530
a(7-H)	0.106
ΔH_{msl}	0.040

hfs / mT

FlH$_2$$^{+\cdot}$

a(5-N)	0.630
a(5-H)	1.411
a(8-Me)	0.305
a(10-N)	0.477
a(10-CH$_2$)	0.477
ΔH_{msl}	0.080

a

g = 2.0036

$\xrightarrow{\text{H}}$
1.0 mT

b

g = 2.0031

$\xrightarrow{\text{H}}$
1.0 mT

Figure 37. The ESR spectra of LuH$_2$$^{+\cdot}$ (**a**) and FlH$_2$$^{+\cdot}$ (**b**) formed by the photoreduction of lumazine (8.1 × 10^{-3} M) and tetraacetylriboflavin (3.0 × 10^{-3} M) by p-ClC$_6$H$_4$CH$_2$OH (5.0 × 10^{-2} M) and p-MeC$_6$H$_4$CH$_2$OH (5.0 × 10^{-2} M), respectively, in the presence of HClO$_4$ (0.17 M) in deaerated MeCN. The dotted line spectra show the corresponding computer simulation by using the hfs values listed above.[124]

which disappear either by the back electron transfer to regenerate the reactant pair or by the proton transfer from X-C$_6$H$_4$CH$_2$OH$^{+\cdot}$ to FlH·, followed by the hydrogen transfer to yield X-C$_6$H$_4$CHO and FlH$_3$$^+$. In the absence of dioxygen, FlH$_3$$^+$ is converted to FlH$_2$$^{+\cdot}$ by the comproportionation with FlH$^+$ (Scheme 30). According to Scheme 30, the limiting quantum yield may be determined by the competition between the back electron transfer (k_b) and the proton transfer (k_H). As is discussed in the substrate-selective photocatalytic oxidation of X-C$_6$H$_4$CH$_2$OH (Scheme 25),[109] the strongly electron-donating substituents favor the electron transfer process, but disfavor the proton transfer process. This may be

$$X\text{-}C_6H_4CH_2OH \quad catH^+ \quad H_2O_2$$

$$h\nu$$

$$X\text{-}C_6H_4CHO \quad catH_3^+ \quad O_2$$

Scheme 29.

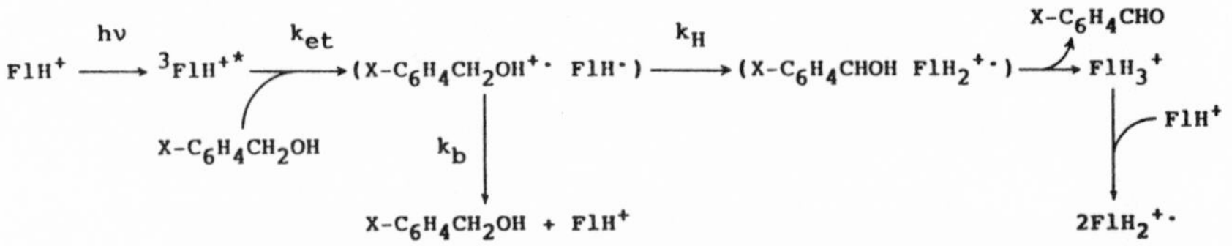

$$\text{FlH}^+ \xrightarrow{h\nu} {}^3\text{FlH}^{+*} \xrightarrow{k_{et}} (\text{X-C}_6\text{H}_4\text{CH}_2\text{OH}^{+\cdot} \ \text{FlH}^{\cdot}) \xrightarrow{k_H} (\text{X-C}_6\text{H}_4\text{CHOH} \ \text{FlH}_2^{+\cdot}) \xrightarrow{\text{X-C}_6\text{H}_4\text{CHO}} \text{FlH}_3^+$$

X-C$_6$H$_4$CH$_2$OH k_b

X-C$_6$H$_4$CH$_2$OH + FlH$^+$ 2FlH$_2^{+\cdot}$

FlH$^+$

Scheme 30.

the reason why the limiting quantum yield with the strongly electron-donating substituents (X = p-HO and p-MeO) becomes significantly smaller as compared with the other substituents. Conversely, the strongly electron-withdrawing substituent (X = p-NO$_2$) disfavors the electron transfer process and thus, photocatalytic reaction may not be started from the beginning. The excited state involved in the reaction in the absence of dioxygen may be the triplet state ^{3}FlH^{+*}, since the excited-state quenching constants obtained from the linear plots between Φ^{-1} and [X-C$_6$H$_4$CH$_2$OH]$^{-1}$ are more than 10-fold larger than the fluorescence quenching constants.[124] In the presence of dioxygen, however, the triplet state is quenched by dioxygen, and thus, the contribution of the singlet excited state ^{1}FlH^{+*} becomes dominant.[121]

7.2. Oxygenation

Photooxygenation of Tetraalkyltin Compounds

Flavin-Mg^{2+} complexes can also catalyze photoinduced oxygenation of R$_4$Sn *via* photoinduced electron transfer from R$_4$Sn to ^{1}Fl*-Mg^{2+} in MeCN at 298 K.[126]

$$\text{Me}_4\text{Sn} + \text{O}_2 \xrightarrow[\text{Fl-Mg}^{2+}]{h\nu} \text{MeO}_2\text{SnMe}_3 \qquad (107)$$

For example, irradiation of an oxygen saturated acetonitrile solution containing a flavin analogue (**1**)-Mg^{2+} complex (c.f. Table 16) and Me$_4$Sn with visible light results in the formation of MeO$_2$SnMe$_3$ (Eq. 107).[126] Yields of MeO$_2$SnMe$_3$ based on the initial amount of (**1**) reach 1000% in 15 hr, indicating that the (**1**)-Mg^{2+} complex acts as a photocatalyst in the photoinduced oxygenation of Me$_4$Sn. Neither thermal nor photoinduced oxygenation of Me$_4$Sn occurs in the absence of the (**1**)-Mg^{2+} complex. The Mg^{2+} ion plays an essential role, since in the absence of Mg^{2+} ion, no photoinduced oxygenation occurs.[126] The role of Mg^{2+} ion is not only to increase the oxidizing ability of the excited state of (**1**) but also stabilize (**1**) against irradiation of the visible light to prevent the photodegradation of (**1**) by forming the complex (Eq. 104). In fact, the fluorescence of (1)-Mg^{2+} can be readily quenched by electron transfer from Me_4Sn but no quenching of $^1(1)^*$ alone occurs.

The photoinduced electron transfer form Me_4Sn to Fl^*-Mg^{2+} initiates the radical chain reactions (Eqs. 108–111), similar to those for autoxidation of

$$\text{Initiation} \quad Me_4Sn + Fl^*\text{-}Mg^{2+} \longrightarrow Me^\cdot + Me_3Sn^+ + Fl^{-\cdot}\text{-}Mg^{2+} \quad (108)$$

$$\text{Propagation} \quad Me^\cdot + O_2 \xrightarrow{\text{fast}} MeO_2^\cdot \quad (109)$$

$$MeO_2^\cdot + Me_4Sn \longrightarrow MeO_2SnMe_3 + Me^\cdot \quad (110)$$

$$\text{Termination} \quad 2MeO_2^\cdot \longrightarrow MeOH + HCHO \quad (111)$$

alkylborons[127] and alkylzirconocenes.[128] Since the one-electron oxidation of Me_4Sn results in the facile fragmentation of Me_4Sn to yield $Me^\cdot$ (Eq. 108), the oxygenation of Me_4Sn proceeds by the radical chain reactions (Eqs. 109 and 110). The termination step of primary alkyl peroxyl radicals such as $Me^\cdot$ is the bimolecular reaction to give equal amounts of alcohol and aldehyde (Eq. 111).[77] The rate-determining step is the S_{H2} reaction of Me_4Sn with $MeO_2^\cdot$ (Eq. 110), when the quantum yield increases linearly with an increase in $[Me_4Sn]$.[126]

In contrast with the case of Me_4Sn, the photooxidation of Pr^i_4Sn by dioxygen, catalyzed by a Fl-Mg^{2+} complex, gives no peroxyl compound, but instead approximately equal amounts of isopropyl alcohol and acetone (Eq. 112). In the case of Pr^i_4Sn, the photoinitiation step becomes dominant with little contribution

$$Pr^i_4Sn + O_2 \xrightarrow[Fl\text{-}Mg^{2+}]{h\nu} Pr^iOH + Me_2C{=}O \quad (112)$$

from the chain-propagation step, to give mainly the termination products (isopropyl alcohol and acetone), when the quantum yield is independent $[Pr^i_4Sn]$.[126] Such a difference between the photooxidation of Me_4Sn and that of Pr^i_4Sn may be ascribed to the more efficient photoinitiation in the case of Pr^i_4Sn than the case of Me_4Sn as predicted by the stronger donor ability of Pr^i_4Sn as well as the higher reactivity of $MeO_2^\cdot$ than $Pr^iO_2^\cdot$ in the propagation step (Eq. 110). In any case, the photocatalyst is regenerated by the fast oxidation of the reduced species $Fl^{-\cdot}$-Mg^{2+} by dioxygen (Eq. 113).[129]

$$Fl^\cdot\text{-}Mg^{2+} + O_2 \xrightarrow{\text{fast}} Fl\text{-}Mg^{2+} + O_2^{-\cdot} \quad (113)$$

Flavin-Sensitized Photooxygenation of Unsaturated Fatty Acids

As described above, flavin-metal ion complexes as well as protonated flavins can act as photocatalysts in oxidation of various substrates by dioxygen *via* the photoreduction of flavins by substrates. On the other hand, flavins are also able to sensitize photoinduced oxygenation of appropriate substrates by the singlet excited state of dioxygen ($^1O_2^*$) formed by energy transfer from the triplet excited states of flavins to dioxygen in its ground state.[130] The singlet dioxygen $^1O_2^*$ ($^1\Sigma_g$) is well known to oxidize a variety of substrates.[131] Thus, photoinduced dioxygenation of unsaturated fatty acids or esters (LH = oleic acid, linoleic acid, methyl linoleate, and linolenic acid) proceeds efficiently in the presence of a riboflavin derivative, riboflavin-2′,3′,4′,5′-tetraacetate (Fl) in MeCN, although no photoreduction of Fl occurs by LH in the absence of dioxygen.[130]

The quantum yields for the formation of the total hydroperoxides (Φ) and conjugated diene hydroperoxides (Φ_{conj}) in the Fl-sensitized photooxygenation of various fatty acids or ester in MeCN are listed in Table 18. While no hydroperoxides are produced from fatty acids containing no double bond (isobutyric acid, valeric acid, and pivalic acid), the Fl-sensitized photooxygenation of unsaturated fatty acids or ester (oleic acid, linoleic acid, methyl linoleate, and linolenic acid) proceeds efficiently. The Φ values of unsaturated fatty acids or ester containing 1,4-diene unit, i.e., linoleic acid, methyl linoleate, and linolenic acid, are larger than the corresponding Φ_{conj} values, indicating that both conjugated and non-conjugated hydroperoxides are formed in the Fl-sensitized photooxidation. The ratios of conjugated and non-conjugated hydroperoxides are determined from the values of $\Phi_{conj}/(\Phi - \Phi_{conj})$; the ratios are 0, 1.1, 1.1, and 2.1 for oleic acid, linoleic acid, methyl linoleate, and linolenic acid, respectively (Table 18). Such product ratios of hydroperoxides are well known as characteristic of the oxidation of unsaturated fatty acids and esters by singlet dioxygen.[132] In contrast, the free radical oxidation of unsaturated fatty acids and ester (linoleic acid, methyl linoleate, and linoleic acid) by triplet dioxygen is known to produce only the corresponding conjugated hydroperoxides.[133] Since the position of the hydroperoxide group in the oxidation by singlet dioxygen is the carbon atom located at both sides of the double bond, the number of isomers produced is two times of the number of double bonds in fatty acids and esters. The double bond shifts to the adjacent position and thereby both conjugated and non-conjugated isomers may be formed for unsaturated fatty acids and esters containing 1,4-diene units as shown in Scheme 31 for linoleic acid or methyl linoleate. When the attack of singlet dioxygen on the double bonds is assumed to be random, the ratios of conjugated and non-conjugated hydroperoxides formed from oleic acid, linoleic acid (or methyl linoleate), and linolenic acid should be 0 (non-conjugated 9,10-isomers), 1 (conjugated 9,13-isomers and non-conjugated 10,12-isomers), and 2 (conjugated 9,12,13,16-isomers and non-conjugated 10,15-isomers), respec-

Table 18. Quantum Yields for the Formation of Conjugated Diene Hydroperoxides (Φ_{conj}) and Total Hydroperoxides (Φ) in the F1-Sensitized Photooxidation of Fatty Acids or Ester (LH 0.10 M) in the Presence of F1 (1.5×10^{-4} M) in an Oxygen-Saturated MeCN Solution Under Irradiation of Light of λ 442 nm[130]

LH	$\Phi_{conj}{}^a$	Φ^b	$\Phi_{conj}/(\Phi - \Phi_{conj})^c$
isobutyric acid	d	d	
valeric acid	d	d	
pivalic acid	d	d	
oleic acid	d	0.21	0
linoleic acid	0.16	0.30	1.1
methyl linoleate	0.16	0.30	1.1
linolenic acid	0.30	0.44	2.1

[a] Determined from the absorbance at λ 233 nm. The experimental errors are within $\pm 10\%$. [b] Determined by the iodometry. The experimental errors are within $\pm 5\%$. [c] The value corresponds to the ratio of conjugated and nonconjugated hydroperoxides formed in the reaction. [d] No reaction.

tively. These product ratios expected from the oxidation by singlet oxygen agree well with those observed in the Fl-sensitized photooxidation in Table 18, indicating the involvement of singlet oxygen in the photooxidation. The involvement of singlet oxygen in the Fl-sensitized photooxidation of linoleic acid as well as linolenic acid is also confirmed by the inhibitory effect of tetramethylethylene and β-carotene, which are well known as strong quenchers of single oxygen.[131,134]

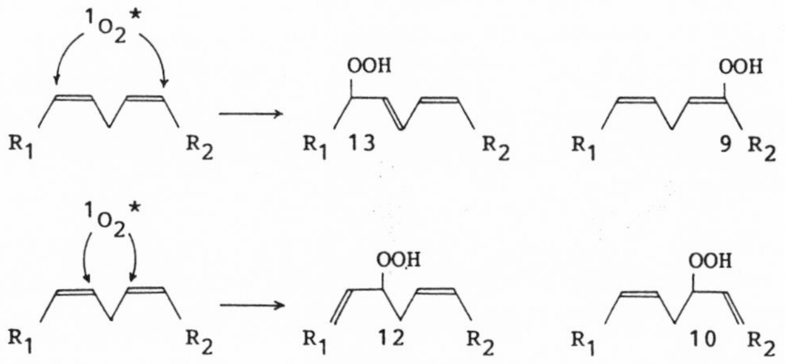

Scheme 31.

Based on the above results, the Fl-sensitized mechanism is summarized as shown in Eqs. 114–117, where τ is the lifetime of $^1O_2^*$ ($^1\Sigma_g$) 30 μs in MeCN,[135] and k_R corresponds to the rate constant for the rate-determining step of the ene

$$\text{Fl} \xrightarrow{h\nu} {}^1\text{Fl}^* \longrightarrow {}^3\text{Fl}^* \quad (\Phi_T) \tag{114}$$

$$^3\text{Fl}^* + {}^3O_2(^3\Sigma_g^-) \longrightarrow {}^1O_2^*(^1\Delta_g) + \text{Fl} \tag{115}$$

$$^1O_2^*(^1\Delta_g) \xrightarrow{\tau^{-1}} {}^3O_2(^3\Sigma_g^-) \tag{116}$$

$$^1O_2^* + \text{LH} \xrightarrow{k_R} \text{LOOH} \tag{117}$$

reaction between $^1O_2^*$ and LH. According to Eqs. 114–117, the quantum yield Φ for the formation of total hydroperoxides (LOOH) may be given by Eq. 118, which is rewritten by Eq. 119. The validity of Eq. 119 is confirmed by the plots

$$\Phi = \Phi_T k_R \tau [\text{LH}]/(1 + k_R \tau [\text{LH}]) \tag{118}$$

$$\Phi^{-1} = \Phi_T^{-1}[1 + (k_R \tau [\text{LH}])^{-1}] \tag{119}$$

of Φ^{-1} vs. $[\text{LH}]^{-1}$ which give linear correlations as shown in Figure 38. Each intercept of the plots gives the same value ($\Phi_T = 0.65$), which agree well with the reported quantum yield of the intersystem crossing of riboflavin ($\Phi_{isc} = 0.67$).[136] The rate constants k_R for the reaction of $^1O_{2*}$ with LH are obtained from the slopes and intercepts of the linear plots in Figure 38 and the lifetime of $^1O_2^*$ (τ 30μs),[31] and the k_R values are listed in Table 19. The k_R value increases with an increase in the number of double bonds in LH; oleic acid < linoleic acid < linolenic acid. The reported k_R value (4.0×10^7 $M^{-1}s^{-1}$)[31] of tetramethylethylene is much larger than those of linoleic acid (2.8×10^5 $M^{-1}s^{-1}$) and linolenic acid (6.4×10^5 $M^{-1}s^{-1}$) in Table 19. This may be the reason why tetramethylethylene inhibited the Fl-sensitized photooxygenation of linoleic acid and linolenic acid efficiently.

Oxygenation and Oxidative Coupling of Alkyl Ligands of cis-Dialkylcobalt(III) Complexes

The oxidizing ability of ground states of flavin and pterin analogues is also enhanced by the protonation in an aprotic solvent (MeCN). In this section we show that organometallic compounds such as *cis*-dialkylcobalt(III) complexes,

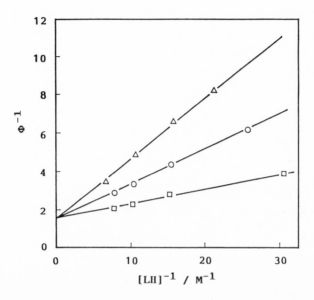

Figure 38. Plots of Φ^{-1} vs $[LH]^{-1}$ for the Fl-sensitized photooxidation of oleic acid ($\triangle$), linoleic acid ($\bigcirc$), and linoleinic acid ($\square$) in the presence of Fl (1.5×10^{-4} M) in an oxygen-saturated MeCN solution under irradiation of light of λ 442 nm.[130]

which are stable to dioxygen, can be oxidized by dioxygen in the presence of a catalytic amount of protonated flavin and pterin analogues in the presence of $HClO_4$ in MeCN.[137] In general, the oxygenation of alkyl ligands of alkyl-cobalt(III) complexes (RCo) are known to be induced by thermal homolytic cleavage of cobalt-carbon bonds (Eq. 120),[138] followed by the reactions of the dissociated alkyl radicals with dioxygen (Eq. 121).[139] In other cases, oxidation of dialkylmetal complexes (R_2M) by dioxygen leads to oxidative coupling of the

$$RCo \;\rightleftharpoons\; (R \cdot Co) \tag{120}$$

$$(R \cdot Co) + O_2 \longrightarrow ROO \cdot + Co \tag{121}$$

alkyl ligands (Eq. 122).[140,141] In the coenzyme-catalyzed oxidation of *cis*-dialkylcobalt(III) complexes by dioxygen, both oxygenation and oxidative cou-

$$R_2M + O_2 \longrightarrow R-R + M^+ + O_2^- \tag{122}$$

pling processes occur depending on the difference in the alkyl ligands as shown below.[137]

cis-$[(PhCH_2)_2Co(bpy)_2]ClO_4$ (bpy = 2,2'-bipyridine) shows no reactivity toward dioxygen or redox coenzyme analogues, riboflavin (RFl), riboflavin-2′,3′,4′,5′-tetraacetate (Fl), lumazine (Lu), and aminopterin (AP), in MeCN at 298 K.[137] When a strong acid such as perchloric acid ($HClO_4$) is added to an oxygen-saturated MeCN solution of cis-[$(PhCH_2)_2Co(bpy)_2$]$^+$ in the presence of a catalytic amount of coenzyme analogue, however, cis-[$(PhCH_2)_2Co(bpy)_2$]$^+$ is readily oxidized by dioxygen to produce benzyl hydroperoxide (Eq. 123).[137] A typical example of the coenzyme-catalyzed oxygenation

$$\underline{cis}\text{-}[(PhCH_2)_2Co(bpy)_2]^+ + O_2 + H^+ \xrightarrow{\text{RFl, Fl, L, or AP}} [PhCH_2Co(bpy)_2]^{2+} + PhCH_2OOH \quad (123)$$

reaction of cis-[$(PhCH_2)_2Co(bpy)_2$]$^+$ is shown in Figure 39, where cis-[$(PhCH_2)_2Co(bpy)_2$]$^+$ (3.0×10^{-2} M) reacts with dioxygen in the presence of catalytic amount of lumazine (5.3×10^{-3} M) in CD_3CN (0.60 cm^3) containing $HClO_4$ (0.12 M) to produce $PhCH_2OOH$ which decomposes to yield benzaldehyde (PhCHO) as the final oxygenated product.[140] Other redox coenzyme analogues (RFl, Fl, and AP) can also catalyze the oxygenation of the benzyl ligand of cis-[$(PhCH_2)_2Co(bpy)_2$]$^+$ in the presence of $HClO_4$ in MeCN at 298 K.[137]

Flavin analogues are protonated at the N(1) position in a strongly acidic aqueous solution ($pK_a = 0$).[141] In MeCN, the protonation of flavin analogues occurs much more readily than that in H_2O as is evident from the large protonation constant in MeCN (2.7×10^6 M^{-1}).[122,123] Other coenzyme analogues (RFl,

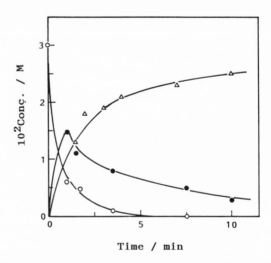

Figure 39. Oxygenation of the benzyl ligand of cis-[$(PhCH_2)_2Co(bpy)_2$]$^+$ (3.0×10^{-2} M) in the presence of $HClO_4$ (1.2×10^{-1} M) and a catalytic amount of lumazine (5.3×10^{-3} M) in CD_3CN at 298 K; cis-[$(PhCH_2)_2Co(bpy)_2$]$^+$ (○), $PhCH_2OOH$ (●), PhCHO (△).[137]

Fl, Lu, AP) exist in the protonated form ($RFlH^+$, FlH^+, LuH^+, APH^+) in the presence of an excess amount of $HClO_4$ in MeCN. The enhanced oxidizing ability of coenzyme analogues in the presence of $HClO_4$ makes it possible to undergo electron transfer from cis-$[(PhCH_2)_2Co(bpy)_2]^+$ that initiates the catalytic cycle of the coenzyme-catalyzed oxygenation of the benzyl ligand of cis-$[(PhCH_2Co(bpy)_2]^+$ (Bz_2Co^+) shown in Scheme 32.[137] The electron transfer form Bz_2Co^+ to FlH^+ in the presence of $HClO_4$ yields radical pair (Bz_2Co^{2+} $FlH_2^{+\cdot}$) in which one cobalt-benzyl bond is readily cleaved to give benzyl radical ($Bz\cdot$), followed by the facile trap by dioxygen to produce benzylperoxyl radical ($BzOO\cdot$) which then gives benzyl hydroperoxide ($BzOOH$) by the abstraction of hydrogen atom from $FlH_2^{+\cdot}$, accompanied by regeneration of FlH^+ (Scheme 32). The benzyl hydroperoxide may decompose to give the final product, benzaldehyde.[140] In the absence of dioxygen, the benzyl radical reacts with $BzCo^{2+}$ to yield the coupling product of the alkyl ligands, and thus the stoichiometric oxidation of cis-$[R_2Co(bpy)_2]^+$ ($R = PhCH_2$) by FlH^+ occurs to yield R-R and $FlH_2^{+\cdot}$ (Eq. 124).[137] Essentially the same reaction scheme is applied for the case of LuH^+.

$$cis\text{-}[R_2Co(bpy)_2]^+ + 2FlH^+ + 2H^+$$
$$\longrightarrow R\text{-}R + [Co(bpy)_2]^{3+} + 2FlH_2^{+\cdot} \quad (124)$$

The coenzyme-catalyzed oxidation of other cis-dialkylcobalt(III) complexes, cis-$[R_2Co(bpy)_2]^+$ ($R = Me$, Et), by dioxygen also proceeds efficiently in the presence of $HClO_4$ in MeCN at 298 K. In this case, however, no oxygenation of the alkyl ligands occurs, but instead coupling products of the alkyl groups are obtained upon the catalytic oxidation of cis-$[R_2Co(bpy)_2]^+$ by dioxygen in the presence of $HClO_4$ (Eq. 125).[137] The formation of the coupling products of alkyl

$$cis\text{-}[(C_2H_5)_2Co(bpy)_2]^+ + O_2 + 2H^+ \xrightarrow{Fl}$$
$$C_4H_{10} + [Co(bpy)_2]^{3+} + H_2O_2 \quad (125)$$

ligands of cis-$[R_2Co(bpy)_2]^+$ ($R = Et$, Me), which could only arise *via* the corresponding dialkylcobalt(IV) complexes,[142,143] demonstrates clearly the in-

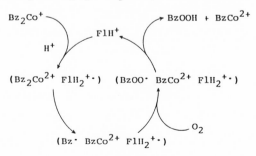

Scheme 32.

volvement of an electron transfer process in the coenzyme-catalyzed oxidation of cis-$[R_2Co(bpy)_2]^+$. The catalytic cycle in the case of FlH^+ is shown in Scheme 33, where an acid-catalyzed electron transfer from the dialkylcobalt(III) complex (R_2Co^+) to FlH^+ occurs to give the corresponding dialkylcobalt(IV) complex (R_2Co^{2+}) and $FlH_2^{+\cdot}$, followed by the facile reductive elimination of the alkyl ligands to yield the coupling product R-R. The resulting cobalt(II) complex may reduce $FlH_2^{+\cdot}$ in the presence of $HClO_4$ to give Co^{3+},[144] and a protonated dihydroflavin FlH_3^+. The fully reduced form of flavin (FlH_3^+) is known to be readily oxidized by dioxygen to regenerate the oxidized form (FlH^+) accompanied by the formation of H_2O_2.[123] In the absence of dioxygen, the dihydroflavin radical cation $FlH_2^{+\cdot}$ is formed by the comproportionation reaction (c.f. Scheme 30).[122,123]

Rates of the coenzyme-catalyzed oxidation of cis-$[R_2Co(bpy)_2]^+$ by dioxygen in the presence of $HClO_4$ in MeCN obey pseudo-first-order kinetics when the concentrations of oxidants and $HClO_4$ are maintained at >10 fold excess of the concentration of cis-$[R_2Co(bpy)_2]^+$. The pseudo-first-order rate constants $k^{(1)}$ increase linearly with an increase in the concentration of a coenzyme catalyst [Cat]. Thus, the rate of disappearance of cis-$[R_2Co(bpy)_2]^+$ is given by Eq. 126.

$$-d[R_2Co^+]/dt = k_{obs}[R_2Co^+][Cat] \qquad (126)$$

The k_{obs} value in air-saturated MeCN was the same as that in oxygen-saturated MeCN. When FlH^+ or LuH^+ is used as a catalyst for the catalytic oxidation of cis-$[Et_2Co(bpy)_2]^+$ by dioxygen in the presence of $HClO_4$ in MeCN, the log k_{obs} value increases linearly with an increase in the log $[HClO_4]$ value with a slope of unity as shown in Figure 40, indicating that the acid-catalyzed electron transfer from cis-$[Et_2Co(bpy)_2]^+$ to FlH^+ or LuH^+ is the rate-determining step in the catalytic cycle in Scheme 33. When APH^+ is used as a catalyst, however, the log k_{obs} value remains constant with increasing $[HClO_4]$ in the low concentration

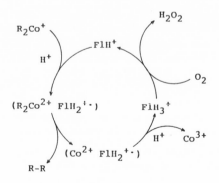

Scheme 33.

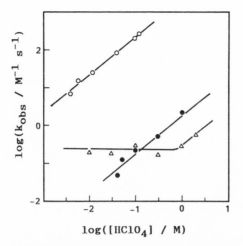

Figure 40. Plots of the observed second-order rate constants log k_{obs} vs log[HClO$_4$] for the oxidation of *cis*-[Et$_2$Co(bpy)$_2$]$^+$ with dioxygen, catalyzed by FlH$^+$ (O), LuH$^+$ (●), and APH$^+$ (△) in the presence of HClO$_4$ in MeCN at 298 K.[137]

region (log[HClO$_4$] < 0) when no protonation of APH$^+$ occurs and increases linearly with an increase in the log[HClO$_4$] value in the higher concentration region with a slope of unity (Figure 40). The HClO$_4$ used in Figure 40 contains 30% H$_2$O. As such no APH$_2$$^{+\cdot}$ has been detected in the stoichiometric oxidation of *cis*-[R$_2$Co(bpy)$_2$]$^+$ with APH$^+$ in the presence of HClO$_4$ (< 1 M), while FlH$_2$$^{+\cdot}$ and LuH$_2$$^{+\cdot}$ are formed in the reactions with FlH$^+$ and LuH$^+$ in deaerated MeCN, respectively (Eq. 124). The addition of H$_2$O to an MeCN solution of 0.10 M HClO$_4$ results in a significant decrease in the k_{obs} value, as shown in Figure 41, where the log k_{obs} values of the FlH$^+$-catalyzed oxidation of *cis*-[Et$_2$Co(bpy)$_2$]$^+$ by dioxygen are plotted against the log[H$_2$O] values.[145] Thus, use of an aprotic solvent is essential for the acid-catalyzed electron transfer to proceed efficiently.

In the absence of a coenzyme analogue, the cobalt-carbon bond of *cis*-[R$_2$Co(bpy)$_2$]$^+$ in both deaerated and oxygen-saturated MeCN is cleaved by the electrophilic attack of proton to yield [RCo(bpy)$_2$]$^{2+}$ and RH, Eq. 127. The rate of electrophilic cleavage of *cis*-[R$_2$Co(bpy)$_2$]$^+$ by HClO$_4$ decreases in the order

$$\underline{cis}\text{-}[R_2Co(bpy)_2]^+ + H^+ \longrightarrow RH + [RCo(bpy)_2]^{2+} \qquad (127)$$

R = Me > Et > PhCH$_2$. Under the conditions such that the contribution from the electrophilic cleavage reaction by HClO$_4$ can be neglected, the k_{obs} values of *cis*-[R$_2$Co(bpy)$_2$]$^+$ (R = PhCH$_2$, Et, Me) are compared by using the same catalyst (FlH$^+$) as shown in Figure 42, where the log k_{obs} values are plotted against the log[HClO$_4$] values. The k_{obs} value at the same concentration of HClO$_4$ decreases in the order R = PhCH$_2$ > Et > Me.

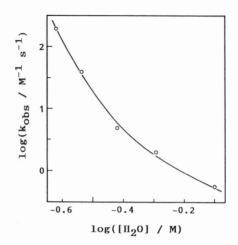

Figure 41. Plots of the observed second-order rate constants log k_{obs} vs log [H$_2$O] for the FlH$^+$-catalyzed oxidation of *cis*-[Et$_2$Co(bpy)$_2$]$^+$ in the presence of HClO$_4$ (0.10 M) in MeCN containing various concentrations of H$_2$O at 298 K.[137]

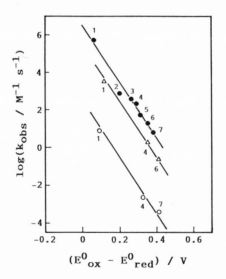

Figure 42. Plots of log k_{obs} for electron transfer reactions from *cis*-[R$_2$Co(bpy)$_2$]$^+$ [R = PhCH$_2$ (○), Et (●), Me (△)] to oxidants vs the difference in the redox potentials between E^0_{ox} of *cis*-[R$_2$Co(bpy)$_2$]$^+$ and E^0_{red} of the oxidants.[137] Numbers refer to the oxidants; 1 = 2,3-dichloro-5,6-dicyano-*p*-benzoquinone, 2 = Fe(C$_5$H$_5$)$_2$$^+$, 3 = Fe(BuC$_5H_4$)(C$_5H_5$)$^+$, 4 = 2,3-dicyano-*p*-benzoquinone, 5 = Fe(MeC$_5$H$_4$)$_2$$^+$, 6 = TCNE, 7 = TCNQ.[137]

Comparison between Scheme 32 and Scheme 33 reveals the origin of the difference in the oxygenation and oxidative coupling processes, that is, the much lower reactivity of benzyl radicals as compared to methyl or ethyl radicals in the coupling reactions, resulting in the trap of benzyl radical by dioxygen to lead to the oxygenated product, benzyl hydroperoxide (Scheme 32). As such, *cis*-$[(PhCH_2)_2Co(bpy)_2]^+$ is the least reactive in the one-electron oxidation in the absence of dioxygen because of the slow coupling process,[143] but it becomes the most reactive in the coenzyme catalyzed reaction in the presence of dioxygen (Figure 42) because of the facile trap of benzyl radical by dioxygen. In the case of *cis*-$[R_2Co(bpy)_2]^+$ (R = Et, Me), the cleavage of Co-R bond upon the one-electron oxidation may also occur in a stepwise manner as shown in Scheme 32. However, rates of the reactions of $R^{\cdot}$ ($Et^{\cdot}$ or $Me^{\cdot}$) with $[RCo(bpy)_2]^{2+}$ as compared to $PhCH_2^{\cdot}$ may be so fast that $R^{\cdot}$ radicals cannot be trapped by dioxygen and that only the net coupling of the alkyl ligands of $[R_2Co(bpy)_2]^{2+}$ can occur to yield the coupling products R-R exclusively (Scheme 33).

8. EPILOGUE

I have focussed on the acid-base catalysis in both thermal and photoinduced electron transfer processes involving redox coenzymes in aprotic media. Such acid- (or base-) catalyzed electron transfer has been shown to play an essential role in reducing the activation barrier of over-all redox reactions of biological significance. In particular, thermal and photoinduced reduction of various substrates has been made possible by employing an acid-stable NADH analogue in the presence of $HClO_4$ in MeCN. The presence of H_2O prevents significantly the acid-catalyzed electron transfer processes. As such, mysteriously active function of the NADH-dependent enzymes may be largely ascribed to simple acid catalysis in electron transfer from NADH to substrates in hydrophobic environment, which causes a drastic decrease in the activation barrier of the over-all biological redox reactions. Similarly, base catalysis in electron transfer from substrates to NAD^+ analogues, that should certainly require further scrutiny, may also play an important role in the overall oxidation of substrates. In the simple and primitive homogeneous system, however, the activation of substrates (electron acceptors) by acid is inherently accompanied by the deactivation of the coenzymes (electron donors) that are more easily protonated by acid. Nonetheless, the choice of appropriate electron transfer catalytic system even in the homogeneous system makes it possible to construct electron transfer chain from an NADH analogue to dioxygen.

By its nature, any delineation of mechanisms depends largely on the eyes of the beholder. In this context, mechanisms and catalysis in electron transfer chemistry of redox coenzyme analogues discussed here will hopefully stimulate further researches including those from a different view at a different level so that better and more general understanding of biological redox reactions could be obtained.

ACKNOWLEDGMENTS

I gratefully acknowledge the contributions of my collaborators mentioned in the references and especially Professor Toshio Tanaka for his continued encouragement. I express my heartfelt appreciation to Professor Jay K. Kochi who guided me into the exciting field of electron transfer chemistry. I also thank Professor M. Chanon for my stay at Université d'Aix-Marseille with his kind hospitality and helpful discussion in Faculté de St Jérome at which this article was completed. Financial support has been provided by the Ministry of Education, Science and Culture, Japan.

REFERENCES

1. Stryer, L. *Biochemistry*, 3rd ed; Freeman, New York, 1988, Chap. 17.
2. (a) Alberts, B.; Bray, D.; Lewis, J.; Raff, M.; Roberts, K.; Watson, J. D. *Molecular Biology of the Cell*. Garland Publishing, New York, 1983. (b) Capaldi, R. A. Ed. *Membrane Proteins in Energy Transduction*. Dekker, New York, 1979.
3. (a) Hatefi, Y. *Ann. Rev. Biochem.* **1985**, *54*, 1015. (b) Hassinen, I. E. *Biochim. Biophys. Acta* **1986**, *853*, 135.
4. Dixon, M.; Webb, E. C.; Thorne, C. J. R.; Tipton, K. F. *Enzymes*, 3rd ed.; Academic Press, New York, 1979, p. 684.
5. (a) Sund, H., Ed. *Pyridine-nucleotide Dependent Dehydrogenase*. Walter de Gruyter: West Berlin, 1977. (b) Kellogg, R. M. *Top. Curr. Chem.* **1982**, *101*, 111. (c) Ohno, A.; Ushida, S. *Lecture Notes in Bioorganic Chemistry, Mechanistic Models of Asymmetric Reductions*. Springer-Verlag, Berlin, 1986, p. 105.
6. (a) Eisner, U.; Kuthan, *Chem. Rev.* **1982**, *72*, 1. (b) Shinkai, S. *Kagaku* **1980**, *35*, 170. (c) Stout, D. M.; Meyer, A. I. *Chem. Rev.* **1982**, *82*, 223.
7. (a) Walsh, C. *Acc. Chem. Res.* **1980**, *13*, 148. (b) Bruice, T. C. *Acc. Chem. Res.* **1980**, *13*, 256. (c) Shinkai, S. *Kagaku Sousetsu* 1982, *35*, 151. (d) Massey, V.; Palmer, G.; Ballou, D. P. *Oxidases and Related Redox Systems*, King, T. E., Mason, H. S., Morrison, M., Eds., Vol. 1, Univ. Park Press, Baltimore, 1973, p.25. (e) Massey, V.; Hemmerich, P. *Enzymes*, **1975**, *12*, 191.
8. (a) Powell, M. F.; Bruice, T. C. *J. Am. Chem. Soc.* **1983**, *105*, 7139. (b) Carlson, B. W.; Miller, L. L. *J. Am. Chem. Soc.* **1985**, *107*, 479. (c) Miller, L. L.; Valentine, J. R. *J. Am. Chem. Soc.* **1988**, *110*, 3982.
9. (a) Sigman, D. S.; Hajdu, J.; Creighton, D. J. *Bioorganic Chemistry*; van Tamelen, E. E., Ed. Academic Press, New York, 1978; Vol. IV, p. 385. (b) Yasui, S.; Ohno, A. *Bioorg. Chem.* 1986, *14*, 70.
10. Fukuzumi, S.; Tanaka, T. *Photoinduced Electron Transfer*, Fox, M. A.; Chanon, M., Eds. Elsevier, Amsterdam, 1988, Part C, Chap. 10 and references cited therein.
11. (a) Fukuzumi, S.; Kondo, Y.; Tanaka, T. *Chem. Lett.* **1982**, 1591; (b) Fukuzumi, S.; Kondo, Y.; Tanaka, T. *Chem. Lett.* **1983**, 751. (c) Fukuzumi, S.; Kondo, Y.; Tanaka, T. *J. Chem. Soc., Perkin Trans. 2* **1984**, 673.
12. Fukuzumi, S.; Hironaka, K.; Nishizawa, N.; Tanaka, T. *Bull. Chem. Soc. Jpn.* **1983**, *56*, 2220.

13. Fukuzumi, S.; Nishizawa, N.; Tanaka, T. *Bull. Chem. Soc. Jpn.* **1982**, *55*, 3482.

14. Carlson, B. W.; Miller, L. L.; Neta, P.; Grodkowski, J. *J. Am. Chem. Soc.* **1984**, *106*, 7233.

15. (a) Okamoto, T.; Ohno, A.; Oka, S. *J. Chem. Soc., Chem. Commun.* **1977**, 7. (b) Powell, M. F.; Wu, J. C.; Bruice, T. C. *J. Am. Chem. Soc.* **1984**, *106*, 3850. (c) Sinha, A.; Bruice, T. C. *J. Am. Chem. Soc.* **1984**, *106*, 7291.

16. Fukuzumi, S.; Koumitsu, S.; Hironaka, K.; Tanaka, T. *J. Am. Chem. Soc.* **1987**, *109*, 305.

17. (a) Westheimer, F. H. *Chem. Rev.* **1961**, *61*, 265. (b) Kreevoy, M. M. *Isotopes in Organic Chemistry. Vol. 2. Isotopes in Hydrogen Transfer Processes*; Buncel, E., Lee, C. C., Eds. Elsevier, Amsterdam, 1976, Chap. 1. (c) More O'Ferrall, R. A. *Proton-Transfer Reactions*, Caldin, E. F.; Gold, V., Eds. Chapman and Hall, London, 1975, Chap. 8.

18. For the solvent effects for the pKa values, see ref. 16 and 20.

19. (a) Fukuzumi, S.; Tanaka, T. *Chem. Lett.* **1982**, 1513. (b) Fukuzumi, S.; Nishizawa, N.; Tanaka, T. *J. Org. Chem.* **1984**, *49*, 3571.

20. Ishikawa, M.; Fukuzumi, S. *J. Chem. Soc., Faraday Trans.* **1990**, *86*, 3531.

21. Marcus, R. A. *J. Phys. Chem.* **1968**, *72*, 891.

22. Fukuzumi, S.; Kitano, T.; Ishikawa, M. *J. Am. Chem. Soc.* **1990**, *112*, 5631.

23. Ishikawa, M.; Fukuzumi, S.; Goto, T.; Tanaka, T. *Bull. Chem. Soc. Jpn.* **1989**, *62*, 3754.

24. Kraeutler, B.; Jaeger, C. D.; Bard, A. J. *J. Am. Chem. Soc.* **1978**, *100*, 4903.

25. (a) Davies, A. G. *Organic Peroxides*. Butterworth, London, 1961, p. 51. (b) Pryor, W. A. *Free Radicals*, McGraw-Hill, New York, 1966, p. 290.

26. (a) Volz, H.; Lotsch, W. *Tetrahedron Lett.* **1969**, 2275. (b) Wasielewski, M. R.; Breslow, R. *J. Am. Chem. Soc.* **1976**, *98*, 4222.

27. Kochi, J. K. *Organometallic Mechansims and Catalysis*. Academic Press, New York, 1978.

28. (a) Czochralska, B.; Lindqvist, L. *Chem. Phys. Lett.* **1983**, *101*, 297. (b) Lindqvist, L.; Czochralska, B.; Grigorov, I. *Chem. Phys. Lett.* **1985**, *119*, 494.

29. (a) Peters, K. S.; Pang, E.; Rudzki, J. *J. Am. Chem. Soc.* **1982**, *104*, 5535. (b) Manring, L. E.; Peters, K. S. *J. Am. Chem. Soc.* **1983**, *105*, 5708. (c) Manring, K. E.; Peters, K. S. *J. Am. Chem. Soc.* **1985**, *107*, 6452.

30. Fukuzumi, S.; Mochizuki, S.; Tanaka, T. *J. Chem. Soc., Dalton Trans.* **1990**, 695.

31. Fukuzumi, S.; Kitano, T. *Chem. Lett.* **1990**, 1275.

32. Wetrz, J. E.; Bolton, J. R. *Electron Spin Resonance. Elementary Theory and Practical Applications*. McGraw-Hill, New York, 1972.

33. Fukuzumi, S.; Mochizuki, S.; Tanaka, T. *J. Phys. Chem.* **1990**, *94*, 722.

34. (a) Fukuzumi, S.; Ishikawa, M.; Tanaka, T. *J. Chem. Soc., Chem. Commun.* **1985**, 1069. (b) Fukuzumi, S.; Ishikawa, M.; Tanaka, T. *Tetrahedron* **1986**, *42*, 1021.

35. Fukuzumi, S.; Kondo, Y.; Tanaka, T. *Chem. Lett.* **1983**, 485.

36. Carlson, B. W.; Miller, L. L. *J. Am. Chem. Soc.* **1985**, *107*, 479.

37. (a) Rehm, D.; Weller, A. *Isr. J. Chem.* **1970**, *8*, 259. (b) Rehm, D.; Weller, A. *Bunsenges. Phys. Chem.* **1969**, *73*, 834.

38. (a) Fukuzumi, S.; Kochi, J. K. *Bull. Chem. Soc. Jpn.* **1983**, *56*, 969. (b) Fukuzumi, S.; Wong, C. L.; Kochi, J. K. *J. Am. Chem. Soc.* **1980**, *102*, 2928. (c) Fukuzumi, S.; Kitano, T. *Inorg. Chem.* **1990**, *29*, 2558.

39. (a) Kochi, J. K. *Angew. Chem. Int. Ed. Engl.* **1988**, *27*, 1227. (b) Klingler, R. J.; Fukuzumi, S.; Kochi, J. K. *ACS Symp. Ser.* **1983**, *211*, 117.

40. (a) Mulliken, R. S.; Person, W. B. *Molecular Complexes. A Lecture and Reprint Volume*. Wiley-Interscience, New York, 1969. (b) Foster, R. *Organic Charge-Transfer Complexes*. Academic Press, New York, 1969.

41. (a) Fukuzumi, S.; Nishizawa, N.; Tanaka, T. *Chem. Lett.* **1983**, 1755. (b) Fukuzumi, S.; Nishizawa, N.; Tanaka, T. *J. Chem. Soc., Perkin Trans. 2* **1985**, 371.

42. Eklund, H.; Branden, C.-I. *Zinc Enzymes*, Spiro, T. G., Ed. Wiley-Interscience, New York, 1983; Chap. 4.

43. (a) Rich, P. R.; Bendall, D. S. *Biochim. Biophys. Acta* **1980**, *592*, 506. (b) Meisel, D.; Czapski, G. *J. Phys. Chem.* **1975**, *79*, 1503.
44. Fukuzumi, S.; Ishikawa, K.; Hironaka, K.; Tanaka, T. *J. Chem. Soc., Perkin Trans. 2* **1987**, 751.
45. (a) Fukuzumi, S.; Ishikawa, M.; Tanaka, T. *Chem. Lett.* **1989**, 1227. (b) Fukuzumi, S.; Ishikawa, M.; Tanaka, T. *J. Chem. Soc., Perkin Trans. 2* **1989**, 1811.
46. (a) Johnston, C. C.; Gardner, J. L.; Suelter, C. H.; Metzler, D. E. *Biochemistry* **1963**, *2*, 689. (b) van Eikeren, P.; Grier, D. L.; Eliason, J. *J. Am. Chem. Soc.* **1979**, *101*, 7406. (c) Skibo, E. B.; Bruice, T. C. *J. Am. Chem. Soc.* **1983**, *105*, 3316.
47. The potential vs. NHE is converted to that vs. SCE by subtracting 0.24 V.
48. Fukuzumi, S.; Chiba, M.; Tanaka, T. *Chem. Lett.* **1989**, 31.
49. Fukuzumi, S.; Mochizuki, S.; Tanaka, T. *J. Am. Chem. Soc.* **1989**, *111*, 1497.
50. Ishikawa, M.; Fukuzumi, S. *J. Chem. Soc., Chem. Commun.* **1990**, in press.
51. Fukuzumi, S.; Yorisue, T. *Chem. Lett.* **1990**, 871.
52. Boughriet, A.; Wortel, M. *J. Chem. Soc., Chem. Commun.* **1989**, 809.
53. (a) Fukuzumi, S.; Chiba, M.; Tanaka, T. *J. Chem. Soc., Chem. Commun.* **1989**, 941. (b) Fukuzumi, S.; Chiba, M. *J. Chem. Soc., Perkin Trans. 2* **1991**, 1393.
54. Mason, R. P. *Free Radicals in Biology*, Pryor, W. A., Ed. Academic Press, New York, 1982, Vol. V, p. 161.
55. Fukuzumi, S.; Mochizuki, S.; Tanaka, T. *Bull. Chem. Soc. Jpn.* **1989**, *62*, 3049.
56. Inoue, H.; Aoki, R.; Imoto, E. *Chem. Lett.* **1974**, 1157.
57. Tanner, D. D.; Stein, A.R. *J. Org. Chem.* **1988**, *53*, 1642.
58. (a) Mukaiyama, T. *Angew. Chem. Int. Ed. Engl.* **1977**, *16*, 817. (b) Schinzer, S., Ed. *Proceedings of the NATO Advanced Research Workshop on Selectivities in Lewis Acid Promoted Reactions.* Kluwer Academic Publishers. Dordrecht, 1989.
59. (a) Tanabe, K. *Solid Acids and Bases.* Academic Press, New York, 1970. (b) Knozinger, H. *Adv. Catal.* **1976**, *25*, 184. (c) Benesi, H. A.; Winquist, B. H. C. *Adv. Catal.* **1978**, *27*, 97.
60. Fukuzumi, S.; Chiba, M.; Ishikawa, M.; Ishikawa, K.; Tanaka, T. *J. Chem. Soc., Perkin Trans. 2*, **1989**, 1417.
61. Ono, Y.; Takagiwa, H.; Fukuzumi, S. *J. Catal.* **1977**, *50*, 181.
62. (a) Fukuzumi, S.; Kondo, Y.; Tanaka, T. *J. Chem. Soc., Chem. Commun.* **1985**, 1053. (b) Fukuzumi, S.; Kondo, Y.; Mochizuki, S.; Tanaka, T. *J. Chem. Soc., Perkin Trans. 2* **1989**, 1753.
63. Buchler, J. W. *Porphyrins and Metalloporphyrins*; Smith, K. M., Ed.; Elsevier: New York, 1975; p. 157.
64. (a) Antonini, E.; Brunori, M. *Hemoglobin and Myoglobin in Their Reactions with Ligands*; North-Holland: Amsterdam, 1971. (b) Lemberg, R.; Borrett, J. *Cytochromes*; Academic Press: New York, 1973.
65. (a) Cheng, R.-J.; Latos-Grazynski, L.; Balch, A. L. *Inorg. Chem.* **1982**, *21*, 2412. (b) Behere, D. V.; Mitra, S. *Inorg. Chem.* **1979**, *18*, 1723.
66. (a) Kadish, K. M.; Bottomley, L. A. *Inorg. Chem.* **1980**, *19*, 832. (b) Kadish, K. M.; Bottomley, L. A.; Beroiz, D. *Inorg. Chem.* **1978**, *17*, 1124. (c) Kadish, K. M.; Kelly, S. *Inorg. Chem.* **1979**, *81*, 2968.
67. (a) Jahnke, H.; Schonborn, M.; Zimmerman, *Top. Curr. Chem.* **1976**, *61*, 133. (b) Buttry, D. A.; Anson, F. C. *J. Am. Chem. Soc.* **1984**, *106*, 59. (c) Forshey, P. A.; Kuwana, T.; Kobayashi, N.; Osa, T. *Adv. Chem. Ser.* **1982**, *201*, 601. (d) Bettelheim, A.; White, B. A.; Raybuck, S. A.; Murray, R. W. *Inorg. Chem.* **1987**, *26*, 1009.
68. (a) Collman, J. P.; Denisevich, P.; Konai, Y.; Marrocco, M.; Koval, C.; Anson, F. C. *J. Am. Chem. Soc.* **1980**, *102*, 6027. (b) Durand, R. R.; Bencosme, C. S.; Collman, J. P.; Anson, F.C. *J. Am. Chem. Soc.* **1983**, *105*, 2710. (c) Chang, C. K.; Liu, H. Y.; Abdalmuhdi, I. *J. Am. Chem. Soc.* **1984**, *106*, 2725.
69. Collman, J. P.; Kim, K. *J. Am. Chem. Soc.* **1986**, *108*, 7847.

70. (a) Fukuzumi, S.; Mochizuki, S.; Tanaka, T. *J. Chem. Soc., Chem. Commun.* **1989**, 391. (b) Fukuzumi, S.; Mochizuki, S.; Tanaka, T. *Inorg. Chem.* **1990**, *29*, 653.

71. (a) Fukuzumi, S.; Mochizuki, S.; Tanaka, T. *Chem. Lett.* **1989**, 27. (b) Fukuzumi, S.; Mochizuki, S.; Tanaka, T. *Inorg. Chem.* **1989**, *28*, 245.

72. (a) Chanon, M.; Tobe, M. *Angew. Chem. Int. Ed.* **1982**, *21*, 1. (b) Julliard, M.; Chanon, M. *Chem. Rev.* **1983**, *83*, 425.

73. Fukuzumi, S.; Ishikawa, M.; Tanaka, T. *J. Chem. Soc., Perkin Trans. 2* **1989**, 1037.

74. (a) Sawyer, D. T.; Calderwood, T. S.; Yamaguchi, K.; Angelis, C. T. *Inorg. Chem.* **1983**, *22*, 2577. (b) Sawyer, D. T.; Valentine, J. S. *Acc. Chem. Res.* **1981**, *14*, 393.

75. (a) Symons, M. C. R. *Pure Appl. Chem.* **1981**, *53*, 223. (b) Chanon, M.; Rajzmann, M.; Chanon, F. *Tetrahedron* **1990**, *46*, 6193.

76. (a) Fukuzumi, S.; Hironaka, K.; Tanaka, T. *Chem. Lett.* **1982**, 1583. (b) Fukuzumi, S.; Hironaka, K.; Tanaka, T. *J. Am. Chem. Soc.* **1983**, *105*, 4722.

77. Howard, J. A. *Adv. Free Radical Chem.* **1972**, *4*, 49.

78. (a) Fukuzumi, S.; Kochi, J. K. *J. Org. Chem.* **1980**, *45*, 2654. (b) Fukuzumi, S.; Kochi, J. K. *J. Am. Chem. Soc.* **1980**, *102*, 2141.

79. (a) Fukuzumi, S.; Mochizuki, S.; Tanaka, T. *Chem. Lett.* **1988**, 1983. (b) Fukuzumi, S.; Mochizuki, S.; Tanaka, T. *J. Chem. Soc., Perkin Trans. 2.* **1989**, 1583.

80. Behar, D.; Neta, P. *J. Phys. Chem.* **1981**, *85*, 690.

81. Neta, P.; Behar, D. *J. Am. Chem. Soc.* **1981**, *103*, 103.

82. Ishikawa, M.; Fukuzumi, S. *J. Am. Chem. Soc.* **1990**, *112*, 8864.

83. (a) Marcus, R. A. *J. Chem. Phys.* **1965**, *43*, 679. (b) Marcus, R. A. *Ann. Rev. Phys. Chem.* **1964**, *15*, 155.

84. (a) Andrieux, C. P.; Blocman, C.; Dumas-Bouchiat, J. M.; Saveant, J.-M. *J. Am. Chem. Soc.* **1979**, *101*, 3431. (b) Andrieux, C. P.; Blocman, C.; Dumas-Bouchiat, J. M.; M'Halla, F.; Saveant, J.-M. *J. Am. Chem. Soc.* **1980**, *102*, 3806.

85. (a) Andrieux, C. P.; Gallardo, I.; Saveant, J.-M.; Su, K.-B. *J. Am. Chem. Soc.* **1986**, *108*, 638. (b) Andrieux, C. P.; Saveant, J.-M.; Su, K. B. *J. Phys. Chem.* **1986**, *90*, 3815. (c) Saveant, J.-M. *J. Am. Chem. Soc.* **1987**, *109*, 6788.

86. (a) Lund, T.; Lund, H. *Acta Chem. Scand.* **1986**, *B40*, 470. (b) Lund, T.; Lund, H. *Acta Chem. Scand.* **1987**, *B41*, 93. (c) Eberson, K.; Ekstrom, M.; Lund, T.; Lund, H. *Acta Chem. Scand.* **1989**, *43*, 101. (d) Lund, H.; Michel, M.-A.; Simonet, J. *Acta Chem. Scand.* **1974**, *B24*, 900.

87. Eberson, L. *Acta Chem. Scand.* **1982**, *B36*, 533.

88. For the discussion whether the radical anions of alkyl halides have a finite lifetime or not; see: Symons, M. C. R. *J. Chem. Res. (S)* **1978**, 360; Garst, J. F.; Roberts, R. D.; Pacifici, J. A. *J. Am. Chem. Soc.* **1977**, *99*, 3538.

89. (a) Klassen, N. V.; Ross, C. K. *J. Phys. Chem.* **1987**, *91*, 3668. (b) Klassen, N. V.; Ross, C. K. *Chem. Phys. Lett.* **1986**, *132*, 478.

90. (a) Shiotani, M.; Williams, F. *J. Am. Chem. Soc.* **1976**, *98*, 4006. (b) Wang, J. T.; Williams, F. *J. Am. Chem. Soc.* **1980**, *102*, 2860.

91. Hironaka, K.; Fukuzumi, S.; Tanaka, T. *J. Chem. Soc., Perkin Trans. 2* **1984**, 1705.

92. (a) Rakshys, J. W., Jr. *Tetrahedron Lett.* **1971**, 4745. (b) Bank, S.; Bank, J. F. *Tetrahedron Lett.* **1969**, 4533.

93. (a) Baizer, M. M.; Chruma, J. L. *J. Org. Chem.* **1972**, *37*, 1951. (b) Covitz, F. H. *J. Am. Chem. Soc.* **1967**, *89*, 5403.

94. Boch, C. R.; Connor, J. A.; Gutierrez, A. R.; Meyer, T. J.; Whitten, D. G.; Sullivan, B. P.; Nagle, J. K. *J. Am. Chem. Soc.* **1979**, *101*, 4815.

95. (a) Elving, P. J. *Topics in Bioelectrochemistry and Bioenergetics*; Milazzo, G., Ed.; Wiley: New York, 1976; Vol.1, p. 179. (b) Carelli, V.; Liberatore, F.; Casini, A.; Mondelli, R.; Arnone, A.; Carelli, I.; Retilio, G.; Mavelli, I. *Bioorg. Chem.* **1980**, *9*, 342.

96. Sakurai, H. *J. Organomet. Chem.* **1980**, *200*, 261.

97. Fukuzumi, S.; Kitano, T.; Mochida, K. *J. Am. Chem. Soc.* **1990,** *112,* 3246.
98. (a) Mochida, K.; Itani, A.; Yokoyama, M.; Tsuchiya, T.; Worley, S.D.; Kochi, J. K. *Bull. Chem. Soc. Jpn.* **1985,** *58,* 2149. (b) Mochida, K.; Worley, S. D.; Kochi, J. K. *Bull. Chem. Soc. Jpn.* **1985,** *58,* 3389.
99. (a) Walther, B. W.; Williams, F.; Lau, W.; Kochi, J. K. *Organometallics* **1983,** *2,* 688. (b) Wang, J. T.; Williams, F. *J. Chem. Soc., Chem. Commun.* **1981,** 666.
100. Fukuzumi, S.; Kitano, T.; Mochida, K. *J. Chem. Soc., Chem. Commun.* **1990,** 1236.
101. Fukuzumi, S.; Kitano, T.; Mochida, K. *Chem. Lett.* **1989,** 2177.
102. (a) Poulos, A. T.; Hammond, G. S.; Burton, M. E. *Photochem. Photobiol.* **1981,** *34,* 169. (b) Gebert, H.; Regenstein, W.; Bending, J.; Kreysig, D. *Z. Phys. Chem. (Leipzig)* **1982,** *263,* 65.
103. Fukuzumi, S.; Kitano,T.; Mochida, K. *Chem. Lett.* **1990,** 1741.
104. Dithionite is known as such reducing agent for the reduction of NAD$^+$ analogues; for example: Blankenhorn, G.; Moore, E. G. *J. Am. Chem. Soc.* **1980,** *102,* 1092.
105. (a) Fukuzumi, S.; Mochida, K.; Kochi, J. K. *J. Am. Chem. Soc.* **1979,** *101,* 5961. (b) Fukuzumi, S.; Kochi, J. K *Inorg. Chem.* **1980,** *19,* 3022. (c) Fukuzumi, S.; Kochi, J. K. *J. Am. Chem. Soc.* **1980,** *102,* 7290.
106. Fukuzumi, S.; Kuroda, S.; Tanaka, T. *J. Chem. Soc., Chem. Commun.* **1986,** 1553.
107. Fukuzumi, S.; Kitano, T.; Tanaka, T. *Chem. Lett.* **1989,** 1231.
108. Eberson, L.; Nyberg, K. *Encyclopedia of Electrochemistry of Elements, Organic Section,* Bard, A. J., Lund, H., Ed. Marcel Dekker, New York, 1978, Chap. XII-2.
109. Fukuzumi, S.; Kuroda, S.; Tanaka, T. *J. Chem. Soc., Chem. Commun.* **1987,** 120.
110. Fukuzumi, S.; Tanii, K.; Ishikawa, M.; Tanaka, T. *J. Chem. Soc., Perkin Trans.* 2 **1989,** 1801.
111. (a) Schlesener, C. J.; Amatore, C.; Kochi, J. K. *J. Am. Chem. Soc.* **1984,** *106,* 7472. (b) Martin, A.; Nicholas, P.; Arnold, D. R. *Can. J. Chem.* **1982,** *60,* 2165.
112. Ishikawa, M.; Fukuzumi, S. *Chem. Lett.* **1990,** 963.
113. (a) Epling, G. A.; Florio, E. *J. Chem. Soc., Chem. Commun.* **1986,** 185. (b) Epling, G. A.; Florio, E. *Tetrahedron Lett.* **1986,** *27,* 675.
114. Roberts, R. M. G.; Ostovic, D.; Kreevoy, M. M. *Faraday Discuss. Chem. Soc.* **1982,** *74,* 257.
115. Fukuzumi, S.; Tanaka, T. *Photoinduced Electron Transfer,* Fox, M. A., Chanon, M., Eds. Elsevier: Amsterdam, 1988, Part C, Chapter 11.
116. (a) Heelis, P. F. *Chem. Soc. Rev.* **1982,** *11,* 15. (b) Penzer, G. R.; Radda, G. K. *Q. Rev.,* **1967,** *21,* 43.
117. (a) Fukuzumi, S.; Kuroda, S.; Tanaka, T. *Chem. Lett.* **1984,** 417. (b) Fukuzumi, S.; Kuroda, S.; Tanaka, T. *J. Am. Chem. Soc.* **1985,** *107,* 3020.
118. Fukuzumi, S.; Kuroda, S.; Tanaka, T. *Chem. Lett.* **1984,** 1375.
119. Chahidi, C.; Aubailly, M.; Momzikoff, A.; Bazin, M.; Santus, R. *Photochem. Photobiol.* **1981,** *33,* 641.
120. Mengel, R.; Pfleiderer, W.; Knappe, W.-R. *Tetrahedron Lett.* **1977,** 2817.
121. Fukuzumi, S.; Tanii, K.; Tanaka, T. *J. Chem. Soc., Chem. Commun.* **1989,** 816.
122. Fukuzumi, S.; Kuroda, S.; Goto, T.; Ishikawa, K.; Tanaka, T. *J. Chem. Soc., Perkin Trans.* 2 **1989,** 1047.
123. Fukuzumi, S.; Goto, T.; Ishikawa, K.; Tanaka, T. *Chem. Lett.* **1988,** 1923.
124. Fukuzumi, S.; Tanii, K.; Tanaka, T. *Chem. Lett.* **1989,** 35.
125. Muller, F.; Hemmerich, P.; Ehrenberg, A. *Flavins and Flavoproteins,* Kamin, H., Ed. University Park Press, Baltimore, 1971, pp. 107–122.
126. Fukuzumi, S.; Kuroda, S.; Tanaka, T. *J. Chem. Soc., Perkin Trans.* 2 **1986,** 25.
127. (a) Davies, A. G.; Ingold, K. U.; Roberts, B. P.; Tudor, R. *J. Chem. Soc. B* **1971,** 698. (b) Korcek, S.; Watts, G. B.; Ingold, K. U. *J. Chem. Soc., Perkin Trans.* 2 **1972,** 242.

128. Brindley, P. B.; Scotton, M. J. *J. Chem. Soc., Perkin Trans. 2* **1981**, 419.
129. Faraggi, M.; Hemmerich, P.; Pecht, I. *FEBS Lett.* **1975**, *51*, 47.
130. Fukuzumi, S.; Tanii, K.; Tanaka, T. *J. Chem. Soc., Perkin Trans. 2* **1989**, 2103.
131. (a) Foote, C. S. *Acc. Chem. Res.* **1968**, *1*, 104. (b) Kearns, D. R. *Chem. Rev.* **1971**, *71*, 395. (c) Stephenson, L. M.; Grdina, M. J.; Orfanopoulos, M. *Acc. Chem. Res.* **1980**, *13*, 419.
132. (a) Thomas, M. J.; Pryor, W. A. *Lipids* **1980**, *15*, 544. (b) Matsushita, S.; Terao, J.; Yamauchi, R. *Tocopherol, Oxygen and Biomembranes*, De Duve, C.; Hayaishi, O., Eds. Elsevier, 1978, p. 23.
133. (a) Porter, N. A.; Lehman, L. S.; Weber, B. A.; Smith, K. J. *J. Am. Chem. Soc.* **1981**, *103*, 6477. (b) Fukuzumi, S.; Tanii, K.; Tanaka, T. *J. Chem. Soc., Perkin Trans. 2* **1989**, 2035.
134. Garner, A.; Wilkinson, F. *Singlet Oxygen Reaction with Organic Compounds and Polymers*, Ranby, B.; Rabek, J. F., Eds. Wiley, New York, 1978, p. 48.
135. Merkel, P.B.; Kearns, D. R. *J. Am. Chem. Soc.* **1972**, *94*, 7244.
136. Grodowski, M. S.; Veyret, B.; Weiss, K. *Photochem. Photobiol.* **1977**, *26*, 341.
137. Ishikawa, K.; Fukuzumi, S.; Goto, T.; Tanaka, T. *J. Am. Chem. Soc.* **1990**, *112*, 1577.
138. (a) Halpern, J. *Acc. Chem. Res.* **1982**, *15*, 238. (b) Halpern, J. *Bull. Chem. Soc. Jpn.* **1988**, *61*, 13.
139. (a) Blau, R. J.; Espenson, J. H. *J. Am. Chem. Soc.* **1985**, *107*, 3530. (b) Schrauzer, G. N.; Grate, J. H. *J. Am. Chem. Soc.* **1981**, *103*, 541.
140. The decomposition of $PhCH_2OOH$ to $PhCHO$ occurs in the presence of $HClO_4$ in MeCN; see: Fukuzumi, S.; Ishikawa, K.; Tanaka, T. *Chem. Lett.* **1986**, 1.
141. (a) Hemmerich, P.; Veeger, C.; Wood, H. C. S. *Angew. Chem.* **1965**, *77*, 699. (b) Dudley, K. H.; Ehrenberg, A.; Hemmerich, P.; Muller, F. *Helv. Chim. Acta* **1964**, *47*, 1354.
142. (a) Fukuzumi, S.; Ishikawa, K; Tanaka, T. *J. Chem. Soc., Dalton Trans.* **1985**, 899. (b) Fukuzumi, S.; Ishikawa, K.; Tanaka, T. *Nippon Kagaku Kaishi* **1985**, 62.
143. (a) Fukuzumi, S.; Ishikawa, K.; Tanaka, T. *Chem. Lett.* **1986**, 1801. (b) Ishikawa, K.; Fukuzumi, S.; Tanaka, T.; *Inorg. Chem.* **1989**, *28*, 1661.
144. The $[Co(bpy)_2]^{3+}$ formed is converted to $[Co(bpy)_3]^{3+}$ which is the most stable form of the cobalt (III) complexes with bpy ligands; see: Fukumi, S.; Ishikawa, K.; Tanaka, T. *Organometallics* **1987**, *6*, 358; Fukuzumi, S.; Ishikawa, K.; Tanaka, T. *Chem. Lett.* **1985**, 1355.
145. The H_2O is added to the reaction system in order to slow down the reaction rate. Such a retarding effect of H_2O on acid-catalyzed redox reactions in MeCN has recently reported; see Ref 48.

ELECTRON TRANSFER CHEMISTRY
OF MONOAMINE OXIDASE

Richard B. Silverman

1. INTRODUCTION

Monoamine oxidase (MAO) is one of the enzymes responsible for the degradation of various amine neurotransmitters and xenobiotics (foreign compounds that

Advances in Electron Transfer Chemistry,
Volume 2, pages 177–213
Copyright © 1992 by JAI Press Inc.
All rights of reproduction in any form reserved.
ISBN: 1-55938-168-X

enter the body by ingestion or from the environment).[1] The enzyme exists in two distinct isoenzymic forms which have been termed MAO A and MAO B.[2] Although these two isoenzymes have different substrate specificity, tissue distribution, and primary structures,[3] they, most likely, catalyze the substrate reaction by the same mechanism. Therefore, for the purposes of this chapter, no distinction will be made between the two isoenzymes. Compounds that block the catalytic action of MAO A, which is selective for the degradation of norepinephrine and serotonin, have been shown to exhibit antidepressant activity and are used for the treatment of depression. A compound that inhibits the action of MAO B, which degrades dopamine in the brain, is now on the drug market as an adjunct to the treatment of Parkinson's disease.[4] In order to design new classes of inactivators (compounds that irreversibly block the enzyme action) of MAO it would be valuable to understand the catalytic mechanism of MAO. In this chapter the evidence for an electron transfer mechanism for MAO is discussed.

In 1877 Schmiedeberg[5] reported that benzylamine was converted in dogs to hippuric acid, and suggested that the benzylamine must have undergone oxidative deamination to benzaldehyde, which was further oxidized and converted to the amide. In 1883 Minkowski[6] showed that incubation of benzylamine with liver homogenates leads to the formation of benzoic acid, and in 1910 Ewins and Laidlaw[7] demonstrated the oxidation of tyramine and tryptamine to p-hydroxyphenylacetic acid and 3-indoleacetic acid, respectively, in perfused organs. Monoamine oxidase was probably the enzyme responsible for the initial oxidation of the amines. However, it was not until 1928 that Hare[8] showed that an enzyme in liver oxidized tyramine with the concomitant uptake of oxygen and the formation of ammonia and hydrogen peroxide. The enzyme was not inhibited by cyanide and therefore was an exception to the Warburg[9] hypothesis that all cellular oxidases were iron dependent (cyanide inhibits iron-dependent enzymes). The enzyme that Hare named tyramine oxidase was later renamed by Zeller[10] as monoamine oxidase because it was found that this same enzyme catalyzed the oxidation of a variety of monoamines.[11] A separate enzyme that catalyzed the oxidation of histamine and other diamines was named diamine oxidase[10] to differentiate it from MAO.

2. CHARACTERISTICS OF MONOAMINE OXIDASE

Monoamine oxidase is a flavoenzyme in which the cofactor (flavin adenine dinucleotide) is covalently attached at the 8α-position to a cysteine residue at the active site of the protein (1).[12] Although iron was once believed to be important for enzyme catalysis,[13] highly purified MAO is fully active with negligible amounts of iron present.[14] No other cofactors are required for enzyme activity. The primary amino acid sequence of both isoenzymes from a variety of sources has been deduced from cDNA clones,[15] however, nothing is known about the tertiary structure of the enzyme. On the basis of chemical modification studies it

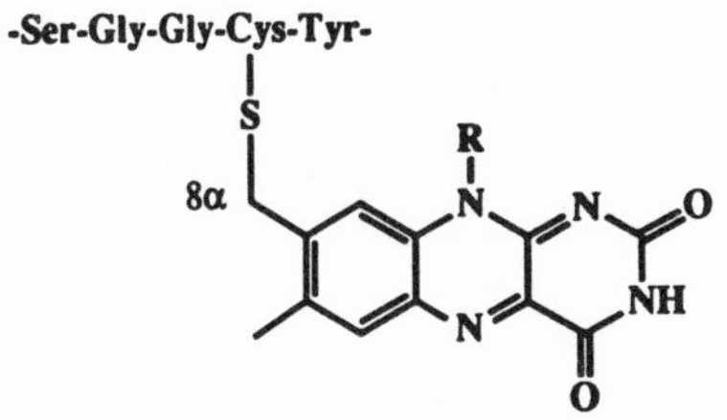

-Ser-Gly-Gly-Cys-Tyr-

1

has been suggested that there are two essential histidine residues[16] and two essential cysteine residues.[17]

The enzyme catalyzes the oxidation of monoamines to the corresponding immonium ion with concomitant reduction of the flavin (Scheme 1). The flavin is then converted back into the oxidized form by reaction with molecular oxygen which is reduced in the process to hydrogen peroxide. MAO is a promiscuous enzyme, catalyzing the oxidation of a variety of aliphatic and arylalkyl primary, secondary, and tertiary amines.[18] Compounds having α-substitution are either very poor substrates or are not substrates at all.[19] MAO-catalyzes the stereo-specific removal of the *pro-R* proton of various substrates.[20] In addition to the stereospecificity of proton removal, stereoisomers of substrates with chiral centers, such as ß-phenylethanolamine[21] or epinephrine and norepinephrine[22] or chiral inactivators such as tranylcypromine[23] or allenic amines[24] show an enantiomeric preference for oxidation by MAO.[25]

The oxidation reaction involves an anaerobic phase and an aerobic phase. The amine is first oxidized to the corresponding imine anaerobically. This was demonstrated by Yasunobu and Oi[26] by the anerobic oxidation of N-methyl-benzylamine to one equivalent of methylamine (presumably from hydrolysis of

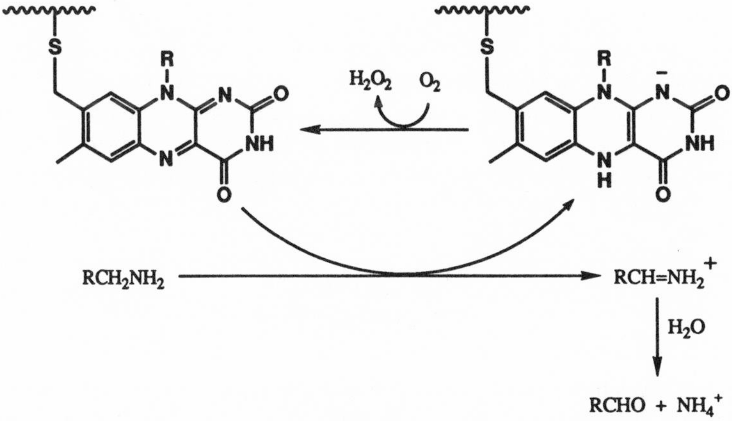

$RCH_2NH_2 \longrightarrow RCH=NH_2^+$

$RCH=NH_2^+ \xrightarrow{H_2O} RCHO + NH_4^+$

Scheme 1.

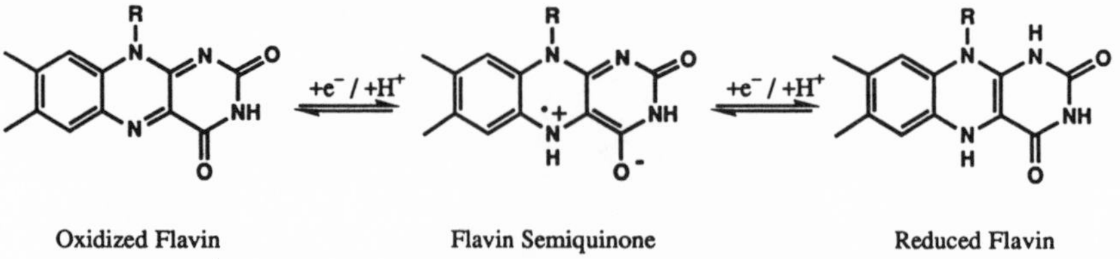

Oxidized Flavin   Flavin Semiquinone   Reduced Flavin

Scheme 2.

the corresponding imine) with the concomitant reduction of the flavin cofactor. Following the introduction of oxygen, the reduced flavin was converted back to the oxidized form.

Smith et al.[27] first proposed that the imine formed from amine oxidation is hydrolyzed nonenzymatically. MAO-catalyzed oxidation of N,N-dimethyltryptamine in [^{18}O]water produced the corresponding aldehyde having ^{18}O in the aldehyde oxygen. Since N,N-dimethyltryptamine-N-oxide is not a substrate, it was concluded that the N-oxide is not an intermediate, but this experiment does not necessarily rule out that possibility. Hellerman and co-workers[28] treated a solution of MAO and phenethylamine with sodium boro[^{3}H]hydride and obtained a small amount of tritiated phenethylamine (none formed in the nonenzymatic control), suggesting that an imine product was formed which was reduced by the borohydride prior to hydrolysis.

The oxidation of the reduced flavin by molecular oxygen is enzyme catalyzed; the dissociation constants for oxygen with MAO vary depending upon the substrate, but they are close to the concentration of oxygen in air-saturated water at 37 °C.[29] Consequently, although the MAO is working below its maximum rate in vivo, the enzyme has evolved so that when processing low concentrations of amine substrates the rate is relatively insensitive to fluctuations in oxygen concentration.

Flavins are capable of accepting one electron to give the semiquinone radical or two electrons to give the fully reduced form (Scheme 2). Oxidized flavin is planar and highly conjugated, but reduced flavin, with its interrupted conjugation, is bent to avoid antiaromaticity.[30] The oxidized form of the flavin is yellow and has an absorbance in the visible region at 480 nm; the reduced form of the enzyme is colorless. The structural differences between the oxidized and reduced forms allow proteins to regulate their redox potentials by selective binding of one form.

3.   ENZYME MECHANISM

There are four basic mechanisms for MAO-catalyzed amine oxidation that should be considered: a hydride mechanism; a carbanion mechanism; a group transfer (addition-elimination) mechanism, and a radical mechanism.

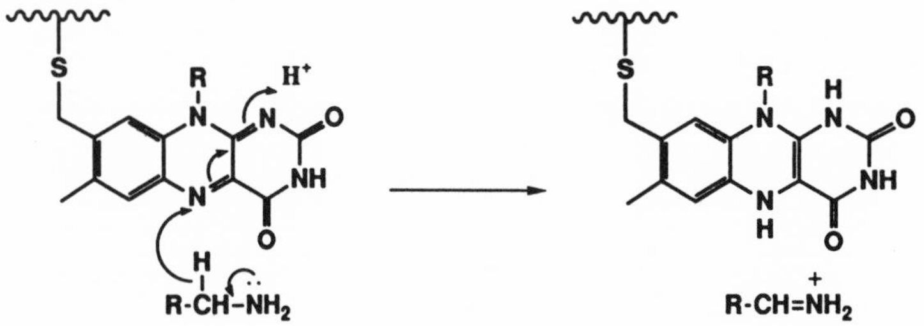

Scheme 3.

3.1. Hydride Mechanism

On the basis of the increased MAO activity with increased pH, Smith et al.[27] proposed that MAO catalyzed a hydride transfer from the substrate to the flavin (Scheme 3). The evidence against this mechanism stems from electronegativity considerations and from the fact that a hydride transfer is a high energy process.[31] Hydride transfer would necessitate the removal of electrons from elements with electronegativities similar to or greater than hydrogen and the localization of those electrons on hydrogen. Furthermore, as discussed later in this chapter, a variety of cyclopropylamines[32] and cyclobutylamines[33] undergo ring opening reactions with MAO that lead to inactivation of the enzyme. These results cannot be rationalized in terms of a hydride mechanism.

3.2. Carbanionic Mechanism

Belleau and Moran[34] measured the isotope effect on the binding and rate of oxidation of [α-^{2}H$_2$]tyramine and [α-^{2}H$_2$] kynuramine during MAO catalysis and concluded that the bond-breaking step was already much advanced upon enzyme-substrate complex formation, and that the bound amine resembles the transition state more than it does the ground state. On the basis of their measured isotope effects, they concluded that the rate limiting step is the abstraction of the α-proton. This carbanionic mechanism (Scheme 4A shows N-5 attack; Scheme 4B shows C-4a attack) is highly unlikely considering that the pK_a of the α-proton is greater than 30.[35] Also, McEwen et al.[19] and Williams[36] established that it is the unprotonated form of the amine that is bound to the enzyme; therefore, there is no carbanion stabilization by an adjacent ammonium ion. Other evidence against a carbanionic mechanism is that 2-chloro-2-(phenyl)ethylamine is a substrate for MAO, but essentially no β-elimination product is formed.[37] In the case of another flavoenzyme whose mechanism is believed to proceed, at least initially, by a carbanion mechanism, a β-halogenated substrate gave mostly the elimination product.[38] Weyler[37] noted, however, that the dihedral angles of the amine constrained within the enzyme active site may have been such that the antiperiplanar orientation preferred for elimination is not achieved.

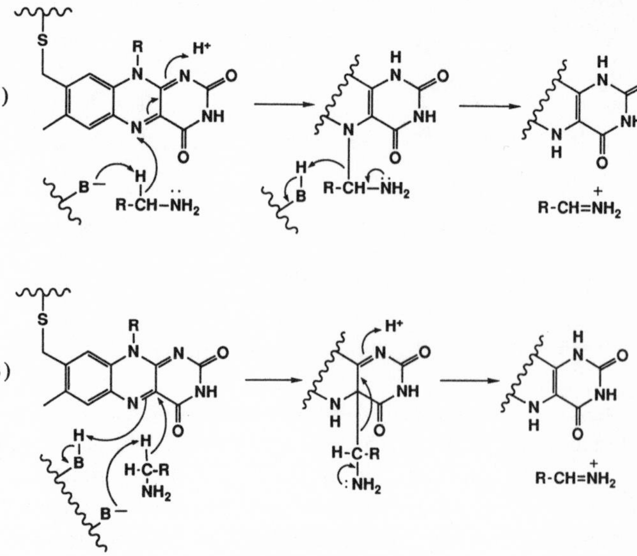

Scheme 4.

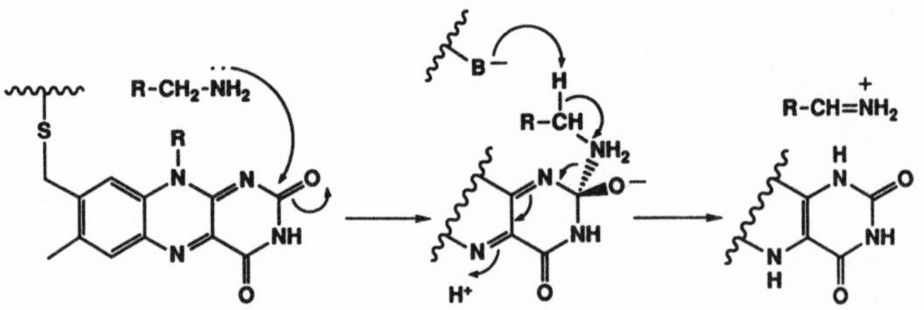

Scheme 5.

3.3. Group Transfer Mechanisms

Two other group transfer (addition-elimination) mechanisms have been proposed. Hellerman and Erwin[39] proposed a mechanism based on their work with amino acid oxidases (Scheme 5). In their mechanism, the substrate nitrogen attacks the carbonyl group at C-2 to generate a flavin hemiaminal intermediate after which an active site base removes a substrate α-proton to generate the imine product by β-elimination. Since the most electrophilic sites of flavin have been calculated to be C-4a and N-5 rather than C-2,[40] this mechanism was revised by Hamilton (Scheme 6).[31] In this version of the mechanism the substrate amino group attacks the C-4a position of the flavin followed by deprotonation and β-elimination (attack at N-5 would be equivalent). These hypotheses, however, may violate the principle of microscopic reversibility which states that for a

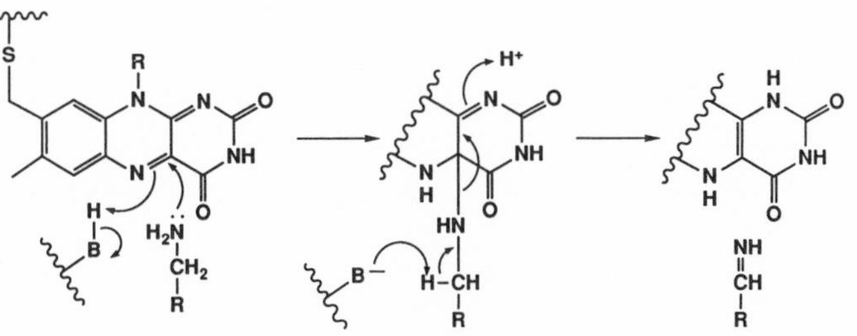

Scheme 6.

reversible reaction the pathway followed in the forward and back directions must be identical, since it affords the lowest energy barrier for either process.[41] On the assumption that the MAO-catalyzed reaction is reversible (there is no evidence for this), the principle of microscopic reversibility would require the enamine carbon of the reduced flavin (C-4a) to attack the imine nitrogen of the product (the reverse of Scheme 6), a much higher energy process than attack at the imine carbon. The carbanionic mechanism is consistent with the principle of microscopic reversibility, but has other problems associated with it, as noted above. Since the group transfer mechanism involves a β-elimination as the second step, it might be predicted that 2-chloro-2-(phenyl)ethylamine would undergo β-elimination of the chloride, but, as noted above, this does not occur.[37] The low acidity of the β-proton in the adduct also argues against this pathway. Furthermore, as pointed out by Maycock et al.,[42] few covalent substrate-flavin intermediates have been detected in enzyme-catalyzed reactions.

3.4. Radical Mechanism

The fourth class of mechanisms is the radical pathway. The notion that radicals were involved in MAO-catalyzed reactions was in the literature since at least the early 1960s.[43] One radical mechanism, modeled after the work on other flavoenzymes by Bruice,[44] Massey and Ghisla,[45] and more recently, Liu and co-workers,[46] would be initiated by carbanion formation followed by two single electron transfers to the flavin (Scheme 7). This is an attractive mechanism for flavoenzymes that are capable of generating a substrate carbanion; however, as discussed above, MAO-catalyzed carbanion formation does not appear to be a favorable process.

The non-enzymatic oxidation of amines is a relatively facile process and can occur with chemical oxidizing agents,[47] electrochemically,[48] and photochemically.[49] All of these nonenzymatic processes occur by electron transfer mechanisms; the mechanism for electrochemical oxidation of amines is shown in Scheme 8. Consequently, we[50] and the Krantz group[51] proposed that monoamine oxidase also should function by an electron transfer mechanism (Scheme 9 shows a more elaborate mechanism than what was originally published). One-electron transfer

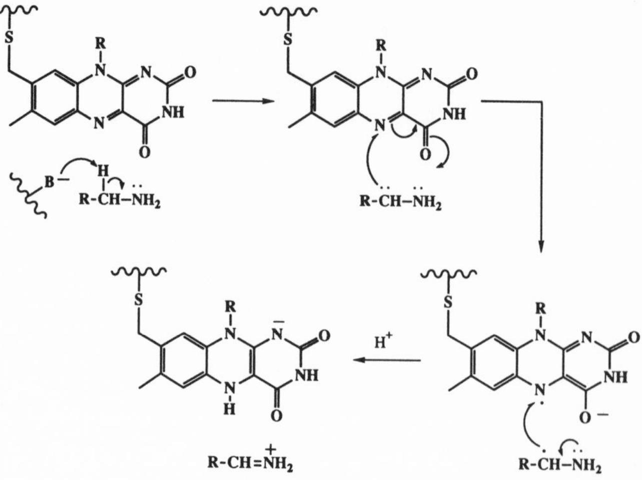

Scheme 7.

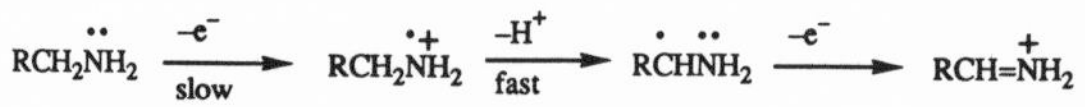

$$RCH_2\overset{\cdot\cdot}{N}H_2 \xrightarrow[\text{slow}]{-e^-} RCH_2\overset{\cdot+}{N}H_2 \xrightarrow[\text{fast}]{-H^+} R\overset{\cdot}{C}H\overset{\cdot\cdot}{N}H_2 \xrightarrow{-e^-} RCH=\overset{+}{N}H_2$$

Scheme 8.

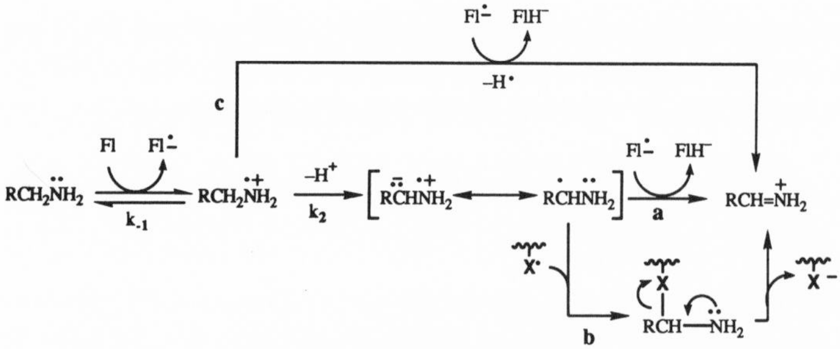

Scheme 9.

from the amino group to the flavin would give the amine radical cation which can lose a proton to give the carbon radical. Whereas the pK_a of the α-proton of amines is much higher than an enzyme should be capable of removing, the pK_a of the α-proton of an amine radical cation is only about 10.[52] Since the pH optimum of the enzyme is 9.0, this proton can be removed readily by the enzyme. The radical generated by deprotonation can be oxidized further either by second electron transfer (pathway a) or by radical combination with an active site radical (either the flavin radical just generated or an amino acid radical generated by hydrogen atom transfer from the amino acid to the flavin; vide infra) followed by β-elimination to the immonium product (pathway b).

In order to rationalize the kinetic isotope effects observed on the oxidation of $[\alpha,\alpha\text{-}^2H_2]$substrates,[34,53] Krantz and co-workers suggested that the first electron transfer is reversible[51] and, therefore, not rate determining. Depending on the relative rates of k_{-1} (the reverse of the initial electron transfer) and k_2 (proton abstraction) for each substrate, the kinetic isotope effect may range from 1–7. The reversibility of the first step of this reaction is reasonable considering the thermodynamics of the uncatalyzed reaction. The reduction potential of free riboflavin is approximately -0.25 V, whereas the oxidation potential of normal primary amine substrates is about $+1.5$ V. This means that the transfer of the first electron from the amine to the flavin would be endothermic by about 1.75 V, and, therefore, the reverse reaction would be exothermic by the same amount. This apparently large energy barrier to the reaction catalyzed by MAO may not be as unsurmountable as it first appears. For one thing, the nonenzymatic potential observed may be much different than the apparent potential for the amine substrate at the active site of the enzyme. The oxidation potential of the amine and the reduction potential of the flavin could be lowered by intrinsic binding[54] which could distort the bonds of the amine and the flavin. In the case of the amine, the distortion could result in the lowering of the energy required to remove a nonbonded electron from the amine nitrogen which would lower the oxidation potential of the molecule.[55] Likewise, bending of the oxidized form of the flavin would distort it toward the structure of reduced flavin, thereby lowering the LUMO energy of the flavin.

Another factor that can affect the oxidation potential is the solvent. For an irreversible electrochemical reaction, the $E_{1/2}$ of an organic compound can change by 0.5 V just by changing the molar ratio of an organic solvent to water mixture.[56] Presumably, the degree of hydrophobicity at the enzyme active site (MAO has a highly hydrophobic active site) will be best suited for lowering the oxidation potential of the substrate. Other ways that the enzyme can utilize its binding energy to make the reaction more favorable, apart from the obvious role of holding the substrate in close proximity to the flavin cofactor, are to bind the reduced form of the flavin selectively, which would lower the reduction potential of flavin, and to bind the flattened amine radical cation selectively, thereby modulating the redox potential of the amine substrate. As mentioned above, intrinsic binding may be one mechanism to accomplish this.

The fact that Weyler[37] observed a small amount of elimination product during MAO-catalyzed oxidation of 2-chloro-2-(phenyl)ethylamine may be a reflection of the extent of carbanionic character that exists when the α-proton is removed from the amine radical cation (see the resonance structures in Scheme 9). Bordwell and Lynch[57] have generated the α-amino radicals of a variety of 9-aminofluorenes and they conclude that the contribution of the resonance structure having carbanionic character is larger than expected. Of course, this system is set up for aromatic carbanion stabilization, so it would show a larger than usual contribution of this resonance structure.

Until fairly recently (vide infra) there was no evidence for a radical intermediate in MAO-catalyzed amine oxidations. Yasunobu and co-workers[58] found no EPR spectral evidence for a radical intermediate in the MAO-catalyzed oxidation of benzylamine, even in the presence of spin traps. Singer and co-workers[53a] failed to observe any evidence for a flavin semiquinone radical during stopped flow experiments with benzylamine and phenethylamine as substrates. However, this may be due to the formation of a radical ion pair between the flavin and the substrate during the reaction or the fact that because of the rapid reversibility of the initial electron transfer there is too small of a concentration of these radical intermediates to be observed spectrometrically.[51]

3.5. Mechanism-Based Enzyme Inactivation by Cyclopropyl- and Cyclobutylamines

The Silverman group took a different approach to the elucidation of radical intermediates in the MAO-catalyzed reaction.[32,33] The strategy involved the use of mechanism-based enzyme inactivators[59] to reveal the mechanism of the enzyme. A mechanism-based inactivator is an unreactive compound that has a structural similarity to the substrate or product for the target enzyme. Once inside the active site of the enzyme it is converted, by the *normal catalytic mechanism* of the enzyme, into a product that inactivates the enzyme. These kinds of inactivators have been shown to be quite useful in the study of enzyme mechanism because they are really nothing more than substrates for the enzyme. They happened to be converted into products that inactivate the enzyme, but the mechanism by which they inactivate the enzyme proceeds, at least initially, by the catalytic mechanism. Therefore, any information that is obtained regarding the inactivation mechanism can be directly related to the catalytic mechanism. With this approach in mind, a chemical probe for an amine radical cation was sought; if this intermediate were formed, the chemical probe would take an altered path indicative of the presence of the radical intermediate. From product analysis (either a released product or the inactivated enzyme) the intermediate could be inferred.

Silverman and co-workers[60,61] had been studying the mechanism of inactivation of MAO by cyclopropylamines and determined that these compounds had the properties of mechanism-based inactivators. However, the inactivation mechanism initially proposed (Scheme 10) was incorrect. It was not until N-(1-methylcyclopropyl)benzylamine, which has no C-1 proton for removal, was found to inactivate MAO[62] that it became apparent that the originally proposed inactivation mechanism (Scheme 10) was not correct. A paper by Maeda and Ingold[63] clarified what was happening. They found that when a cyclopropylaminyl radical was generated by laser flash photolysis, the cyclopropyl ring homolytically cleaved at a rate too fast for them to measure (Scheme 11). Not only did this provide a rationalization for the mechanism of inactivation of MAO by cyclopropylamines, but it also suggested a probe for the mechanism of MAO-catalyzed amine oxidation in general. If an aminyl radical is a viable intermediate

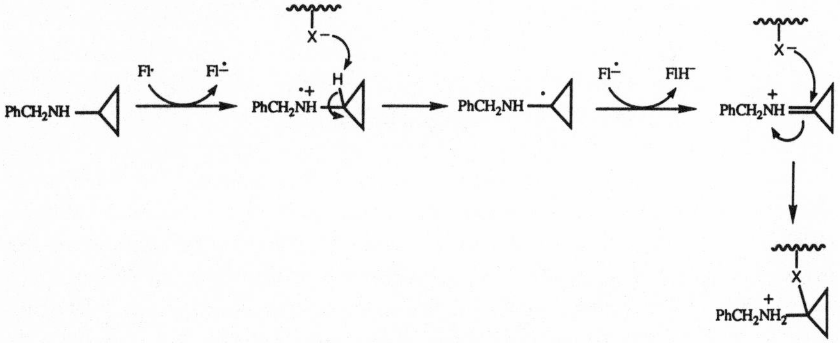

Scheme 10.

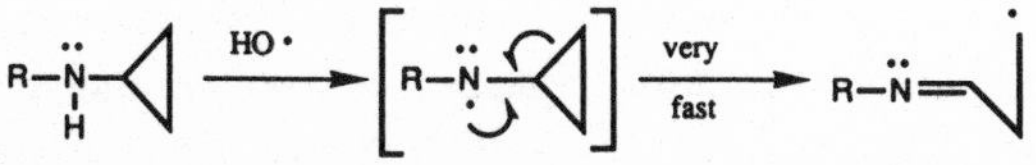

Scheme 11.

during MAO-catalyzed amine oxidation, then a cyclopropyl substituent should signal its presence by undergoing rapid homolytic cleavage. This also would account for the inactivation of the enzyme by cyclopropylamines; ring opening would generate a reactive radical that could combine with an active site radical and produce a stable covalent bond to the enzyme.

Consequently, a series of cyclopropylamines was synthesized as modified substrates to probe the intermediate in the enzyme reaction. The first cyclopropylamine investigated was the antidepressant drug, tranylcypromine (**2**, Scheme 12).[64] Oxidation of the amine to the amine radical cation should induce the rapid homolytic cleavage of the cyclopropyl ring. In this case there are two different modes of ring cleavage; pathway a leads to the resonance-stabilized benzyl radical and pathway b generates a primary radical. When [^{14}C]-labeled tranylcypromine was used, one equivalent of radioactivity became attached to the

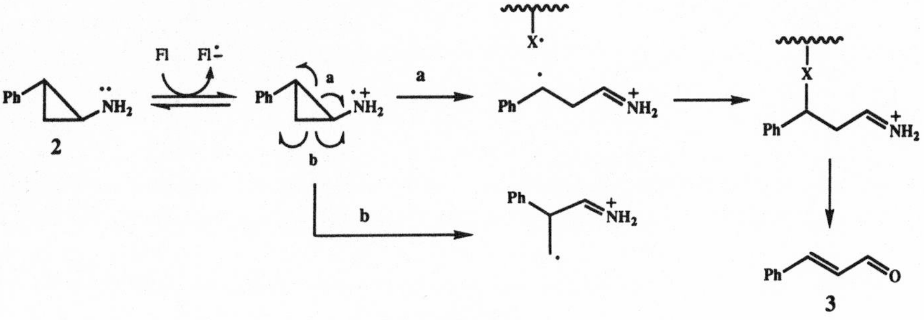

Scheme 12.

Scheme 13.

enzyme. The enzyme remained inactivated until it was denatured, which released all of the radioactivity as cinnamaldehyde (**3**), isolated as the 2,4-dinitrophenyl-hydrazone. Paech et al.[65] provided evidence that tranylcypromine does not become attached to the flavin, and suggested that it may be bound to an active site cysteine. If the X in Scheme 12 is the sulfur of cysteine, then a retro-Michael reaction under denaturing conditions to give cinnamaldehyde[66] is reasonable. If β-elimination is responsible for cinnamaldehyde formation, then reduction of the imine should prevent the release of the cinnamaldehyde. In fact, treatment of the inactivated enzyme with sodium borohydride blocked the release of about a third of the radioactivity. Since the cinnamaldehyde is released upon denaturation and these conditions are needed to get the sodium borohydride into the active site, it is difficult to reduce all of the adduct before it is released from the enzyme. A thiyl radical (S·) could be generated by hydrogen atom abstraction from the cysteine residue by the flavin semiquinone that was produced in the first electron transfer step (Scheme 13). A single electron transfer (SET) photochemical model study by Mariano and co-workers[66a] for the reaction of **2** with a model flavin supported the proposed enzymatic SET mechanism (in the model study, however, a flavin adduct was formed because thiols could not be used); hydrolysis gave cinnamaldehyde, as in the case of the enzyme reaction.

A detailed study of the mechanism of inactivation of MAO by N-(1-methylcyclopropyl)benzylamine (**3**) also revealed that an apparent cyclopropylaminyl ring cleavage was occurring; the mechanism in Scheme 14 was hypothesized.[67] Three

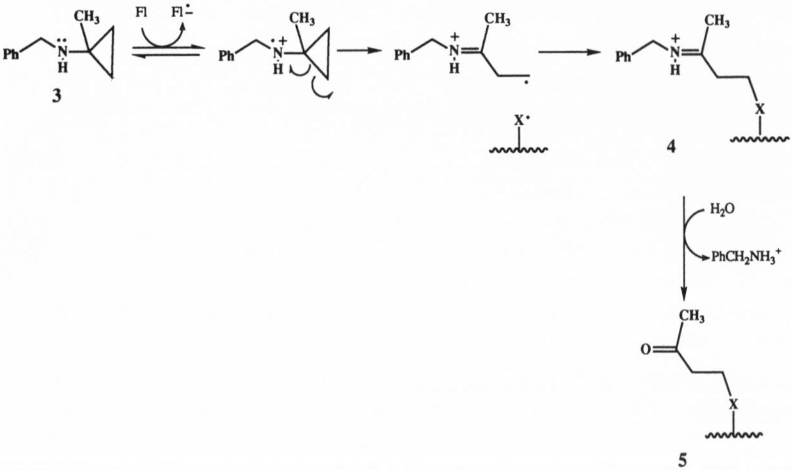

Scheme 14.

different [^{14}C]-labeled analogues were synthesized (**3a**, **3b**, **3c**) in order to determine which part of the molecule remains bound to the enzyme and which part is released during inactivation. After inactivation and removal of excess inactivator (these experiments are always done with a large excess of inactivator relative to enzyme), essentially no [^{14}C] from **3a** was bound to the inactivated enzyme, but approximately one equivalent of [^{14}C] each from **3b** and **3c** remained attached to the inactivated enzyme. When the enzyme was inactivated with **3a** and dialyzed, benzylamine and benzaldehyde, the oxidation product of benzylamine, were isolated. Reduction of the enzyme with sodium cyanoborohydride prior to removal of the excess **3a** resulted in the attachment of about one equivalent of the radioactivity, suggesting that the benzyl group is released during removal of the excess inactivator as a result of hydrolysis of an imine (cyanoborohydride rapidly reduces protonated imines but very slowly reacts with aldehydes and ketones);[68] the imine, presumably, is reduced by the cyanoborohydride to a stable amine. The ease of hydrolysis of this imine is consistent with the lability to hydrolysis of Schiff bases of aliphatic ketones[69] and evidence for the conversion of **4** to **5**. Several reactions on the inactivated enzyme were carried out to confirm the presence of **5**. MAO was inactivated with unlabeled **3**, dialyzed, and treated with sodium[^{3}H]borohydride. One equivalent of tritium was incorporated into the inactivated enzyme that did not remain bound to the uninactivated enzyme, indicating that a ketone may be part of the structure of the adduct. The presence of a methyl ketone in **5** was confirmed by carrying out the iodoform reaction, a test for methyl ketones, on **3b**-inactivated MAO. Incubation with basic potassium triiodide released all of the radioactivity as [^{14}C]iodoform (with **3b** inactivation the radioactivity ends up in the methyl group of the methyl ketone). Attachment of the inactivator to the flavin was suggested by the observation that following inactivation and denaturation, the flavin absorption spectrum resembled that of reduced flavin. Since flavins are highly susceptible to air oxidation, this indicates that there is a substituent attached to the flavin that is preventing it from being oxidized.

Lewis and Correa[70] found two competing pathways from secondary amine radical cations that were generated photochemically. In addition to the favored C-H proton transfer to give the carbon radical, N-H proton transfer to the aminyl radical also occurred (Scheme 15). If aminyl radical formation is the predominant pathway on the enzyme, then a different inactivation mechanism must be sought. To test this, *N*-methyl-*N*-(1-methylcyclopropyl)benzylamine (**6**) was used to inactivate MAO. If this compound inactivates MAO by the same mechanism as does the desmethyl analogue (Scheme 14), then there would not be an N-H bond available for proton removal from the amine radical cation. The

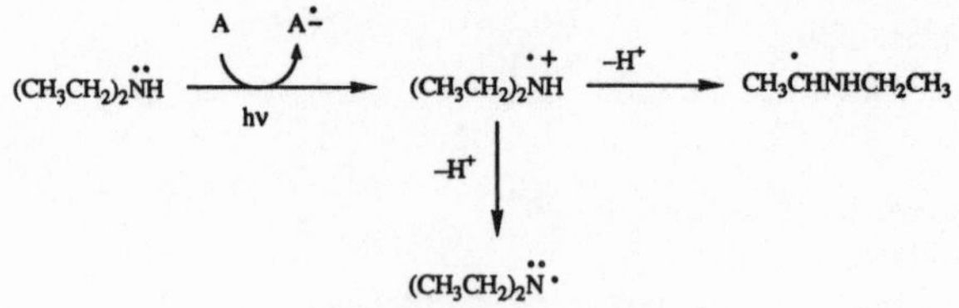

Scheme 15.

N-methylated analogue (6) inactivates MAO at the same rate as 3; consequently, deprotonation of the amine radical cation is not relevant to the inactivation mechanism.

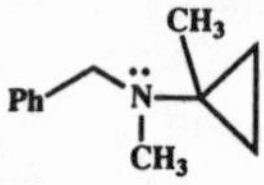

6

Once the radical cation is generated there are potentially two competing pathways: cyclopropyl ring cleavage (pathway a) and α-proton removal (pathway b, Scheme 16). Given the magnitude of the rate of cyclopropyl ring cleavage,[62] it might be surprising to expect *any* competing α-deprotonation to occur. However, in addition to inactivation, **3b** and **3c** produced 0.1–0.2 equivalent of 1-methylcyclopropylamine (**7**), the product of oxidation at the benzyl methylene. This suggests that cyclopropyl ring opening is only 5 to 10 times faster than benzyl proton abstraction which indicates that the normal catalytic process (α-proton removal) is a very efficient process. This could account for why intermediates of this type have not been observed spectrophotometrically.

If the amine radical cation is a viable intermediate, then the ratio of these competing reactions, namely inactivation versus α-deprotonation, should vary

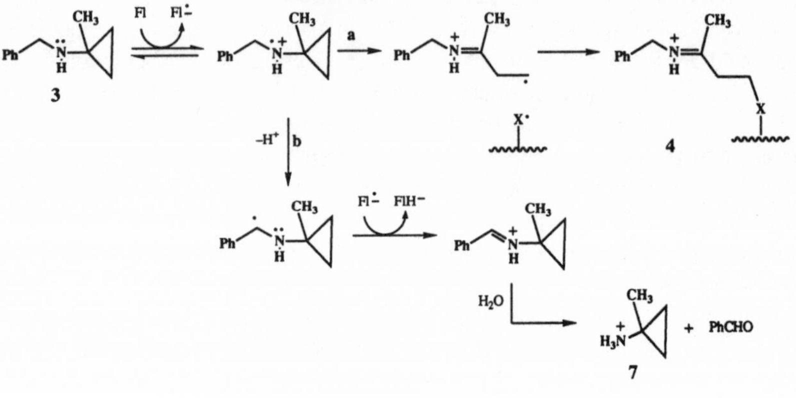

Scheme 16.

with substitution that affects the rates of the two competing reactions. It is known that for electrochemical oxidations of secondary amines, the ratio of α-proton removal from the two substituents generally depends on the kinetic acidities of the protons adjacent to the incipient amine radical cation. As a carbon atom becomes more substituted, the pK_a of a proton attached to the central carbon generally increases. Since there is a kinetic isotope effect on α-proton removal during MAO-catalyzed amine oxidation,[34,53] the amount of α-proton removal could be decreased by increasing the kinetic acidity of the α-proton. Consequently, radioactively-labeled *N*-cyclopropylbenzylamine (**8**, R = H) and *N*-cyclopropyl-α-methylbenzylamine (**8**, R = CH$_3$) were synthesized to determine the effect of α-methylation on the ratio of these competing pathways.[71] Whereas the partition ratio (the ratio of pathway b/a) of α-deprotonation (as measured by the formation of radioactive benzaldehyde and cyclopropylamine) to equivalents of radioactivity bound was 1.0 for **8**, R = H, the partition ratio for **8**, R = CH$_3$ was 0.012 (Scheme 17). Since the pK_a for methylated compounds is, in general, about two units higher than for the corresponding parent compound,[72] the partition ratio drop for **8**, R = CH$_3$ to only 1% that for **8**, R = H is a reasonable reflection of the kinetic acidity of the α-proton and is consistent with an amine radical cation intermediate that can partition in two pathways. This is not just a steric effect because α-methylbenzylamine binds to MAO even better than does benzylamine, and there is no difference in the binding of the (*R*)- and (*S*)-enantiomers of α-methylbenzylamine. However, since α-methylbenzylamine is a very poor substrate for MAO,[71] initial electron transfer may be difficult.

A study of inactivation of MAO by 1-phenylcyclopropylamine (**9**)[73] revealed that depending upon whether the inactivator became attached to the flavin or to an amino acid residue, the resultant adduct had different stabilities. Incubation of MAO with **9** completely inactivated the enzyme; however, dialysis of the inactivated enzyme led to the partial restoration of enzyme activity. The percentage of activity restored was dependent upon the concentration of **9** used and the length of the incubation period. Titration of the enzyme for an extended period of

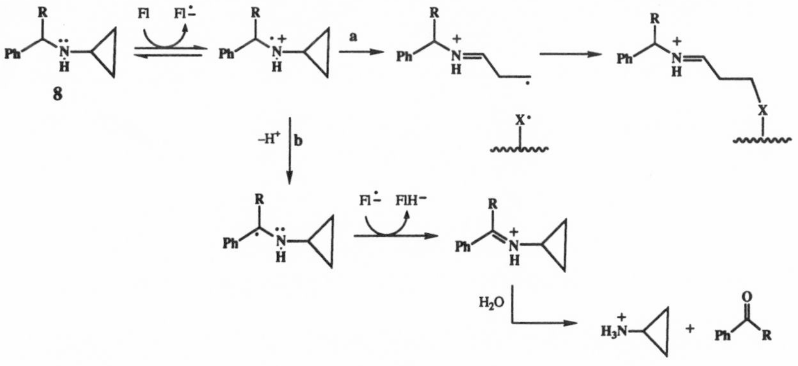

Scheme 17.

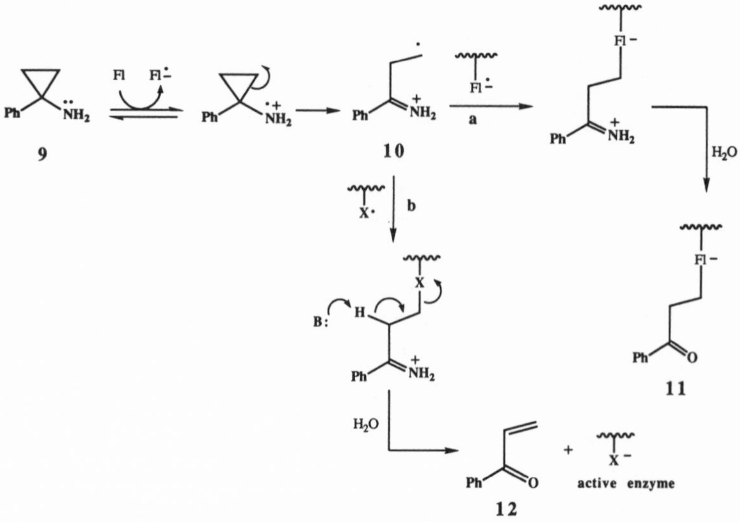

Scheme 18.

time revealed that it took eight equivalents of **9** to completely inactivate MAO and to incorporate one equivalent of radioactivity (from 1-[phenyl-^{14}C]**9**) into the enzyme. This suggests that seven molecules of **9** are being metabolized and one is reacting to form a stable adduct with the enzyme. A mechanism to account for these observations is shown in Scheme 18. Three organic reactions were carried out on the inactivated enzyme in order to determine if adduct **11** is a reasonable hypothesis (Scheme 19). As described above for *N*-(1-methylcyclopropyl)benzylamine (**3**), the enzyme inactivated with **9** was treated with sodium [^{3}H]borohydride and 0.73 equivalent of tritium was incorporated into the inactivated

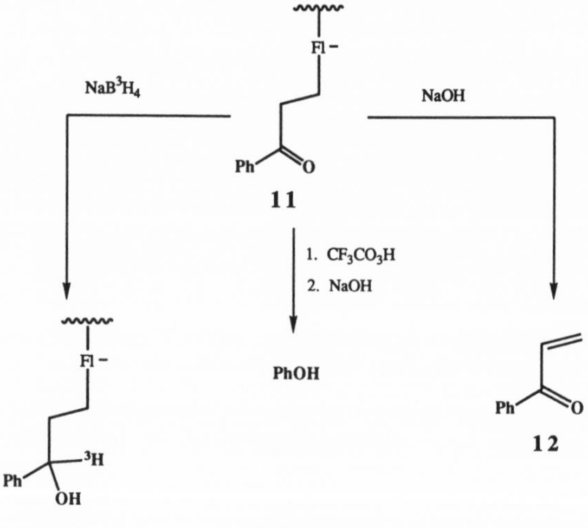

Scheme 19.

enzyme that was not incorporated into the native enzyme, consistent with the presence of a keto group. Phenyl alkyl ketones undergo a Baeyer-Villiger reaction[74] with peroxytrifluoroacetic acid to give phenyl esters; saponification of the phenyl ester gives phenol. When this same reaction was carried out on MAO that was inactivated with 1-[phenyl-^{14}C]9, dialyzed to remove the excess inactivator, protease digested to assure solution chemistry, incubated with peroxytrifluoroacetic acid, then saponified, 82% of the theoretical amount of [^{14}C]phenol was recovered. This indicates the presence of a phenyl ketone. The third reaction used to characterize the structure of the adduct was a base-catalyzed retro Michael reaction.[75] Base treatment of MAO inactivated with 1-[phenyl-^{14}C]9 resulted in the time-dependent release of [^{14}C]acrylophenone (12). When the labeled enzyme was first treated with sodium borohydride to reduce the ketone, then incubated with base, no acrylophenone was formed. The identity of the group attached to the inactivator in Scheme 18 was determined to be the flavin: the radioactively-labeled enzyme was protease digested and the radioactive fragments that were isolated by gel filtration chromatography corresponded to the fragments that had a flavin absorption spectrum. On the basis of a titratable proton with a pKa of 7.1-7.5 and the effect of the change of pH on the absorption spectrum, the attachment of the inactivator appeared to be at the N-5 position of the flavin.

The other seven molecules of 9 that are consumed also react with MAO and form a covalent adduct at a rate that is seven times that for the formation of the covalent adduct to the flavin; however, this adduct is unstable, spontaneously releasing acrylophenone at pH 7.2 with a $t_{1/2}$ of 80 minutes. When the flavin has one equivalent of inactivator bound, seven equivalents of acrylophenone are produced. This suggests that an adduct similar to that formed with the flavin also is produced with the other seven molecules of 9, but that it is inherently less stable. If X in Scheme 18 is not the flavin, and is a very good leaving group, then it may account for the different stabilities of the two adducts. Denaturation of the enzyme that is mostly in the form of the unstable adduct revealed that, unlike the stable flavin adduct, the flavin spectrum was that of oxidized flavin, indicating that attachment was to an amino acid residue not to the flavin. Attachment of the inactivator to an amino acid residue could occur by the mechanism shown in Scheme 18. The X would be generated by hydrogen atom abstraction of an amino acid residue by the flavin semiquinone radical as shown previously in Scheme 13. If hydrogen atom transfer occurs seven times faster than the reaction of 10 with the flavin semiquinone radical, then seven out of eight turnovers of the inactivator would result in attachment to the amino acid residue (pathway b) and only one to the flavin (pathway a). Since the adduct to the amino acid residue is reversible and the one to the flavin is not, eventually all of the inactivated enzyme would end up as the flavin adduct (11), as is observed.

The amino acid to which 9 becomes attached in the reversible adduct was identified.[76] If the mechanism for the formation and release of the reversible adduct is as shown in Scheme 18, then X has to be an amino acid capable of easy

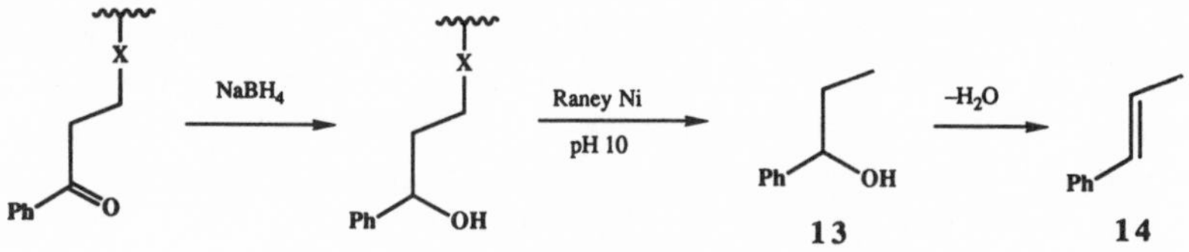

Scheme 20.

hydrogen atom abstraction. Also, once the adduct is formed, X has to be an amino acid that readily undergoes β-elimination. The two most likely candidates that fit that description are cysteine[77] and tyrosine. Two experiments were carried out that identified the amino acid X as a cysteine residue. MAO was treated with 1-[phenyl-^{14}C]9 for a short enough time that mostly the reversible adduct was formed, then it was reduced with sodium borohydride so that the adduct would not be released by β-elimination. The labeled enzyme then was treated with Raney nickel, a reducing agent known to cleave carbon-sulfur bonds specifically;[78] in proteins Raney nickel exclusively reduces cysteine and methionine residues (to alanine and 2-aminobutanoic acid, respectively).[79] One radioactive product was released from the enzyme by Raney nickel, *trans*-β-methylstyrene (**14**, Scheme 20). Cleavage of the carbon-sulfur bond of the sodium borohydride-reduced adduct was predicted to give 1-phenyl-1-propanol (**13**); however, in a nonenzymatic control it was shown that under the conditions of the experiment, 1-phenyl-1-propanol is dehydrated to *trans*-β-methylstyrene. This supports cysteine as the X amino acid and further characterizes the structure of the reversible adduct. The second experiment carried out to identify the X amino acid was to determine the effect of reversible inactivation on the number of cysteine residues in the enzyme. A 5,5'-dithiobis(2-nitrobenzoic acid) titration of the cysteine residues revealed that the native enzyme has six cysteines, but after reversible adduct formation, there are only five cysteine residues. These results support two different pathways available for MAO-catalyzed amine oxidations (Scheme 21). Both pathways could involve either direct second electron transfer or radical combinations followed by β-elimination. The mechanism shown in pathway b could involve direct hydrogen atom transfer; however, hydrogen atom abstraction *by* a thiyl radical is not a favorable process. Further support for these two pathways is described below (vide infra). An elegant SET photochemical model study by Mariano and co-workers[66a] for the reaction of **9** with MAO using a model flavin as the electron acceptor showed that a SET mechanism does, indeed, produce a flavin adduct of general structure **11** (Scheme 18). This is strong support for the involvement of a SET mechanism in the inactivation of MAO by **9**.

Two phenethylamine analogues were prepared to see if reactions similar to those observed with the benzylamine analogue **9** occur.[80] 1-Benzylcyclopropyl-amine appears to be inactivating MAO by the same two pathways as does 1-phenylcyclopropylamine. 1-(Phenylcyclopropyl)methylamine (**15**), however,

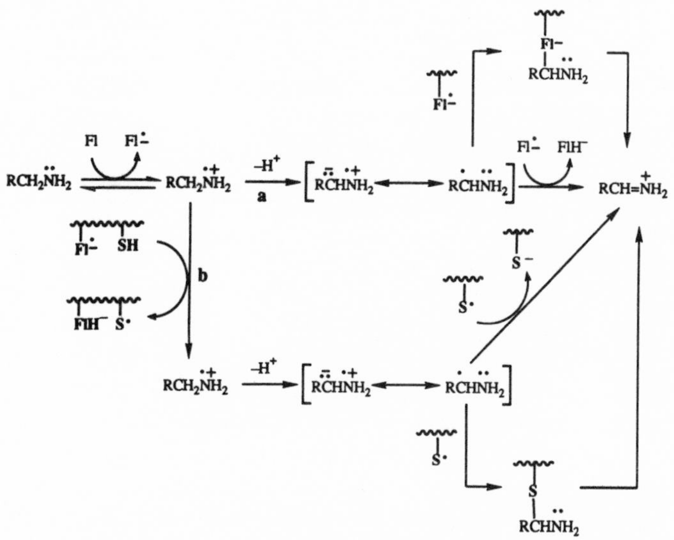

Scheme 21.

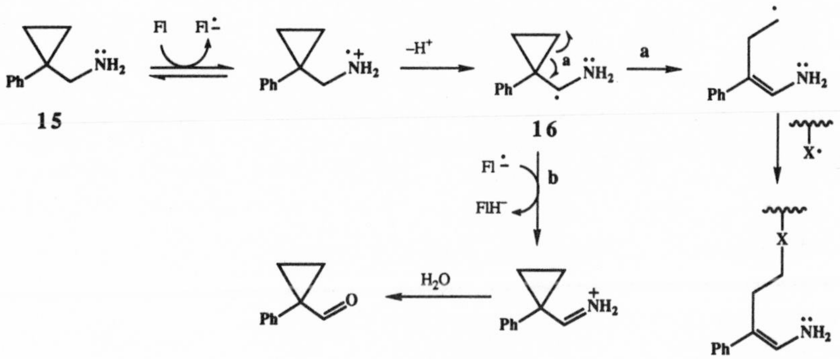

Scheme 22.

is not an inactivator of MAO, but it is a substrate. If electron transfer-proton transfer occurs, a cyclopropylcarbinyl radical would be formed (**16**, Scheme 22). Hypothetically, this could undergo ring cleavage and inactivation (pathway a). Instead, it appears that prior to ring cleavage, second electron transfer occurs to give the imine of the product, 1-phenylcyclopropanecarboxaldehyde (pathway b). Although cyclopropylcarbinyl radicals usually lead to rapid ring cleavage,[81] this is not always the case,[82] especially when the cyclopropyl methyl radical is adjacent to a heteroatom.[83] As described above, the rate of proton transfer and second-electron transfer compètes with cyclopropylaminyl radical ring cleavage. Since the rate of cyclopropylcarbinyl radical opening is measurable (1×10^8 sec^{-1} at 25 °C),[84] but the rate of cyclopropylaminyl radical opening occurs too fast to measure,[63] it is not unreasonable that a cyclopropylcarbinyl radical

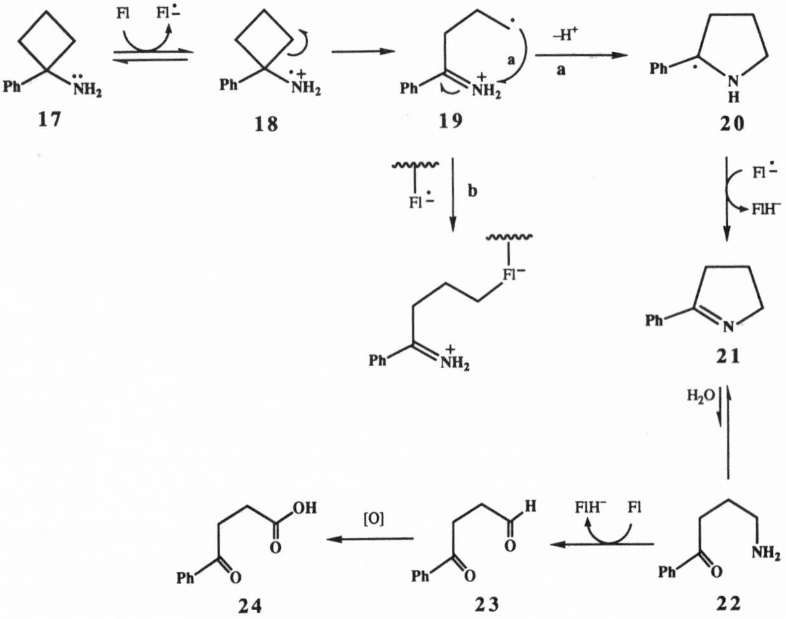

Scheme 23.

intermediate may not cleave prior to second electron transfer. Of course, the alternative explanation is that proton transfer-electron transfer is not the catalytic mechanism, and hydrogen atom transfer occurs instead. This mechanism bypasses the cyclopropylcarbinyl radical; however, as described above, this is not a favored pathway.

The above reactions with cyclopropylamines provide circumstantial evidence that an amine radical intermediate is important in MAO-catalyzed reactions. Taking this approach one step further, if MAO catalyzes an electron transfer mechanism, then it should give the same product expected of a nonenzymatic one-electron reaction. In order to test this approach, 1-phenylcyclobutylamine (**17**) was incubated with MAO and the products were identified (Scheme 23). Cyclobutylaminyl radicals also are known to undergo homolytic ring cleavage, albeit at a slower rate than do cyclopropylaminyl radicals.[63] Therefore, if **18** is formed in the first step, then the cyclobutyl ring would be expected to cleave to **19** (there is no α-proton to compete with ring opening). This intermediate has a

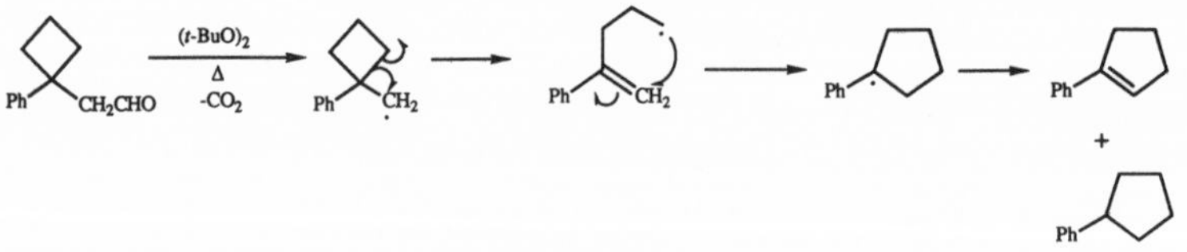

Scheme 24.

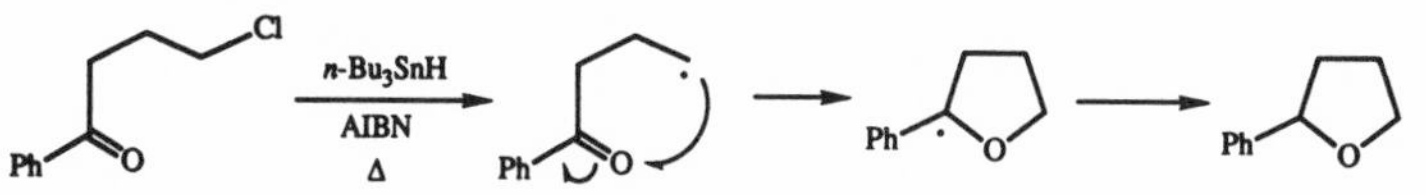

Scheme 25.

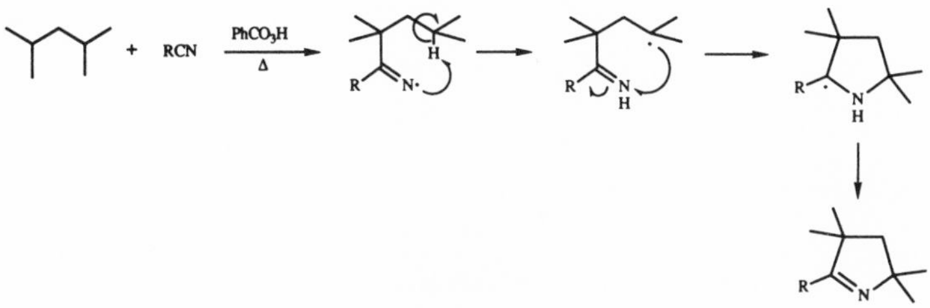

Scheme 26.

built-in radical trap, namely, the imine double bond. There is ample precedence with nonenzymatic reactions that indicate that when a radical is three atoms from a double bond, whether a carbon-carbon (Scheme 24),[85] carbon-oxygen (Scheme 25),[86] or carbon-nitrogen (Scheme 26)[87] double bond, that rapid ring closure can occur to the corresponding cyclopentyl, tetrahydrofuranyl, or piperidinyl radical, respectively. This represents a 5-*endo trig* cyclization which is favored when there is a substituent capable of stabilizing the resultant cyclic radical.[88] Second-electron transfer from intermediate **20** (Scheme 23) would give 2-phenyl-1-pyrroline (**21**) which was isolated as the first metabolite formed in the enzyme reaction. Hydrolysis of **21** would give the amino ketone **22** which should be a good substrate for MAO because 4-phenylbutylamine[89] and 3-keto-3-phenylpro-pylamine[73] are excellent substrates. In fact, after a lag period, a second metabo-lite, 3-benzoylpropanal (**23**) was identified. Since only low concentrations of the amino ketone (**22**) would be formed,[90] and that product is expected to be rapidly oxidized by MAO, it is not surprising that **22** was not detected. A third metabolite, 3-benzoylpropanoic acid (**24**), was shown to be a nonenzymatic oxidation product of the aldehyde (**23**). When MAO was incubated with **21**, both **23** and **24** were formed without a lag period, confirming that they are derived from a MAO-catalyzed oxidation of **21**.

More recently, Bondon et al.[91] found that the enzyme cytochrome P-450, an enzyme that is believed to catalyze one-electron oxidations, also catalyzes the conversion of 1-phenylcyclobutylamine (**17**) to 2-phenyl-1-pyrroline (**21**). This provides enzymatic support that electron transfer chemistry is involved in the MAO-catalyzed oxidation of **17**. MAO also is slowly inactivated by **17**, which becomes covalently attached to the flavin (Scheme 23, pathway b). The mecha-nistic work with the cyclopropylamines and cyclobutylamines suggests that the hydride and carbanion mechanisms for MAO-catalyzed amine oxidation are not reasonable, but that a radical mechanism is quite plausible.

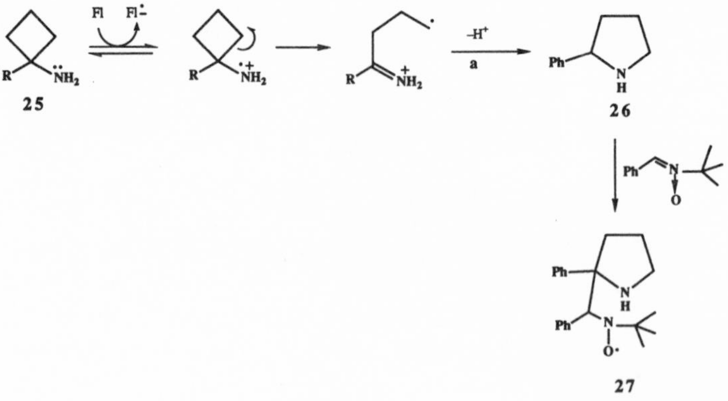

Scheme 27.

Given the above evidence for the potential involvement of a radical mechanism in MAO-catalyzed reactions, it may seem surprising that Tan et al.[58] were unable to detect a radical intermediate by EPR spectroscopy during MAO-catalyzed processing of benzylamine, even in the presence of spin traps. However, the oxidation of benzylamine may be so efficient that the intermediate radical never escapes from the active site, a condition presumably required for the spin trap to be effective. Possibly a poor substrate would have more of a chance to leak from the active site and be spin trapped. 1-Phenylcyclobutylamine (**25**, R = Ph, Scheme 27) and 1-benzoylcyclobutylamine (**25**, R = PhCO) were selected as candidates for an EPR investigation with MAO.[92] Not only are these compounds poor substrates for MAO, but the presumed intermediate (**26**) is equivalent to an α-substituted amine which MAO processes poorly. Incubation of MAO with either 1-phenylcyclobutylamine or 1-benzoylcyclobutylamine in the presence of the radical spin trap α-phenyl *N-tert*-butylnitrone produced the time-dependent build up of a triplet of doublets in the EPR spectrum centered about a *g* value of 2.006 which is what is predicted for **27**, the expected adduct between α-phenyl *N-tert*-butylnitrone and **26** (Scheme 27). This is the first direct evidence for a radical intermediate in the MAO-catalyzed oxidation of amines.

3.6. Inactivation by (Aminomethyl)trimethylsilane

Up to this point in the discussion the only amines used for the investigation of the mechanism of MAO were small cylic amines. It would be intriguing to gain evidence for radical intermediates in the case of acyclic amine substrates. Radicals[93] and radical cations[94] are stabilized by β-silyl group hyperconjugation; therefore, initial electron transfer beta to a silicon atom should be facilitated. This suggested that (aminomethyl)trimethylsilane (**28**, Scheme 28) may be a substrate for MAO.

However, Mariano and co-workers[95] demonstrated in a series of photochemical reactions that the electrophilicity of a silicon atom is greatly enhanced when a strongly electron-deficient atom, particularly a radical cation, is generated beta to the silicon atom. If that is the case, then once the amine radical cation (**29**) is generated, the β-trimethylsilyl group should be activated for attack by an active site nucleophile, leading to silylation (**30**), and possibly inactivation, of the enzyme (Scheme 28, pathway a). Alternatively, **28** may act as a typical substrate for MAO and proceed along pathway b; however, this pathway also can lead to enzyme inactivation depending upon the stability of the adduct **33**. If pathway a is important, then this would be good evidence for an electron transfer mechanism, since it would be difficult to rationalize this pathway by two-electron mechanisms. (Aminomethyl)trimethylsilane was found to be a mechanism-based inactivator of MAO.[96,97] Since neopentylamine (the same compound except with a carbon in place of the silicon) is a substrate for MAO, the silicon atom in **28** must be responsible for the inactivation.

A series of experiments were carried out to differentiate the pathways in Scheme 28. Both of the potential adducts, **30** and **33**, should be relatively labile to hydrolysis. Even trimethylsilyl ethers, the most stable of the possible silylated enzyme heteroatoms, hydrolyze rapidly in aqueous solution.[98] No examples of an acyclic compound of the general structure **33** were found in the literature. Incubation of MAO inactivated with **28** in pH 5.5-9.0 buffer resulted in a time- and pH-dependent return of enzyme activity; the rate of enzyme activity return was slightly faster at low pH than at neutral and high pH. The difference in the rate of reactivation at these pH values was much less than the rate difference for the hydrolysis of trimethylsilyl ethers,[98] suggesting that the adduct is more likely **33** than **30**. Furthermore, incubation of the inactivated enzyme with fluoride ion, known to cleave trimethylsilyl ethers very rapidly, did not affect the rate of reactivation of the **28**-inactivated MAO, again supporting adduct **33**.

A more definitive answer was sought, so isotopically-labeled analogues of **28** were prepared.[97] According to Scheme 28 (pathway a), inactivation of MAO with [1-^{3}H]**28** should lead to inactivation with no incorporation of tritium into the enzyme and concomitant release of tritium into solution as [^{3}H]formaldehyde. Pathway b should give MAO containing tritium and no [^{3}H]formaldehyde. Incubation of MAO with [1-^{3}H]**28** gave both results; about one equivalent of tritium was incorporated into the enzyme, but [^{3}H]formaldehyde also was formed (detected as its 2,4-dinitrophenylhydrazone). This suggests that either both pathway a and b are operative or that only pathway b is important, but that formaldehyde can be obtained somehow from this route. Both of these possibilities are reasonable because acylsilanes (the product of hydrolysis of **32**) are known to hydrolyze to the aldehyde via the Brook rearrangement[99] (Scheme 29, in this case, R = R′ = H). If **32** is released into solution, it can undergo this rearrangement.

In order to differentiate pathways a and b (Scheme 28), [1-^{2}H$_2$]-**28** (**34**, Scheme 30) was synthesized and used to inactivate MAO; Scheme 30 shows the outcomes of inactivation of MAO by **34**. Inactivation by pathway a would produce dideuterated formaldehyde (trapped as the 2,4-dinitrophenylhydrazone),

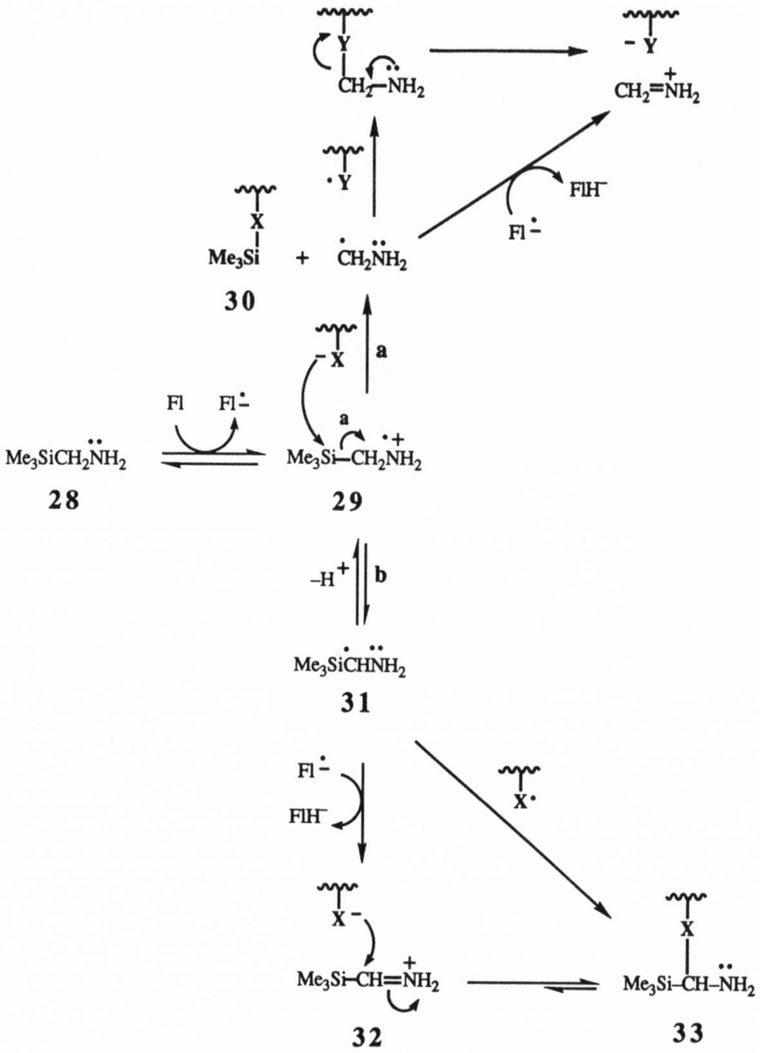

Y
CH_2–NH_2
– Y
CH_2=$\overset{+}{N}H_2$
· Y
FlH⁻
X
Me₃Si
+
$\dot{C}H_2\ddot{N}H_2$
30
Fl·⁻
– X
a
Fl
Fl·⁻
a
$Me_3SiCH_2\ddot{N}H_2$
28
Me_3Si–$CH_2\overset{\cdot+}{N}H_2$
29
–H⁺
b
$Me_3Si\dot{C}H\ddot{N}H_2$
31
Fl·⁻
FlH⁻
X·
X⁻
Me_3Si–CH=$\overset{+}{N}H_2$
32
X
Me_3Si–CH–$\ddot{N}H_2$
33

Scheme 28.

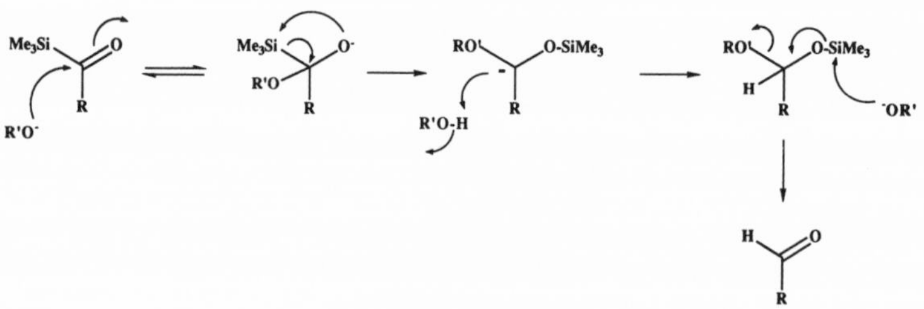

Me₃Si
O
R
R'O⁻
Me₃Si
O⁻
R'O
R
RO
O-SiMe₃
R
R'O-H
RO
O-SiMe₃
H
R
⁻OR'
H
O
R

Scheme 29.

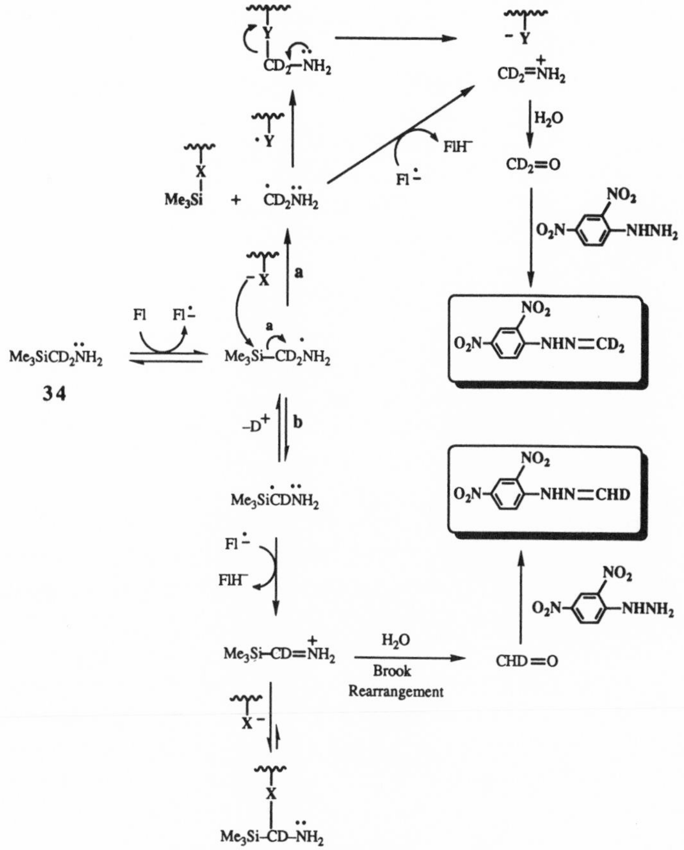

Me3SiCD2NH2
34
Fl
Fl·−
Me3Si–CD2NH2
a
−X
Me3Si
+
CD2NH2
·Y
CD2–NH2
−Y
CD2=NH2
H2O
CD2=O
FlH−
Fl·−
O2N
NO2
NHNH2
NHN=CD2
−D+
b
Me3SiCDNH2
Me3Si–CD=NH2
H2O
Brook
Rearrangement
CHD=O
NHN=CHD
X−
Me3Si–CD–NH2

Scheme 30.

whereas pathway b, following hydrolysis and Brook rearrangement, would give monodeuterated formaldehyde. Furthermore, since other substrates for MAO B such as tyramine and kynuramine,[34] benzylamine,[53a] and dopamine[53b] exhibit kinetic isotope effects on α-C-H bond cleavage, pathway b, but not pathway a, may exhibit a deuterium isotope effect on the rate of inactivation (a C-D bond is broken during inactivation by pathway b, but not by pathway a). Inactivation of MAO by **28** and **34** exhibited a deuterium isotope effect (k^{H}inact/k^{D}inact) of 2.3 with no effect on the K_I. This isotope effect is almost identical to the deuterium isotope effects reported for [1-$^2H_2$]tyramine[34] and for [1-$^2H_2$]dopamine,[53b] and indicates that pathway b is responsible for inactivation of MAO by **28**. Mass spectral analysis of the formaldehyde produced during the inactivation (isolated as the 2,4-dinitrophenylhydrazone) revealed that both monodeuterated (pathway b) and dideuterated (pathway a) formaldehyde were formed in the ratio of 3.5 to 1, respectively. Therefore, both pathway a and pathway b are operative, but pathway b is responsible for inactivation and pathway a results in turnover to product without inactivation.

The converse experiment, namely, the inactivation of MAO by 28 in ^2H_2O, produced a mixture of monodeuterated (pathway b; the Brook rearrangement leads to incorporation of a deuteron from the ^2H_2O) and undeuterated (pathway a) formaldehyde, confirming that the formaldehyde comes from pathway a and pathway b. This also indicates that the [^{3}H]formaldehyde observed during inactivation of MAO by [1-^{3}H]-28 (vide supra) also came from pathway a and pathway b.

The observation of the product from pathway a is strong support for a radical mechanism. Recently, Mariano and co-workers[100] carried out a photochemical study with (diethylaminomethyl)trimethylsilane (N,N-diethyl 28) that was analogous to the enzymatic one described here with 28. The results of their study indicate that upon generation of the amine radical cation, two processes occur, desilylation (equivalent to pathway a in Scheme 28) and deprotonation (equivalent to pathway b in Scheme 28). The ratio of these two pathways is solvent dependent (low-polarity nonhydroxylic solvents favor deprotonation and polar hydroxylic solvents favor desilylation) and base dependent (increased base strength favors deprotonation). Although the products of pathway b could be rationalized by any mechanism that generates intermediate 32 (Scheme 28), the products of pathway a will not form without the generation of a highly electron deficient amino group.

Our earlier precedence for the generation of amine radical cations with cyclopropylamines[32] and cyclobutylamines[33] in conjunction with the model studies of Mariano and co-workers[95] strongly suggest that an amine radical cation intermediate is involved in the case of 28. Since 28 is an acyclic molecule that is structurally related to a substrate (neopentylamine) for MAO, our results with 28 seem to validate the radical mechanism for MAO-catalyzed amine oxidation as the rule, not the exception.

The chemistry of trimethylsilyl groups is, in many ways, that of a "super proton."[101] Therefore, removal of the trimethylsilyl group (pathway a, Scheme 28) and removal of a proton (pathway b) from intermediate 29 are closely related processes, and are not really divergent pathways. Alternatives to pathways a and b would be removal of the trimethylsilyl group or the hydrogen, respectively, as radicals to give directly the immonium ion of formaldehyde or 32, respectively. However, on the basis of the model study work and discussions of Mariano and coworkers[100] and Dinnocenzo and Banach,[52] removal of the trimethylsilyl group or a hydrogen as a radical is not relevant to the oxidation of 28 (or to amine oxidation in general).

Inactivation of MAO by pathway b (Scheme 28) should result in the incorporation of one equivalent of tritium from [1-^{3}H]-28 and one equivalent of ^{14}C from [^{14}C-methyl]-28 (label in the trimethylsilyl group); reactivation of inactivated labeled MAO should release both labels at the same rate with a concomitant return of enzyme activity. Inactivation of MAO with these inactivators led to the incorporation of 1.24 and 3.29 equivalents of radioactivity, respectively. It is not known if the additional two equivalents of ^{14}C radioactivity (presumably, the result of trimethylsilylated nucleophiles) are at the active site. Incubation of the labeled enzymes at pH 7.0 resulted in a pseudo first-order release of both ^3H and ^{14}C and in return of enzyme activity all at comparable rates, suggesting that all three of these processes occur simultaneously, which, again, is consistent with the formation of adduct **33** (Scheme 28), the product formed by pathway b.

Inactivation of MAO by [1-^3H]-**28** results in the reduction of the flavin. This is a common observation for inactivators of MAO, whether or not they become attached to the flavin cofactor. Upon denaturation of the inactivated enzyme, however, the flavin spectrum reverts to that of the oxidized form. This suggests that the attachment is to an amino acid residue, not to the flavin, that is, unless the adduct has hydrolyzed off of the enzyme during denaturation. After denaturation and exhaustive dialysis of the inactivated enzyme, about 0.5 equivalent of tritium still was attached to the denatured protein. Although some hydrolysis of the adduct had occurred during dialysis for removal of the excess inactivator, none of the flavin was in the reduced form. Therefore, attachment of the inactivator to an amino acid residue (most likely, the active site cysteine residue) is a reasonable conclusion.

Studies with cyclopropylamine[32] and cyclobutylamine[33] inactivators have provided good evidence that the first step of amine oxidation by MAO involves a one-electron oxidation of the amino group. However, this earlier work has not clarified whether the mechanism proceeds from the amine radical cation by proton removal followed by α-carbon radical transfer to the flavin (Scheme 9, pathway a), by proton removal followed by radical combination and β-elimination (Scheme 9, pathway b), or by the direct transfer of an α-hydrogen atom to the flavin (Scheme 9, pathway c). The above results with (aminomethyl) trimethylsilane (**28**) support pathways a and b. When R in Scheme 9 is Me$_3$Si, proton removal from the amine radical cation would give a carbon radical that could partition between second electron transfer to give the aldehyde metabolites (pathway a) and radical combination with an active site amino acid radical (presumably a cysteinyl radical) to give a covalent intermediate (pathway b). In the case of (aminomethyl)trimethylsilane this covalent intermediate is stabilized by the α-trimethylsilyl group. Therefore, this compound is acting as if it were a normal substrate for MAO, but it leads to inactivation because the trimethylsilyl group stabilizes the normal covalent intermediate in the enzyme reaction.

3.7. MAO Inhibition by an Oxazolidinone

The reaction of 5-(aminomethyl)-3-aryl-2-oxazolidinones (**35**) with MAO has provided additional support for this pathway. Structure-activity relationship studies of a variety of oxazolidinones uncovered several very potent inhibitors of MAO, some of which were MAO A selective and some MAO B selective.[102] The

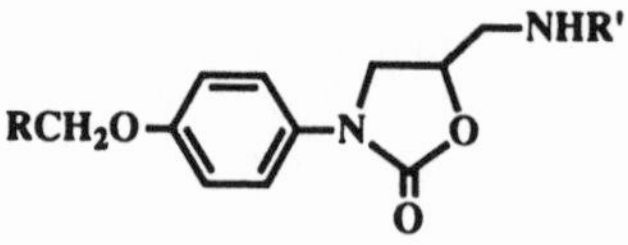

35

most potent of the MAO B inhibitors, **35** (R = 3-chlorophenyl, R' = CH₃),[103] also was found to be an irreversible inactivator of MAO.[104] Since this suggested that these compounds may be reacting covalently with MAO, an investigation of the mechanism of inactivation of MAO by this class of compounds was initiated.[105] On the basis of the earlier work on the mechanism of MAO and the similarity of the structure of these compounds to substrates for the enzyme, several possible inactivation pathways were suggested (Scheme 31). According to this scheme **36** undergoes one-electron transfer to the radical cation **37** from which an α-proton could be removed to give radical **38**. This radical could decompose either heterolytically (pathway a) or homolytically (pathway c). The heterolytic pathway is analogous to the mechanism for the conversion of ethylene glycol to acetaldehyde by Fenton's reagent.[106] Pathway a would result in the loss of CO_2 and in the formation of radical **39**, which could combine with an active site radical (flavin semiquinone radical or amino acid radical) and inactivate the enzyme (**40**). The homolytic pathway c also results in the generation of CO_2 but gives a different radical (**41**) which would inactivate the enzyme (**42**). Pathway b

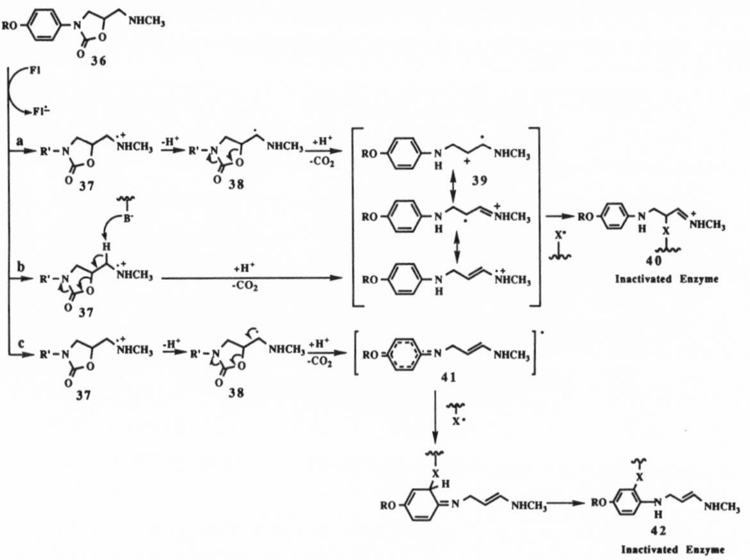

Scheme 31.

utilizes the carbanionic character generated at the α-carbon upon deprotonation (a resonance structure of the α-radical).

Since there was no literature precedence for this radical chemistry, model studies for this reaction were carried out.[107] One model was designed to determine if a radical adjacent to the N-(4-alkoxyphenyl)oxazolidinone ring (intermediate **38**, pathways a and c) would induce decomposition of the oxazolidinone ring with loss of CO_2 (Scheme 32). Treatment of model oxazolidinone **43** with tri-*n*-butylstannane and catalytic AIBN at 190 °C resulted in the formation of a 6% yield of N-allylanisidine (**45**) and a 94% yield of the hydrogen atom rebound product **44**; the loss of CO_2 was detected with lead acetate. The formation of **45** and CO_2 supports the mechanism in Scheme 31 (pathways a and c). Other model reactions carried out[107] provided further support for these mechanisms. The carbanionic mechanism (Scheme 31, pathway b) was supported by the reaction of model oxazolidinone **46** and treatment with magnesium, zinc, or *n*-butyllithium (Scheme 33); in all cases greater than a 90% yield of N-allylanisidine (**45**) was isolated.

In order to test these mechanistic hypotheses several radioactively-labeled analogues were synthesized. Two of the radioactively-labeled analogues (*R*- and *S*-**47**, R = ³H) were synthesized to show that the inactivator molecules become irreversibly attached to MAO after inactivation. Both of these compounds inactivated MAO with attachment, after denaturation, of one equivalent of radioactivity.

An important test of the validity of the proposed inactivation mechanisms (Scheme 31) is whether CO_2 is released during inactivation by **47**. *R*- and *S*-**48** were synthesized; inactivation of MAO was carried out in a closed vessel containing a base trap to collect any ¹⁴CO_2 that was generated. The *R*- and *S*-isomers inactivated the enzyme with release of 3-4 equivalents of ¹⁴CO_2. Loss

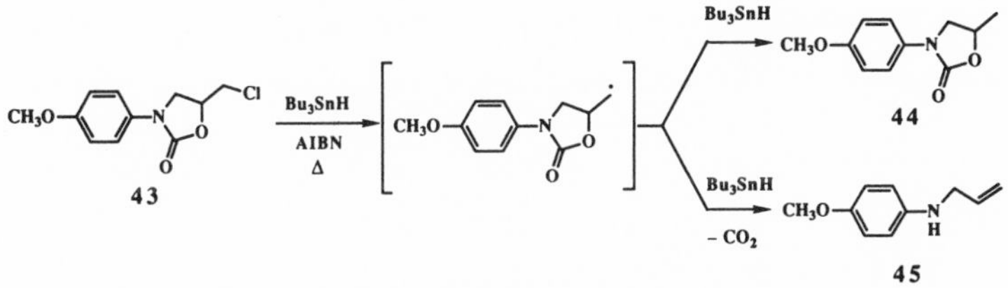

Scheme 32.

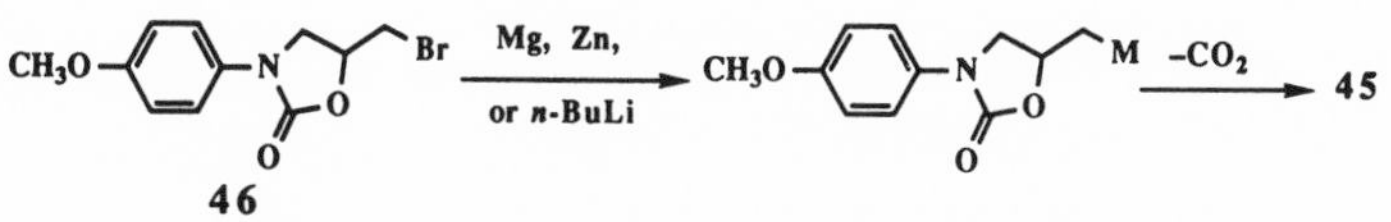

Scheme 33.

47

48

of CO_2 should be a measure of the MAO-catalyzed oxidation of **47** (R = H) by one of the mechanisms in Scheme 31. An alternative oxidation pathway for **47** (R = H) and its analogues is the normal oxidation reaction, namely its conversion to the corresponding imine followed by hydrolysis to the aldehyde, which is a known metabolite of **47** (R = H) oxidation.[108]

So far, the results support the proposed inactivation mechanisms (Scheme 31), but according to these mechanisms no ^{14}C from the oxazolidinone carbonyl group should remain attached to the inactivated enzyme. Inactivation of MAO with (R)- and (S)-**48**, however, led to the incorporation of 1.5 and 1.0 equivalents, respectively, of ^{14}C per enzyme molecule! Therefore, decarboxylation is not involved in the mechanism of inactivation of MAO by the 5-(aminomethyl)-3-aryl-2 oxazolidinones. Decarboxylation must be important, however, in the MAO-catalyzed metabolism of this class of inactivators.

There are several alternative inactivation mechanisms that could be considered, but the most important of these is shown in Scheme 34 (pathway a). This mechanism is a modification of the mechanism of inactivation that was proposed by Dostert et al.[109,110] The stability of the proposed adduct **50** would be derived from the electron-withdrawing oxygen that is at the β position. It is well known that electron-withdrawing groups stabilize α- and β-sp[3] carbons in preference to sp[2] carbons, presumably because of destabilization of the electron-deficient carbonyl. For example, when electron-withdrawing substituents are beta to a keto group, the corresponding hydrate or hemiacetal derivative is strongly preferred over the ketone.[111] A stable α-aminosulfide was isolated that contained a β-halogen,[112] and a fluorohydrin with a β-electron withdrawing group was stable to chromatography.[113] A β-fluoro substituent was used to stabilize a proposed acetal intermediate in the reaction catalyzed by glycosidase, resulting in inactivation of the enzyme.[114]

If the mechanism for inactivation shown in Scheme 34 is correct, then it suggests that any compound containing a β-electron withdrawing group could inactivate MAO. Examples of this class of inactivators may be 2-chloro-2-

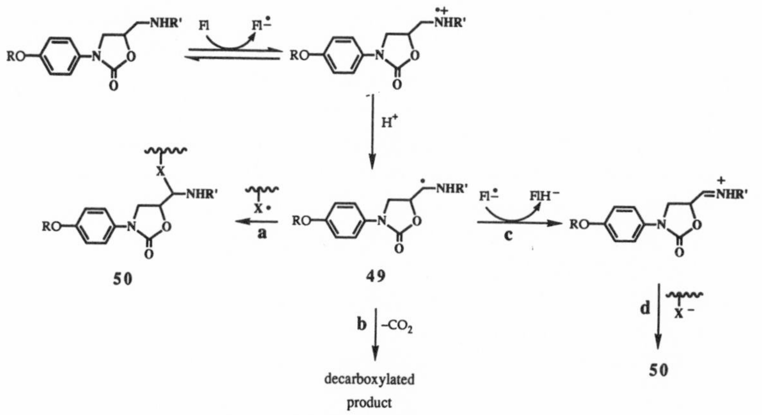

Scheme 34.

phenylethylamine,[37] the inhibitors reported by the group at Hoffmann-La Roche, namely, Ro 19-6327,[115] Ro 16-6491,[116] and the antidepressant drug moclobemide[117] as well as the anticonvulsant agent from Searle, milacemide.[118] Furthermore, if it is the oxygen of the oxazolidinone that is responsible for inactivation, then the oxazolidinone nitrogen is not important for inactivation. Consequently, the two corresponding diastereomeric lactones (**51** and **52**) were synthesized. The rate constant for inactivation of MAO by the *trans*-isomer is 5 times greater

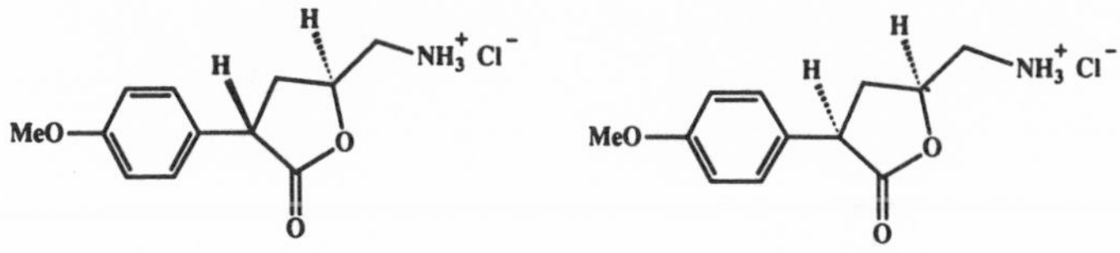

51   **52**

than for the *cis*-isomer and 30 times greater than that for the corresponding oxazolidinone. This supports the hypothesis that the β electron withdrawing group is the essential feature in the oxazolidinones that leads to inactivation after attachment to the enzyme. Since epimerization at the nitrogen of the oxazolidinone is a low energy process, and the *trans*-lactone is a much better inactivator than the *cis*-lactone, it is likely that one configuration of the oxazolidinone also is more active than the other.

Upon inactivation of MAO by oxazolidinone **35** (R = H; R' = CH$_3$), the flavin spectrum became reduced, but after denaturation it was reoxidized. This indicates that attachment of the inactivator is not to the flavin but to an amino acid residue, possibly the active site cysteine.

The results of these studies, in conjunction with our earlier work, provide additional evidence for the mechanism of MAO-catalyzed amine oxidation shown in Scheme 9. Results with (aminomethyl)trimethylsilane and the ox-azolidinones support pathways a and b. Similar to what was described above for (aminomethyl)trimethylsilane, when R in Scheme 9 is an *N*-substituted 2-ox-azolidinon-5-yl unit, proton removal from the amine radical cation would give a carbon radical that could partition between second electron transfer to give the aldehyde metabolites (pathway a) and radical combination with an active site amino acid radical to give a covalent intermediate (pathway b). In the case of the 5-(aminomethyl)-3-aryl-2-oxazolidinones this covalent intermediate is stabilized by the oxygen of the *N*-substituted 5-oxazolidinonyl group. Therefore, this compound is acting as if it were a normal substrate for MAO; however, it leads to inactivation because the built in electron-withdrawing group (the oxazolidinone oxygen) stabilizes the normal covalent intermediate in the enzyme reaction.

4. CONCLUSIONS

One might wonder why Mother Nature would be so careless as to design a redox enzyme with a cysteine residue near to the oxidizing flavin cofactor. It may not be carelessness, however, but a clever design element that allows MAO to catalyze oxidations of a variety of substrates having different second electron oxidation potentials. After oxidation proceeds to the carbon radical intermediate (Scheme 9), depending upon the oxidation potential of that species, the enzyme can continue along two different pathways. For those substrates with low oxida-tion potentials, second electron transfer may occur (pathway a), but for those substrates with high oxidation potentials, radical combination and β-elimination could be an alternative route (pathway b). An electron-withdrawing group at the β-position of a substrate increases the oxidation potential for second electron transfer and would detour the mechanism to pathway b, which results in covalent adduct formation. In these cases the covalent adduct is stabilized and inactivation is the result. But for other molecules that do not lead to a stabilized adduct, since thiolate is a better leaving group than the flavin for β-elimination,[73] the rate of elimination would be *accelerated* by covalent bond formation to a cysteine residue rather than to the flavin. This could account for the positioning of a cysteine group near to the flavin cofactor. Recently, a SET photochemical model study for the oxidation of amines with a model flavin (a MAO model) was carried out by Mariano and co-workers[119] Interestingly, the results differed for primary and secondary amines versus tertiary amines. Following SET the former amines favored abstraction of the proton on the amine radical cation to give the neutral aminyl radical. Hydrogen atom abstraction would result in the oxidized product (see Scheme 9, pathway c, except from the aminyl radical instead of the amine radical cation). With tertiary amines a mechanism related to Scheme 9, pathway b, where X is the flavin seemed most reasonable; however, because no thiols could be included in the model study, any adducts formed had to be between the amines and the model flavin. These flavin adducts were found to be stable under anhydrous conditions, but were very unstable to hydrolysis, resulting in the formation of the corresponding oxidized products. It is likely that the stability of the corresponding cysteine adduct would be even lower than that for the flavin adduct.

Although a mechanism can never be "proven," all of the chemistry that MAO catalyzes can be rationalized in terms of single electron transfer reactions. When alternative substrates are utilized in the investigation of an enzyme mechanism, it always can be said that with non-ideal substrates the mechanism is different than with physiological substrates. That certainly is a possibility, but the evidence to date indicates that MAO is, at least, capable of catalyzing electron transfer chemistry. Since the enzyme may have to deal with highly energetic intermediates, it is not surprising that it has been "designed" to be the most efficient possible to avoid leakages of radicals that may be harmful to the cell during turnover of its substrates to products. This would suggest that only poor substrates may be useful in gaining information regarding the catalytic mechanism of MAO and, therefore, non-ideal evidence for the mechanism may be the best we can do for now.

REFERENCES AND NOTES

1. Strolin Benedetti, M.; Dostert, P.; Tipton, K. F. *Prog. Drug Metab.* **1988,** *11*, 149–174.
2. Johnston, J. P. *Biochem. Pharmacol.* **1968,** *17*, 1285–1297.
3. (a) Bach, A. W. J.; Lan, N. C.; Johnson, D. L.; Abell, C. W.: Bembenek, M. E.; Kwan, S.-W.; Seeburg, P. H.; Shih, J. C. *Proc. Natl. Acad. Sci. USA* **1988,** *85*, 4934–4938. (b) Hsu, Y.-P. P.; Weyler, W.; Chen, S.; Sims, K. B.; Rinehart, W. B.; Utterback, M. C.; Powell, J. F.; Breakefield, X. O. *J. Neurochem.* **1988,** *51*, 1321–1324. (c) Ito, A.; Kuwahara, T.; Inadome, S.; Sagara, Y. *Biochem. Biophys. Res. Commun.* **1988,** *157*, 970–976.
4. Palfreyman, M. G.; McDonald, I. A.; Bey, P.; Schechter, P. J.; Sjoerdsma, A. *Prog. Neuro-Psychopharmacol. & Biol. Psychiat.* **1988,** *12*, 967–987.
5. Schmiedeberg, O. *Naunyum-Schmiedeberg Arch. Pharmakol. Exp. Pathol.* **1877,** *8*, 1–14.
6. Minkowski, O. *Arch. Exp. Pathol. Pharmakol.,* **1883,** *17*, 445–465.
7. Ewins, A. J.; Laidlaw, P. P. *J. Physiol. (London)* **1910,** *41*, 78–87.
8. Hare, M. L. C. *Biochem. J.* **1928,** *22*, 968–979.
9. Warburg, O. *Biochem. Z.* **1923,** *142*, 518–523.
10. Zeller, E. A. *Helv. Chim. Acta* **1938,** *21*, 881–890.
11. (a) Blaschko, H.; Richter, D.; Dchlossmann, H. *Biochem. J.* **1937,** *31*, 2187–2196. (b) Pugh, C. E.; Quastel, J. H. *Biochem. J.* **1937,** *31*, 2306–2321. (c) Bhagvat, K.; Blaschko, H.; Richter, D. *Biochem. J.* **1939,** *33*, 1338–1341.
12. (a)Kearney, E. B.; Salach, J. I.; Walker, W. H.; Seng, R. L.; Kenney, W.; Zeszotek, E.; Singer, T. P. *Eur. J. Biochem.* **1971,** *24*, 321–327. (b) Rucker, R. B.; Wold, F. *FASEB J.* **1988,** *2*, 2252–2261.
13. (a) Oreland, L. *Arch. Biochem. Biophys.,* **1971,** *146*, 410–421. (b) Youdim, M. B. H. In *Flavins and Flavoproteins,* Singer, T. P., Ed. Elsevier/North-Holland, Amsterdam, 1976, pp. 593–604.

14. Weyler, W.; Salach, J. I. *Arch. Biochem. Biophys.*, **1981**, *212*, 147–153.
15. (a) Bach, A. W. J.; Lan, N. C.; Johnson, D. L.; Abell, C. W.; Bembenek, M. E.; Kwan, S.-W.; Seeburg, P. H.; Shih, J. C. *Proc. Natl. Acad. Sci. USA* **1988**, *85*, 4934–4938. (b) Hsu, Y.-P. P.; Weyler, W.; Chen, S.; Sims, K. B.; Rinehart, W. B.; Utterback, M. C.; Powell, J. F.; Breakefield, X. O. *J. Neurochem.* **1988**, *51*, 1321–1324. (c) Ito, A.; Kuwahara, T.; Inadome, S.; Sagara, Y. *Biochem. Biophys. Res. Commun.* **1988**, *157*, 970–976.
16. Hiramatsu, A.; Tsurushiin, S. Yasunobu, K. T. *Eur, J. Biochem.* **1975**, *57*, 587–593.
17. (a) Singer, T. P. *J. Neur. Trans.* **1987 [suppl]**, *23*, 1–23. (b) Gomes, B.; Kloepfer, H. G.; Oi, S.; Yasunobu, K. T. *Biochim. Biophys. Acta* **1976**, *438*, 347–357. (c) Singer, T. P.; Barron, E. S. G. *J. Biol. Chem.* **1945**, *157*, 241–253.
18. Blaschko, H. *Pharmacol. Rev.* **1952**, *4*, 415–458. (b) Alles, G. A.; Heegaard, E. V. *J. Biol. Chem.* **1943**, *147*, 487–503. (c) Guffroy, C.; Fowler, C. J.; Strolin Benedetti, M. *J. Pharm. Pharmacol.* **1982**, *35*, 416–420. (d) Yamasaki, R. B.; Silverman, R. B. *Biochemistry* **1985**, *24*, 6543–6550.
19. McEwen, C. M., Jr.; Sasaki, G.; Lenz, W. R., Jr. *J. Biol. Chem.* **1968**, *243*, 5217–5225.
20. (a) Belleau, B.; Fang, M.; Burba, J.; Moran, J. *J. Am. Chem. Soc.*, **1960**, *82*, 5752–5754. (b) Yu, P. H.; Bailey, B. A.; Duden, D. A.; Boulton, A. A. *Biochem. Pharmacol.*, **1986**, *35*, 1027–1036. (c) Battersby, A. R.; Chrystal, E. J. T.; Staunton, J. *J. Chem. Soc. Perkin Trans. I*, **1980**, 31–42. (d) Battersby, A. R.; Buckley, D. G.; Staunton, J.; Williams, P. J. *J. Chem. Soc. Perkin Trans. I*, **1979**, 2550–2558.
21. Williams, C. H. *Biochem. Soc. Trans.*, **1977**, *5*, 1770–1771.
22. Giachetti, A.; Shore, P. A. *Life Sci.*, **1966**, *5*, 1373–1378.
23. Riley, T. N.; Brier, C. G. *J. Med. Chem.*, **1972**, *15*, 1187–1188.
24. (a) Sahlberg, C.; Ross, S. B.; Fagervall, I.; Ask, A.-L.; Claesson, A. *J. Med. Chem.* **1983**, *26*, 1036–1042. (b) White, R. L.; Smith, R. A.; Krantz, A. *Biochem. Pharmacol.*, **1983**, *32*, 3661–3664.
25. Dostert, P. L.; Strolin Benedetti, M.; Tipton, K. F. *Med. Res. Rev.*, **1989**, *9*, 45–89.
26. (a) Yasunobu, K. T.; Oi, S. In *Monoamine Oxidase-New Vistas*, Costa, E.; Sandler, M., Eds. Raven Press, New York, 1972, Vol. 5, pp. 91–105. (b) Oi, S.; Yasunobu, K. T. *Biochem. Biophys. Res. Commun.* **1973**, *53*, 631–637.
27. Smith, T. E.; Weissbach, H.; Udenfriend, S. *Biochemistry* **1962**, *1* 137–143.
28. (a) Hellerman, L.; Chuang, H. Y. K.; DeLuce, D. C. In *Monoamine Oxidase-New Vistas*, Costa, E.; Sandler M., Eds. Raven Press, New York, 1972, Vol. 5, 327–337. (b) Patek, D. R.; Chuang, H. Y. K.; Hellerman, L. *Fed. Proc.* **1972**, *31*, 420.
29. Tipton, K. F.; O'Carroll, A.-M.; McCrodden, J. M. *J. Neur. Trans.* **1987 [suppl]**, *23*, 35–35.
30. Kierkegaard, P., In *Flavins and Flavoproteins*, Kamin, H. Ed. University Park Press, Baltimore, 1971, Vol. 3, p. 13.
31. Hamilton, G. A. In *Progress in Bioorganic Chemistry*, Kaiser, E. T.; Kézdy, F. J., Eds. John Wiley & Sons, New York, 1971, Vol. 1, pp. 83–157.
32. (a) Silverman, R. B.; Hoffman, S. J. *J. Am. Chem. Soc.* **1980**, *102*, 884–886. (b) Silverman, R. B.; Hoffman, S. J.; Catus, W. B., III *J. Am. Chem. Soc.* **1980**, *102*, 7126–7128. (c) Silverman, R. B.; Hoffman, S. J. *Biochem. Biophys. Res. Commun.* **1981**, *101*, 1396–1401. (d) Silverman, R. B. *J. Biol. Chem.* **1983**, *258*, 14766–14769. (e) Silverman, R. B.; Yamasaki, R. B. *Biochemistry* **1984**, *23*, 1322–1332. (f) Silverman, R. B. *Biochemistry* **1984**, *23*, 5206–5213. (g) Silverman, R. B.; Zieske, P. A. *Biochemistry* **1985**, *24*, 2128–2138. (h) Silverman, R. B.; Zieske, P. A. *J. Med. Chem.* **1985**, *28*, 1953–1957. (i) Vazquez, M. L.; Silverman, R. B. *Biochemistry* **1985**, *24*, 6538–6543. (j) Yamasaki, R. B.; Silverman, R. B. *Biochemistry* **1985**, *24*, 6543–6550. (k) Silverman, R. B.; Zieske, P. A. *Biochem. Biophys. Res. Commun.* **1986**, *135*, 154–159.

33. (a)Silverman, R. B.; Zieske, P. A. *Biochemistry* **1986**, *25*, 341–346. (b) Yelekci, K.; Lu, X.; Silverman, R. B. *J. Am. Chem. Soc.* **1989**, *111*, 1138–1140.
34. Belleau, B.; Moran, J. *Ann. N. Y. Acad. Sci.* **1963**, *107*, 822–839.
35. Cram, D. *Fundamentals of Carbanion Chemistry*. Academic Press, New York, 1965, p. 56.
36. Williams, C. H. *Biochem. Pharmacol.* **1974**, *23*, 615–628.
37. Weyler, W. *Arch. Biochem. Biophys.* **1987**, *255*, 400–408.
38. Walsh, C.; Schonbrunn, A.; Abeles, R. *J. Biol. Chem.* **1971**, *246*, 6855.
39. Hellerman, L.; Erwin, V. G. *J. Biol. Chem.*, **1968**, *243*, 5234–5243.
40. Sun, M.; Song, P.-S. *Biochemistry*, **1973**, *12*, 4663–4669.
41. Carey, F. A.; Sundberg, R. J. *Advanced Organic Chemistry*. Plenum Press, New York, 1990, 3rd ed., Part A, p. 193.
42. Maycock, A. L.; Abeles, R. H.; Salach, J. I.; Singer, T. P. *Biochemistry* **1976**, *15*, 114–125.
43. Eberson, L. E.; Persson, K. *J. Med. Pharm. Chem.* **1962**, *5*, 738–752.
44. Bruice, T. C. In *Advances in Chemistry Series 191: Biomemetic Chemistry;* American Chemical Society: Washington, DC, 1980; p. 89.
45. Massey, V.; Ghisla, S. In *Biological Oxidations, 34, Mosbach Colloquium*, Sund, H. Ullrich, V., Ed. Springer, Berlin, 1983; p. 114.
46. (a) Lenn, N. D.; Shih, Y.; Stankovich, M. T.; Liu, H.-w. (b) Lai, M.-t; Liu, L.-d.; Liu, H.-w. *J. Am. Chem. Soc.* **1989**, *111*, 3065–3067. *J. Am. Chem. Soc.* **1991**, *113*, 7388–7397.
47. (a) Hull, L. A.; Davis, G. T.; Rosenblatt, D. H. *J. Am. Chem. Soc.* **1969**, *91*, 6247. (b) Lindsay Smith, J. R.; Mead, L. A. V.*J. Chem. Soc., Perkin Trans.* 2 **1973**, 206–210.
48. Mann, C. K.; Barnes, K. K. *Electrochemical Reactions in Non-Aqueous Systems.* Marcel Dekker, New York, 1970, Chapter 9.
49. (a) Cohen, S. G.; Parola, A.; Parsons, G. H. *Chem. Rev.* **1973**, *73*, 141. (b) Lewis, F. D.; Ho. T. *J. Am. Chem. Soc.* **1980**, *102*, 1751–1752.
50. Silverman, R. B.; Hoffman, S. J. & Catus, W. B., III *J. Am. Chem. Soc.* **1980**, *102*, 7126–7128.
51. (a) Simpson, J. T., Krantz, A., Lewis, F. D. & Kokel, B. *J. Am. Chem. Soc.* **1982**, *104*, 7155–7161. (b) Krantz, A.; Kokel, B.; Sachdeva, Y. P.; Salach, J.; Detmer, K.; Claesson, A.; Sahlberg, C. In *Monoamine Oxidase: Structure, Function, and Altered Functions*, Singer, T. P.; Von Korff, R. W.; Murphy, D. L., Eds. Academic Press, New York, 1979, p. 51.
52. Dinnocenzo, J. P.; Banach, T. E. *J. Am. Chem. Soc.* **1989**, *111*, 8646–8653.
53. (a) Husain, M.; Edmondson, D. E.; Singer, T. P. *Biochemistry* **1982**, *21*, 595–600. (b) Yu, P. H.; Bailey, B. A.; Durden, D. A.; Boulton, A. A. *Biochem. Pharmacol.* **1986**, *35*, 1027–1036.
54. Jencks, W. P. *Ádv. Enzymol. Relat. Areas Mol. Biol.* **1975**, *43*, 219–410.
55. Streitwieser, A., Jr. *Molecular Orbital Theory for Organic Chemists*. Wiley, New York, 1961, p. 185.
56. Tomilov, A. P.; Maironovskii, S. G.; Fioshin, M. Y.; Smirnov, V. A. *Electrochemistry of Organic Compounds*. Halsted Press, New York 1972, p. 69.
57. Bordwell, F. G.; Lynch, T.-Y. *J. Am. Chem. Soc.* **1989**, *111*, 7558–7562.
58. Tan, A.; Glantz, M. D.; Piette, L. H.; Yasunobu, K. T. *Biochem. Biophys. Res. Commun.* **1983**, *117*, 517–523.
59. Silverman, R. B. *Mechanism-Based Enzyme Inactivators: Chemistry and Enzymology*. CRC Press, Boca Raton, FL, 1988, Vol. I and II.
60. Silverman, R. B.; Hoffman, S. J. *J. Am. Chem. Soc.* **1980**, *102*, 884–886.
61. Silverman, R. B.; Hoffman, S. J.; Catus, W. B. III *J. Am. Chem. Soc.* **1980**, *102*, 7126–7128.
62. Silverman, R. B.; Hoffman, S. J. *Biochem. Biophys. Res. Commun.* **1981**, *101*, 1396–1401.
63. Maeda, Y.; Ingold, K. U. *J. Am. Chem. Soc.* **1980**, *102*. 328–331.
64. Silverman, R. B. *J. Biol. Chem.* **1983**, *258*, 14766–14769.

65. Paech, C.; Salach, J. I.; Singer, T. P. *J. Biol. Chem.* **1980**, *255*, 2700–2704.
66. (a) Nielsen, A. T.; Houlihan, W. J. *Org. React.* **1968**, *16*, 1–438. (b) Kim, J.-M.; Bogdan, M. A.; Mariano, P. S. *J. Am. Chem. Soc.* **1991**, *113*, 9251–9257.
67. Silverman, R. B.; Yamasaki, R. B. *Biochemistry* **1984**, *23*, 1322–1332.
68. Borch, R. F.; Bernstein, M. D.; Durst, H. D. *J. Am. Chem. Soc.* **1971**, *93*, 2897–2904.
69. Feeney, R. E.; Blankenhorn, G.; Dixon, H. B. F. *Adv. Prot. Chem.* **1975**, *29*, 135–203.
70. Lewis, F. D.; Correa, P. *J. Am. Chem. Soc.* **1981**, *103*, 7347–7349.
71. Silverman, R. B. *Biochemistry* **1984**, *23*, 5206–5213.
72. Jones, J. R. *The Ionisation of Carbon Acids.* Academic Press, London, 1973, p. 29.
73. Silverman, R. B.; Zieske, P. A. *Biochemistry* **1985**, *24*, 2128–2138.
74. Hassall, C. H. *Org. React.* **1957**, *9*, 73–106.
75. Bergmann, E. D. *Org. React.* **1959**, *10*, 179–555.
76. Silverman, R. B.; Zieske, P. A. *Biochem. Biophys. Res. Commun.* **1986**, *135*, 154–159.
77. Knight, A. R. In *The Chemistry of the Thiol Group;* Patai, S.; Ed.; Wiley, London, 1974, Part 1, pp. 455–479.
78. Pettit, G. R.; Van Tamelen, E. E. *Org. React.* **1962**, *12*, 356–529.
79. Danenberg, P. V.; Heidelberger, C. *Biochemistry* **1976**, *15*, 1331–1337.
80. Silverman, R. B.; Zieske, P. A. *J. Med. Chem.* **1985**, *28*, 1953–1957.
81. Nonhebel, D. C.; Walton, J. C. *Free Radical Chemistry.* Cambridge University Press, Cambridge, 1974, p. 106.
82. (a) Schuster, D. L.; Roberts, J. D. *J. Org. Chem.* **1962**, *27*, 51–53. (b) Brown, H. C.; Borkowski, J. *J. Am. Chem. Soc.* **1952**, *74*, 1894–1902. (c) Beckwith, A. L. J.; Ingold, K. U. In *Rearrangements in Ground and Excited States,* de Mayo, P., Ed. Academic Press, New York, 1980, Vol. 1, p. 161.
83. van Niel, J. C. G.; Pandit, U. K. *J. Chem. Soc., Chem. Commun.* **1983**, 149–150.
84. Newcomb. M.; Glenn, A. G. *J. Am. Chem. Soc.* **1989**, *111*, 275–277.
85. Wilt, J. W.; Maravetz, L. L.; Zawadzki, J. F. *J. Org. Chem.* **1966**, *31*, 3018–3025.
86. Menapace, L. W.; Kuivila, H. G. *J. Am. Chem. Soc.* **1964**, *86*, 3047–3051.
87. Tanner, D. D.; Rahimi, R. J. *J. Org. Chem.* **1979**, *44*, 1674–1677.
88. Beckwith, A. L. J. *Tetrahedron* **1981**, *37*, 3073–3100.
89. Yamasaki, R. B.; Silverman, R. B. *Biochemistry* **1985**, *24*, 6543–6550.
90. Kemppainen, A. E.; Thomas, M. J.; Wagner, P. J. *J. Org. Chem.* **1976**, *41*, 1294–1295.
91. Bondon, A.; Macdonald, T. L.; Harris, T. M.; Guengerich, F. P. *J. Biol. Chem.* **1989**, *264*, 1988–1997.
92. Yelekci, K.; Lu, X.; Silverman, R. B. *J. Am. Chem. Soc.* **1989**, *111*, 1138–1140.
93. (a) Krusic, P. J.; Kochi, J. K. *J. Am. Chem. Soc.* **1969**, *91*, 6161–6164. (b) Kawamura, T.; Kochi, J. K. *J. Am. Chem. Soc.* **1972**, *94*, 648–650.
94. Cooper, B. E.; Owen, W. J. *J. Organometal. Chem.* **1971**, *29*, 33–40.
95. (a) Brumfield, M. A.; Quillen, S. L.; Yoon, U. C.; Mariano, P. S. *J. Am. Chem. Soc.* **1984**, *106*, 6855–6856. (b) Lan, A. J. Y.; Quillen, S. L.; Heuckeroth, R. O.; Mariano, P. S. *J. Am. Chem. Soc.* **1984**, *106*, 6439–6440. (c) Ohga, K.; Yoon, Y. C.; Mariano, P. S. *J. Org. Chem.* **1984**, *49*, 213–219. (d) Chen, S. F.; Ullrich, J. W.; Mariano, P. S. *J. Am. Chem. Soc.* **1983**, *105*, 6160–6162.
96. Silverman, R. B.; Banik, G. M. *J. Am. Chem. Soc.* **1987**, *109*, 2219–2220.
97. Banik, G. M.; Silverman, R. B. *J. Am. Chem. Soc.* **1990**, *112*, 4499–4507.
98. Shirai, N.; Moriya, K.; Kawazoe, Y. *Tetrahedron* **1986**, *42*, 2211–2214.
99. Brook, A. G. *Acc. Chem. Res.* **1974**, *7*, 77–84.
100. (a) Hasegawa, E.; Xu, W.; Mariano, P. S.; Yoon, U.-C.; Kim, J.-U. *J. Am. Chem. Soc.* **1988**, *110*, 8099–8111. (b) Xu, W.; Jeon, Y. T.; Hasegawa, E.; Yoon, U. C.; Mariano, P. S. *J. Am. Chem. Soc.* 1989, *111*, 406–408.
101. Fleming, I. *Chem. Soc. Rev.* **1981**, *10*, 83–111.

102. Dostert, P.; Strolin Benedetti, M. & Jalfre, M. In *Monoamine Oxidase: Basic and Clinical Frontiers*, Kamujo, K., Ed. Excerpta Medica, Amsterdam, 1982, pp. 155–163.
103. Ancher, J. F. *Drugs Future* **1984**, *9*, 585–586.
104. Tipton, K. F.; Fowler, C. J.; McCrodden, J.; Strolin Benedetti, M. *Biochem. J.* **1983**, *209*, 235–242.
105. Gates, K. S.; Silverman, R. B. *J. Am. Chem. Soc.* **1990**, *112*, 9364–9372.
106. Walling, C.; Johnson, R. A. *J. Am. Chem. Soc.* **1975**, *97*, 2405–2407.
107. Gates, K. S.; Silverman, R. B. *J. Am. Chem. Soc.* **1989**, *111*, 8891–8895.
108. Strolin Benedetti, M.; Dow. J. *J. Pharm. Pharmacol.* **1983**, *35*, 238–245.
109. Dostert, P.; Strolin Benedetti, M.; Guffroy, C. *J. Pharm. Pharmacol.* **1983**, *35*, 161–165.
110. The mechanism proposed in Ref. 109 was oxidation of the amine to the imine by an unspecified pathway followed by attack of an active site nucleophile on the imine. The modified version shown in Scheme 34 takes into account previous evidence about the mechanism of the enzyme[32,33] and accounts for the decarboxylation pathway and the known aldehyde metabolite formation.
111. (a) Gambaryan, N. P.; Rokhlin, E. M.; Zeifman, Yu. V.; Chen, C.-Y.; Knunyants, I. L. *Angew Chem. Int. Ed. Engl.* **1966**, *5*, 947–956. (b) Luknitskii, F. I. *Chem. Rev.* **1975**, *75*, 259–289.
112. Weygand, F.; Steglich, W.; Tanner, H. *Liebig's Ann. Chem.* **1962**, *658*, 128–150.
113. Guest, A. W.; Milner, P. H.; Southgate, R. *Tetrahedron Lett.* **1989**, *30*, 5791–5794.
114. Withers, S. G.; Rupitz, K.; Street, I. P. *J. Biol. Chem.* **1988**, *263*, 7929–7932.
115. Cesura, A. M.; Galva, M. D.; Imhof, R.; Kyburz, E.; Picotti, G. B.; Da Prada, M. *Eur. J. Pharmacol.* **1989**, *162*, 457–465.
116. Cesura, A. M.; Imhof, R.; Takacs, B.; Galva, M. D.; Picotti, G. B.; Da Prada, M. *J. Neurochem.* **1988**, *50*, 1037–1043.
117. Da Prada, M.; Kettler, R.; Cesura, A. M.; Richards, J. G. *Pharmacol. Res. Commun.* **1988**, *20 (suppl. IV)*, 21–33.
118. Janssens de Varebeke, P.; Pauwels, G.; Buyse, C.; David-Remacle, M.; De Mey, J.; Roba, J.; Youdim, M. B. H. *J. Neurochem.* **1989**, *53*, 1109–1116.
119. Kjm, J.-M; Cho, I.-S; Mariano, P.S. *J. Org. Chem.* **1991**, *56*, 4943–4955.

PHOTOLYASE:
DNA REPAIR BY PHOTOINDUCED
ELECTRON TRANSFER

Aziz Sancar

Advances in Electron Transfer Chemistry,
Volume 2, pages 215–272
Copyright © 1992 by JAI Press Inc.
All rights of reproduction in any form reserved.
ISBN: 1-55938-168-X

1. INTRODUCTION

Solar UV (290-400 nm) has mutagenic, carcinogenic, and lethal effects and there is evidence that with the gradual depletion of the atmospheric zone these effects will have serious consequences for the biosphere.[1] The most significant cellular target of UV is DNA. The four DNA bases absorb at λ_{max} 250-270 mm and produce numerous UV photoproducts of both purines and pyrimidines.[2] The pyrimidine photoproducts which predominate include thymine and cytosine hydrates, thymine glycols, pyrimidine-pyrimidone[6-4] photoproducts, and pyrimidine dimers (pyrimidine cyclobutadipyrimidines). Pyrimidine dimers (Pyr<>Pyr) are by far the most abundant lesions. All organisms have special molecular mechanisms for eliminating the UV photoproducts from their DNA and thus preventing its harmful effects,[3,4] these are called DNA repair mechanisms.

One of the most interesting repair mechanisms is photoreactivation, which is operationally defined as the reversal of the effects of far UV (200-300 nm) irradiation by subsequent exposure to light of lower energy (350-500 nm). This seemingly paradoxical phenomenon was discovered by Kelner in 1949[5] and has been the subject of considerable interest to both physicists and biologists for a long time, and more recently to chemists. A major breakthrough in understanding this phenomenon was the restoration of the biological activity of UV-damaged DNA by a cell-free extract from *Escherichia coli* plus visible light.[6] This discovery and the subsequent discovery of the thymine dimer (T<>T) from

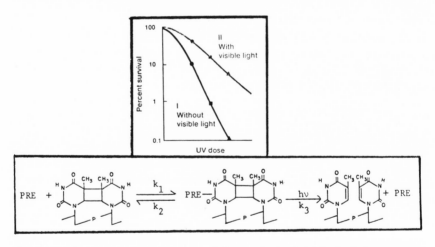

Figure 1. Photoreactivation. (*Top panel*) Shows the basic biological phenomenon: UV-irradiated cells are rescued from killing if they are exposed to visible light prior to growth. (*Bottom panel*) Shows the biochemical mechanism in outline which is responsible for this phenomenon. UV makes Pyr<>Pyr in DNA, photolyase (PRE, photoreactivating enzyme) binds to the photodimers and absorbs a near UV-visible photon, repairs dimer and dissociates from DNA.

irradiated ice of thymine solution[7,8] led to the following molecular model:[9,10] an enzyme, photoreactivating enzyme, DNA photolyase (DNA cyclobutane dipyrimidine photolyase, EC 4.1.99.3) binds to the *c,s*-pyrimidine dimer in DNA in a light-independent step, forms a stable enzyme-substrate complex ($t_{1/2}$ = 1-60 min depending on the source of the enzyme), this complex absorbs a photon which leads to photocycloreversion of the cyclobutane ring and regeneration[11,12] of the two constituent pyrimidines (Figure 1). This is the classic Michaelis-Menten scheme for enzyme catalysis with the notable exception that catalysis is light-initiated. The dependence of catalysis but not complex formation on light offers a great experimental advantage in studies on the enzyme by enabling the investigator to quantify binding or photolysis without the competing reactions by either carrying out the experiments under non-photoreactivating light ($\lambda > 500$ nm), or by using either enzyme or substrate excess such that the component under investigation is completely in the enzyme-substrate complex at the time of initiation of the photoreactivating treatment, either in the form of intense light flashes or continuous illumination.

2. PYRIMIDINE DIMERS

Pyrimidine dimers (cyclobutadipyrimidines) are formed upon irradiation of pyrimidines as bases, nucleosides or nucleotides, or in polynucloetides (DNA). Upon absorbing a photon (typically 254 nm from a germicidal lamp) a pyrimidine is excited to a singlet state which has a lifetime of $\sim 10^{-12}$ sec. This may undergo certain photochemical reactions or is converted to a triplet with a quantum yield of 1.2×10^{-1} to 4.7×10^{-4} depending on the type of pyrimidine.[2] With isolated bases and nucleotides the photodimers are formed almost exclusively from the triplet state while the singlet leads to formation of pyrimidine hydrates. This is to be expected as within the triplet lifetime ($\sim 10^{-5}$ sec) there is a reasonable probability of bimolecular collision essential for dimer formation while the singlet is so short lived ($\sim 10^{-12}$ sec) that it can only react with H_2O at a significant rate and thus only yields photohydrates. In contrast, dimer formation in di-and polynucleotides proceeds both from the singlet and triplet states as the proximity of the pyrimidines as a result of covalent attachment enables the excited pyrimidine to react with its neighbor within the lifetime of the singlet. For the same reason the dimerization reaction proceeds from both singlét and triplet states in frozen aqueous solutions where pyrimidine bases (Pyr) stack through "molecular aggregation-puddle formation."[2]

In addition to these direct mechanisms, Pyr<>Pyr formation may be accomplished through photosensitization with acetone, acetophenone, and benzophenone. These compounds yield triplets at high efficiency and therefore photosensitize for dimer formation via triplet-triplet energy transfer to pyrimidine bases. As a result, in photosensitized dimer formation in DNA, non-dimer photoproducts which are produced from the base singlets are avoided. For this reason photosensitization is frequently used in DNA photochemistry when the effects of pyrimidine dimers on structure and function of DNA are investigated independent of other photoproducts. Of the three photosensitizers listed, aceto-phenone is of special importance. This compound has a very high intersystem crossing efficiency ($\phi_{isc} \sim 1.0$) and therefore generates low-lying triplets in high yield. Furthermore, the acetophenone triplet lies above the triplet of thymine but below those of the other bases (Figure 2). As a result, in acetophenone photosen-sitized irradiation (313 nm) of DNA, thymine dimers (Thy) are formed nearly exclusively.

The silver ion, Ag^{1+} also promotes the formation of Pyr<>Pyr, especially Thy<>Thy to the exclusion of other photoproducts. However, the mechanism is totally different than that of acetophenone. Ag^{1+} is not a photosensitizer in the classic sense; the ion binds to DNA, preferentially at GC sequences but also complexes with A.T pairs at high enough concentrations. Upon irradiation of DNA with 254 nm it increases the rate of formation of Thy<>Thy by a factor of 20-30. It has a similar effect on the intensity of DNA phosphorescence and therefore, it appears that Ag^{1+} promotesThy<>Thy formation by the heavy atom effect on photochemical reactions, that is by facilitating intersystem cross-ing

$$\underset{0}{^1}Thy \xrightarrow{\quad h\nu \quad} \underset{1}{^1}Thy \xrightarrow[isc]{\quad Ag^{1+} \quad} \underset{1}{^3}Thy \qquad (1)$$

$$D^* + A \longrightarrow D + A^*$$

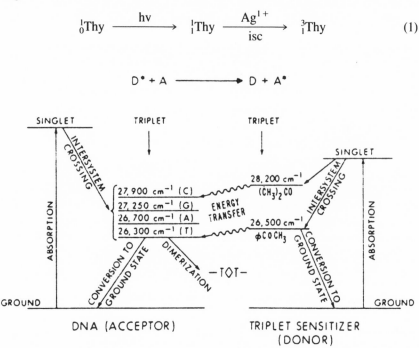

Figure 2. Jablonski diagram for C, G, A, T, and two photosensitizers, acetone and acetophenone. From Wang.[1]

This enhancement, in turn, means that even in DNA the quantum yield for dimer formation is 20-30-fold more efficient from the thy triplet compared to the singlet state. Table 1 summarizes the quantum yields for formation of Pyr<>Pyr under a variety of conditions and in a variety of forms.

Mechanistically, Pyr<>Pyr are formed through $[\pi_s + \pi_s]$ symmetry allowed-concerted photocycloaddition of an excited pyrimidine to a ground state homo- or hetero-pyrimidine.[13] Structurally, there are four types of pyrimidine dimers, T<>T, T<>C, C<>T, and C<>C. Each of these has four isomers, *cis-syn (c,s), trans-syn (t,s), cis-anti (c,a)* and *trans-anti (t,a)*. The structures of these stereoisomers are shown in Figure 3 for Thy<>Thy, which is the predominant pyrimidine photodimer in DNA under most irradiation conditions. Of the four isomers only *c,s* is formed in double-stranded DNA, and in single-stranded DNA *c,s*, and *t,s*, are formed in 7:1 ratio.[2] The other isomers never form in DNA for steric reasons and are isolated only from the irradiated solutions of free bases or nucleotides and are therefore biologically not relevant. Thymine dimers of all compositions and of all stereoisomeric forms do not absorb significantly at $\lambda > 250$ nm as a result of saturation of the 5,6-double bond which is responsible for the 250-270 nm peak typical of DNA bases (Figure 4).

The structure of the *c,s*-thymine dimer has been solved at the base[14] and nucleoside level[15,16] by X-ray crystallography. However, crystallographic data on

Table 1. Quantum Yields for Formation and Photoreversal of Pyr<>Pyr[a]

Compound	Solvent	Quantum Yield[b]	
		Formation	Photoreversal
Thy[c]	H_2O	4.7×10^{-4}	1.0 (280 nm)
Thd[c]	H_2O	5.6×10^{-4}	—
TMP[c]	H_2O	1.0×10^{-4}	—
Ura[c]	H_2O	5×10^{-3}	—
Cyt[c]	H_2O	5×10^{-3}	—
Thy	Ice	2.3×10^{-1}	1.0 (280 nm)
Thd	Ice	1.6×10^{-1}	—
TMP	Ice	3×10^{-3}	—
Ura	Ice	5×10^{-3}	—
Urd	Ice	1.9×10^{-3}	—
UMP	Ice	2.2×10^{-3}	—
TpT	H_2O	1×10^{-2}	—
TpT	Poly (T)	3×10^{-2}	—
TpT	DNA	2×10^{-2}	0.65
TpC (CpT)[d]	DNA	2.2×10^{-3}	—
CpC	DNA	1×10^{-3}	0.15 (265 nm)
TpT	DNA (Ag^{1+})[e]	0.6	—
TpT	DNA (Acϕ)[f]	8×10^{-2} (313 nm)	—

[a] Compiled from Wang[2]. [b] Unless stated otherwise the wavelength is 254 nm. [c] The quantum yields are for 1×10^{-4} M solutions in H_2O. [d] These are isolated as U<>C photodimers. [e] At Ag^{1+} to nucleotide ratio of $r = 1$. [f] At Acetophenone concentration of 10^{-2} M under anaerobic conditions.

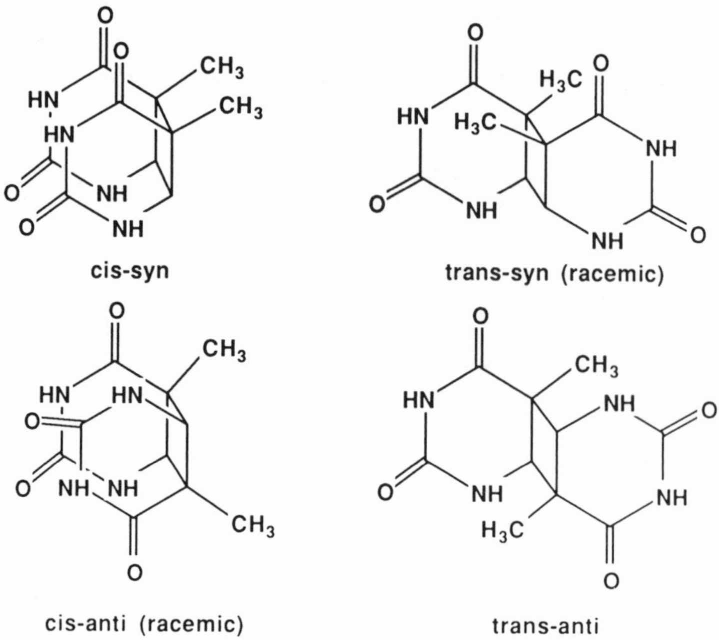

cis-syn   trans-syn (racemic)

cis-anti (racemic)   trans-anti

Figure 3. The four isomers of Pyr<>Pyr. Only c,s-Pyr<>Pyr is formed in dsDNA and in ssDNA the c,s- and t,s-isomers are formed in 7:1 ratio. The other isomers are formed only upon irradiating free bases or nucleotides. Note that both NMR (20) and X-ray crystallographic[15,16] data show that the cyclobutane ring of c,s-T<>T has a puckered conformation causing the bases to be twisted in a right-handed fashion in a B-DNA according to NMR analysis and twisted in a left-handed fashion according to X-ray structure.

an oligonucleotide containing a dimer is not available for lack of suitable crystals. Instead, the effects of a c,s-T<>T on the structure of DNA duplex has been investigated by three alternative methods:

1. Two molecular mechanics studies arrived at essentially opposite conclusions regarding the effect of c,s-T<>T on DNA structure. Rao and Kollman[17] concluded that there was essentially no change in the helical parameters while Pearlman et al.[18] predicted a 27° kink into the major groove at the dimer site.
2. NMR studies by Kemmink et al.,[19] and by Taylor et al,[20] arrived at essentially the same conclusion—the c,s-T<>T causes little perturbation in the helical axis, weakens but does not break the H-bonds of dimerized thymines and causes minor changes in chemical shift, more pronounced on the 3′ side rather than the 5′ side of the dimer. Taylor et al.[20] also

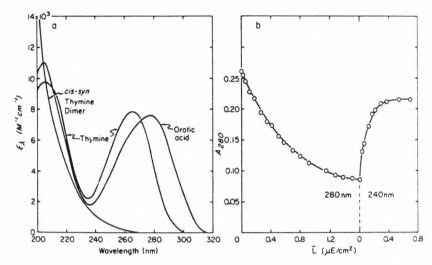

Figure 4. Absorption Spectra of Pyr<>Pyr. (**a**) Absorption spectra of Oro, Thy, and c,s-Thy<>Thy in aqueous solutions. (**b**) Formation of Oro<>Oro with 280 nm followed reversal to a new photosteady state with 240 nm. From Wang.[1]

concluded from NOE data that the cyclobutane ring of the dimer in the DNA duplex was puckered such that the two thymine rings were twisted in a right-handed fashion as are the other DNA bases. This is in contrast to the conformation in the crystal of isolated c,s,-T<>T, where the thymines are twisted in a left-handed fashion.[16] The results are not necessarily contradictory and it has been suggested[20] that they simply mean that the photodimer is conformationally flexible and that the exact conformation is determined by other constraints imposed on the dimer by covalent or packing interactions.

3. Biochemical probes of various kinds, in contrast to the NMR studies, tend to suggest a greater helical deformity is induced by c,s,-T<>T. Hayes et al.[21] from melting temperature studies concluded that c,s-T<>T disrupted the H-bonds of the two thymines in the dimer plus those of two additional base pairs, for a total of four. Ciarrocchi and Pedrini[22] titrated the number of superhelical turns in circular DNA as a function of photodimers in the DNA and concluded that a c,s-T<>T unwinds DNA by about 14°. Husain et al.[23] analyzed the electrophorotic migration of, and the circularization behavior of DNA fragments containing c,s-T<>T in which the photodimers were separated by 32 basepairs and were therefore in phase with the helix screw axis (~3 turns apart) and concluded that a c,s-T<>T bends the DNA duplex by 29°, possibly into the major groove.

It is quite likely that the effect of c,s-T<>T on the overall helix structure is influenced by the neighboring sequences, which may explain some of the discrepancies between the results obtained by these various methods.

3. PHOTOLYASES

Photolyases are enzymes which convert light energy into chemical energy to repair pyrimidine photodimers. All photolyases characterized to date contain two chromophore-cofactors (Figure 5). One is 1,5-dihydroflavin adenine dinucleotide, $FADH_2$[24,27] and the other so-called second chromophore (28) is either methenyltetrahydrofolate, MTHF[29] or 8-hydroxy-5-deazaflavin, 8-HDF.[26,30,31] Accordingly the enzymes have been classified into two groups: (1) the folate class which has its action spectrum maximum at 360-390 nm includes enzymes from *Escherichia coli* and *Saccharomyces cerevisiae,* and; (2) the deazaflavin class which has its action spectrum maximum at 430-460 nm and includes photolyases from *Anacystis nidulans, Streptomyces griseus, Scendesmus acutus, Halobacterium balobium, Methanobacterium thermoautotrophicum.* Although no spectroscopic data are available on photolyases from other sources, photoreactivation action spectra either in vivo or in crude cell-free in vitro systems reveal maxima either at 360-390 nm or 430-460 nm range[1] suggesting that they belong either to the folate or the deazaflavin class. Evolutionarily, photolyases are found in members of all three kingdoms. However, certain species of all three kingdoms lack the enzyme. Thus, of the prokaryota, *E. coli* has photolyase while *Hoemophilus influenzae* does not;[6] of the archaebacteria, *M. thermoautotrophicum* has photolyase while *Methanococcus vannielii* does not;[32] and of the eukaryota, while marsupials are rich in photolyase,[33] mammals including humans do not have the enzyme.[34]

3.1. Structural Properties

Photolyases are monomeric proteins of $M_r = 50,000\text{-}60,000$. Although no X-ray structure is available for any of the enzymes as yet, the genes for the apoenzymes of members of both classes have been cloned and sequenced.[35-40] The sequences reveal a remarkable 30% homology between enzymes from the three kingdoms, the prokaryotes, the archaebacteria, and the eukaryotes. Interestingly, the carboxy-terminal region is conserved among enzymes from both classes while certain stretches in the amino-terminal half are conserved only among members of each class. This observation has led to the proposal that the amino terminal half of the proteins bind the second chromophore (MTHF or 8-HDF) and that the carboxy-terminal half contains the flavin and DNA binding sites. In support of this Li and Sancar[41] found that a Trp ———→Arg (residue 277) change at the carboxy terminal half of *E. coli* photolyase reduced the specific binding of the enzyme by about 10^3 without affecting its spectroscopic or

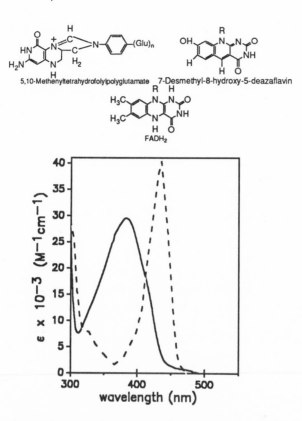

5,10-Methenyltetrahydrofolylpolyglutamate   7-Desmethyl-8-hydroxy-5-deazaflavin

FADH₂

Figure 5. Chromophores and Near-UV Absorption Spectra of Two Classes of Photolyase. Folate class (MTHF + FADH₂), *solid line;* deazaflavin class (8-HDF + FADH₂), *broken line.* The spectra are those of *E. coli* and *M. thermoautotrophicum* photolyases as representatives of the folate and deazaflavin class enzymes, respectively.

photochemical properties. Similarly, Malhotra et al.[42] have isolated a 30 kDa proteolytic fragment carrying the amino-terminal half of yeast photolyase and found that this fragment contains the folate cofactor but has lost its affinity to DNA. Some of the most important biochemical properties of two representative photolyases from each class are summarized in Table 2.

The structures of the chromophores of the folate class photolyases are shown in Figure 6. Note that the native enzymes of this class have reduced flavin but enzymes with all three oxidation states of this cofactor may be obtained during purification. Thus, yellow, blue and green enzymes may be obtained depending on the source of the enzyme and the conditions of purification. The folate cofactor contains three glutamates in γ-linkages, and three glutamates in α-linkage in *E. coli* photolyase. The α-linked glutamates are unique to *E. coli* folates. Therefore, photolyases from other sources are expected to have only the γ-linked

Table 2. Physical and Photochemical Properties of Photolyases

	Photolyase			
	E. Coli	S. cerevisiae	A. nidulans	M. thermoauto
Kingdom	Prokaryote	Eukaryote	Prokaryote	Archaebacterium
Class	Folate	Folate	Deazaflavin	Deazaflavin
Mr	53,994	66,189	54,475	55,000
Subunit	Monomer	Monomer	Monomer	Monomer
Cofactors	$FADH_2$ + MTHF	$FADH_2$ + MTHF	$FADH_2$ + 8 − HDF	$FADH_2$ + 8 − HDF
λ_{max}	384 (480, 580,635)[a]	377	440	440
ϵ_{max}	29,500	27,800	53,000	40,000
Color	Yellow/Blue[a]	Yellow	Yellow/Blue[a]	Yellow/Blue[a]
K_D (M)	$10^{-8} - 10^{-9}$	10^{-8}	10^{-8}	$10^{-10} \times 10^{-11}$
$t_{1/2}$ (min)[b]	1.0	0.5	1.0	43
k_p (mm^{2}erg^{-1})	1×10^{-3}	9.8×10^{-4}	1.1×10^{-3}	1.5×10^{-3}
k_{cat} (min^{-1})[c]	25	12	12	9[d]
Quantum Yield	0.6	0.5	1.0	0.4

[a] The physiological form of *E. coli* photolyase contains $FADH_2$ and therefore, the enzyme is pale yellow in color. However, during purification the flavin is converted to the neutral blue radical form, FADH°, which is responsible for the additional peaks at 480, 580, and 625 nm. [b] This is the half-life of the ES complex in the dark. [c] k_{cat} is dependent on light intensity; these values are obtained at near-saturating intensity and therefore, to a large extent, reflect the rate of the dissociation of the enzyme from repaired DNA. [d] It was later realized that the enzyme used in this measurement was only 10–50% pure; therefore, the actual k_{cat} is more likely 50-500 min^{-1}.

glutamates in their folate cofactor, unless they are overproduced in an *E. coli* host.[29]

3.2. Spectroscopic Properties

Both classes of photolyases have distinctive colors in their native states, the folate class enzymes have a pale yellow color[24,25,43] while the deazaflavin class photolyases have strong yellow color because of higher extinction coefficients. Enzymes from both classes turn blue during purification due to oxidation of flavin to the semiquinone form.

The Folate Class

The absorption and fluorescence spectra of *E. coli* photolyase as a representative of the folate class are summarized in the following.

Absorption Spectra. The absorption spectra of the various forms of *E. coli* photolyase are shown in Figure 7. The native form of the enzyme contains one mole of MTHF and one mole of $FADH_2$ per mole of apoenzyme and its absorption spectrum (Figure 7C) is characterized by a peak at 280 nm mainly due to aromatic residues of the apoenzyme and a peak at 384 nm ($\epsilon = 29.5 \times 10^3$) typical of enzyme-bound MTHF.[29] The spectrum in Figure 7C was actually

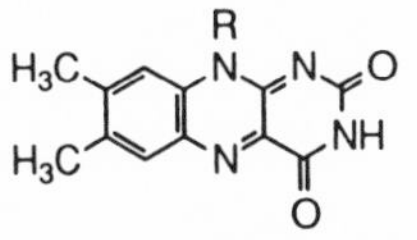

FAD$_{ox}$

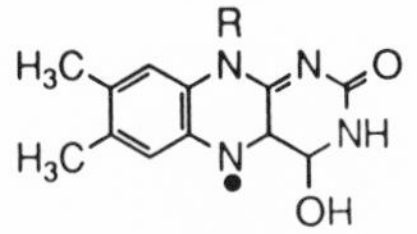

FADH$^{\bullet}$

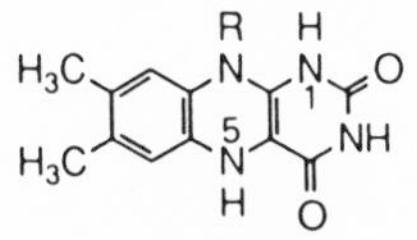

FADH$_2$

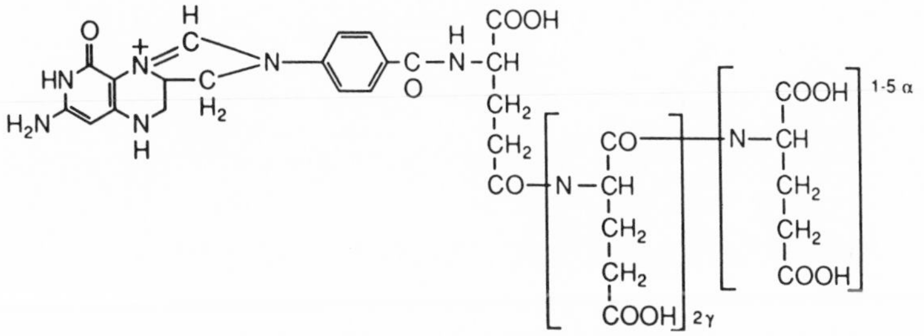

5,10-Methenyltetrahydrofolylpolyglutamate

Figure 6. Structures of *E. coli* photolyase chromophores. The native enzyme contains FADH$_2$ which may become one- or two-electron oxidized during purification. The MTHF chromophore contains three glutamates in γ-linkage followed by one or more in α-linkage.

recorded after photoreduction of flavin to FADH$_2$[44] as this cofactor becomes oxidized to the flavin semiquinone during purification.[28,45] Therefore, the purified *E. coli* photolyase has additional absorption peaks at 480, 580, and 625 nm (Figure 7A) and also has a blue color typical of neutral flavin semiquinone. During purification the enzyme also tends to lose its folate cofactor; a typical purification scheme yielding pure enzyme results in 50-70% loss of the folate chromophore.[46] The rest of the folate can be easily removed by photodecomposition:[47] exposure to intense light (250-400 nm) results in quantitative conversion of MTHF into degradation products which no longer absorb in the near-UV or

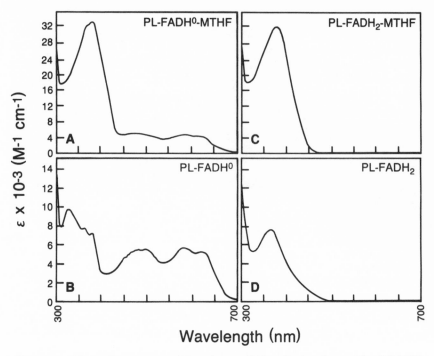

Figure 7. Absorption spectra of four forms of *E. coli* photolyase. The E-FADH$_2$-MTHF form is the physiological species which is converted to the catalytically inert E-FADH°-MTHF during purification. The E-FADH$_2$ form is obtained by photoreduction of flavin and decomposition of folate while the E-FADH° form is produced by selective removal of folate from E-FADH°-MTHF by borohydride treatment or by exposing the E-FADH$_2$ form to air oxidation.

bind to the enzyme. In the presence of reducing agents during irradiation the photodecomposition of MTHF is accompanied with photoreduction of FADH° to FADH$_2$ to yield the E-FADH$_2$ form of the enzyme with its typical absorption spectrum shown in Figure 7D (ε_{366} = 5680). Upon exposure to air the flavin reoxidizes to the semiquinone form to yield the E-FADH° form of the enzyme with the absorption spectrum shown in Figure 7B.

In addition to these photochemical methods the status of the chromophores can be affected by chemical methods: dithionite reduces FADH° to FADH$_2$ without affecting the folate and cyanoborohydride converts MTHF to 5,10-methyl-enetetrahydrofolate and 5-methyltetrahydrofolate (both of which are released from the enzyme) without affecting the FADH° cofactor.[46,48] The MTHF in native enzyme contains 3-6 glutamate residues.[29] Although the polyglutamate form of the cofactor binds to the enzyme with higher affinity even the monoglutamate form binds sufficiently tightly to allow the purification of this form of the enzyme.[49] Upon dilution to nanomolor concentrations, however, the MTHF chromophore falls off the enzyme rapidly at a rate inversely proportional to the length of the polyglutamate tail.[49] Free MTHF has $\lambda_{max} = 355$ nm ($\varepsilon = 25,000$) and is unstable at neutral pH. Upon binding to enzyme there is a red shift and it becomes stable.

The only other photolyase of the folate class that has been characterized spectroscopically is the *S. cerevisiae* (yeast) enzyme. The spectral properties of this enzyme are very similar to those of the physiological form of *E. coli* photolyase except that the absorption peak is at 377 nm ($\varepsilon \sim 29,000$). In addition, this enzyme is more tightly bound to both chromophores. Therefore, the purified enzyme contains shoichiometric amounts of both cofactors.[43,46] Furthermore, the $FADH_2$ cofactor is quite stable to air oxidation and is converted to the semiquinone form only upon prolonged exposure to air[43] and the folate chromophore is completely resistant to photodecomposition.[50]

Fluorescence Spectra. The $FADH_2$ cofactor is only weakly fluorescent and the $FADH°$ flavosemiquinone is non-fluorescent. Therefore the fluorescence properties of the *E. coli* and yeast photolyases are essentially those of enzyme-bound MTHF. Figure 8 (left panel) shows the excitation and emission spectra of E-$FADH_2$-MTHF form of *E. coli* photolyase; the excitation spectrum matches the absorption spectrum of the enzyme-bound MTHF with $\lambda_{max} \sim 384$ nm and the emission spectrum shows a peak at 480 nm. In high resolution spectra such as

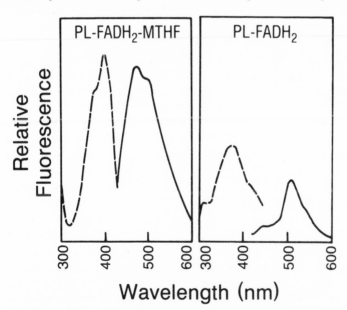

Figure 8. Fluorescence excitation and emission spectra of E-$FADH_2$-MTHF and E-$FADH_2$ forms of *E.coli* photolyase. *Broken line,* Excitation; *solid line,* emission. The fluorescence emission is mainly that of folate in the E-$FADH_2$-MTHF form. The heights of the emission peaks are approximately proportional to the relative intensities of the fluorescence of the two forms.

this a 505 nm shoulder due to $FADH_2$ fluorescence is also observed. The E-FADH°-MTHF form of the enzyme has essentially the same fluoremetric properties except the fluorescence intensity is lower due to higher efficiency of energy transfer from folate to FADH° as compared to $FADH_2$. The flavin fluorescence of the enzyme can be directly observed after depletion of the folate either photochemically or by treatment with cyanoborohydride followed by photoreduction of flavin. Figure 8 (right panel) shows the fluorescence excitation and emission spectra of the E-$FADH_2$ form of *E. coli* photolyase. The excition spectrum follows the absorption spectrum of enzyme-bound $FADH_2$ with a peak at 366 nm and the emission spectrum has a peak at 505 nm typical of fluorescence emission of enzyme-bound flavins.[51] The luminescence properties of yeast photolyase are very similar to the *E. coli* enzyme except the excitation and emission maxima of the holoenzyme are blue-shifted by 5-10 nm compared to those of the *E. coli* photolyase.[43]

Spectral Properties of the Free Chromophores. When the folate class photolyases are denatured at neutral pH the MTHF chromophore is rapidly converted to 5,10-methylenetetrahydrofolate (λ_{max} = 295 nm) resulting in the disappearance of the characteristic blue emission of the folate chromophore.[24,28,43,46] Instead, the near-UV spectrum is dominated by the flavin cofactor which becomes fully oxidized upon release from the enzyme. As a consequence, denatured enzyme yields typical FAD_{ox} absorption and fluorescence spectral properties, absorption and excitation maxima at 375 and 450 nm and an emission peak at 520 nm. However, long-term incubation of the denatured enzyme at room temperature or treatment of the denatured material with a solution of 1% I_2 + 2% KI generates oxidized pterin with its characteristic spectroscopic properties: an absorption and excitation maximum at 365 nm and an emission maximum at 455 nm. If, however, the enzyme is denatured at pH 2 where 5,10-CH^+-H_4 Folate is stable the released chromophore retains its spectral characteristics with an absorption maximum at 360 nm and an emission maximum at 460 nm.[29]

EPR Spectrum. The $FADH_2$ cofactor of *E. coli* photolyase is oxidized to the flavin semiquinone during purification.[45] The purified enzyme yields an EPR spectrum characteristic of flavin neutral radicals with ΔG = 19 Guass and g = 2.0039 (Figure 9). Flavin radical has also been observed in *S. cerevisiae* photolyase with the same properties. In addition *A. nidulans*[27] and *M. thermoautotrophicum* photolyases[31] appear to contain FADH° and are expected to be paramagnetic as well. During photoreduction of photolyase a transient trp neutral radical is produced which can be detected by time-resolved EPR spectroscopy.[52]

The Deazaflavin Class

The absorption spectra of deazaflavin class enzymes is characterized by an absorption peak at 280 nm ($\varepsilon \sim$ 100,000) mostly due to aromatic residues of the

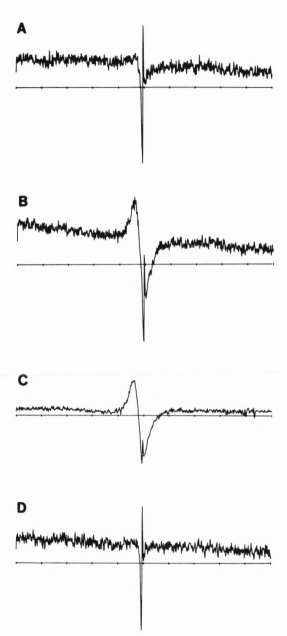

Figure 9. Electron paramagnetic resonance spectra of *E. coli* photolyase. Spectra were recorded at various stages of purification on enzyme samples containing nearly identical concentrations of photolyase. (**A**) Cell-free extract; (**B**) Ammonium sulfate precipitate redissolved; (**C**) Blue-sepharose peak fraction (>95% pure); (**D**) Buffer. From Payne et al.[45]

polypeptide and a visible absorption peak at 440 nm (ε = 53,000) contributed by the enzyme bound 8-hydroxy-5-deazaflavin (oxidized) chromophore. All indications are that the enzyme-bound 8-HDF is in the (two electron) oxidized state. This has important mechanistic implications in considering whether or not deazaflavin functions as a photoantenna or as the redox active center of this class of photolyases. In free form 5-deazaflavins have a strong absorption (ε ~ 45,000) at 420 nm while the reduced forms have a λ_{max} = 320 nm and ε ~ 11,000.[53,54] The near-UV extinction coefficients of deazaflavin class photolyases have been reported to be ε_{440} = 40,000-50,000[26,27,31,55] which could be attributed to oxidized 5-deazaflavin in an apolar environment; thus, both the magnitude and the position of the absorption peak excludes reduced deazaflavin in as a cofactor.

All deazaflavin class enzymes analyzed also contain flavin adenine dinucleotide.[26,27,31,56] However, the spectroscopic signs of this cofactor are not immediately obvious and this may have been a contributing factor to the fact that even though the 8-HDF chromophore in this class was identified in 1981[30] the presence of the flavin cofactor was not realized until 1988.[26] The main problem in this identification is that the ε_{max} of the deazaflavin is so high (ε_{440} = 40,000-50,000) that even though it is far enough removed from that of a potential peak in the 350-400 nm region of enzyme-bound FADH$_2$, the "tail absorptions" of the apoenzyme (ε_{280} = 1.2 × 10^5) and of 8-HDF (ε_{440} = 4.4 × 10^4) makes it impossible to observe a clearly defined peak of ε ~ 5 × 10^3 at λ = 350-400 nm, typical values for enzyme-bound reduced flavins. Furthermore, upon denaturation both 8-HDF and FAD$_{ox}$ are released, but again both the absorbance and the fluorescence of the flavin are obscured by the strongly fluorescent deazaflavin. Nevertheless, in high resolution spectra a "shoulder" is seen at λ ~ 370 nm of the absorption spectrum, which is attributable to the absorption of the FADH$_2$ cofactor.[31] Furthermore, the absorption spectra of photolyases from both *M. thermoautotrophicum*[31,50] and *A. nidulans* (27) show significant absorption in the λ = 500-700 nm region. High resolution analysis of this region in the *A. nidulans* photolyase revealed a typical flavin neutral radical spectrum with peaks at 580 and 625 nm. It was estimated that the FAD chromophore in the *A. nidulans* photolyase was almost quantitatively in the blue radical form[27] whereas a smaller fraction of this cofactor appears to be oxidized to the semiquinone form in the photolyase from *M. thermoautotrophicum*.[31] Thus, it appears that the FADH$_2$ cofactor tends to be oxidized to the flavosemiquinone in the deazaflavin class as well.

The absorption and fluorescence spectra of *M. thermoautotrophicum* photolyase as a representative of the deazaflavin class are shown in Figure 10. The fluorescence excitation and emission maxima of 420 and 460 nm, respectively, correspond to those of free 5-deazaflavin. It has, therefore, been suggested that enzyme-bound 8-HDF is weakly fluorescent or not fluorescent at all, and that the fluorescence observed with these enzymes is entirely due to low level of the strongly fluorescent free 8-HDF contamination of the enzyme preparations.[27,30]

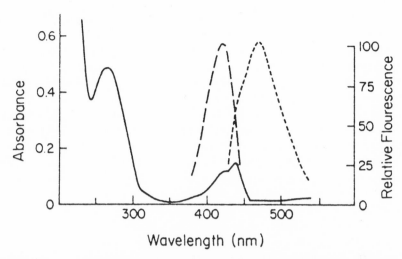

Figure 10. Spectroscopic properties of a deazaflavin class photolyase. Absorption and fluorescence excitation and emission spectra of *M. thermoautotrophicum* photolyase. The λ_{max} is at 440 nm and $\varepsilon \sim 40,000$. The structured absorption at $\lambda > 500$ nm is due to the contribution of FADH° which constitutes about 50% of total FAD content in this particular preparation. It is not clear whether the luminescence spectra are those of enzyme-bound 8-HDF as the enzyme preparation contained an unknown amount of free 5-deazaflavin cofactor. From Kiener et al.[31]

The excitation and emission spectra of denatured enzyme are typical for 8-HDF ($\lambda_{max} = 420$ nm and $\lambda_{em} = 460$ nm). However, upon addition of venom phosphodiesterase to denatured *A. nidulans* photolyase the fluorescence emission peak shifted from 460 nm to 520 nm as a result of conversion of FAD to the much more fluorescent FMN by the phosphodiesterase.[27] Thus the spectroscopic data are consistent with the notion that the deazaflavin class contains 8-HDF in oxidized form and FAD in fully reduced semiquinone form.

4. SUBSTRATE RECOGNITION

Photolyases bind to *c,s*-Pyr<>Pyr in DNA. Theoretically and experimentally the substrate may be considered to have two structural determinants, the unique DNA structure in the immediate vicinity of the photodimer, and the *c,s*-Pyr<>Pyr.

4.1. DNA Recognition

UV irradiation of an *E. coli* cell, which contains 20 photolyase molecules, produces 20 dimers per genome. Using the millisecond flash photolysis technique,[57-68] Harm reported[61] that 10 of the dimers could be repaired with a single light flash, indicating about 10 enzyme-substrate complexes were present at equilibrium. If it is assumed that the remaining ten photolyase molecules were bound non-specifically and that the photolyase binding site covers four nucleotides,[69] then the minimum value for the specificity of photolyase binding (defined as the ratio of specific to non-specific binding constants) is $8 \times 10^6/4 \times 10 = 2 \times 10^5$ (assuming that each of the 8×10^6 nucleotides in the $E.$ $coli$ chromosome constitutes the beginning of a potential non-specific binding site).[70] This level of substrate specificity is nearly optimal for the functioning of DNA binding proteins with a few specific binding sites in the entire chromosome[71] and thermodynamically can be achieved by two different paths: either the binding protein to DNA non-specifically (ionic interactions with phosphates) with high affinity, with additional interactions with the specific site which add to the free energy by about 7-8 kcal, or the binding protein has very little affinity for non-specific DNA and the free energy of binding is mostly due to the unique interactions at the specific site. While most specific DNA binding proteins such as RNA polymerase, repressors, restriction endonucleases fall into the first class[71] thermodynamic and kinetic measurements indicate that $E.$ $coli$ photolyase and perhaps all other photolyases fall into the second category.

The Thermodynamic and Kinetic Parameters

The thermodynamic and kinetic parameters for enzyme-substrate interaction for $E.$ $coli$ DNA photolyase are shown in Table 3. The specific DNA binding constant $K_s = 10^8 - 10^9$ M^{-1} is low compared to other DNA binding proteins such as the $E.$ $coli$ lac repressor ($K_s \sim 10^{12} - 10^{13}$ M^{-1}). However, the non-specific binding constant is proportionally low ($K_{NS} = 10^3 - 10^4$ M^{-1} for photolyase, and $K_{NS} = 10^7 - 10^8$ M^{-1} for lac repressor) suggesting that photolyase makes very few ionic bonds (the main source of non-specific binding energy) with the phosphate backbone of the DNA. Indeed, when the number of ion pairs formed between photolyase and DNA was determined by measuring the binding constant as a function of ionic strength[72,73] it was found that photolyase makes only two salt bridges with the phosphate backbone and as a consequence only about 10% of the free energy of binding comes from ionic interactions.[74-76] This is in contrast with the lac repressor where more than 50% of the binding free energy is due to ionic interactions.

The nature of molecular interactions responsible for the binding free energy also influences the kinetics of the binding reaction. When a protein makes many ionic contacts upon binding DNA specifically the same charged groups partly responsible for specific binding interact with non-specific DNA as well. Therefore, these proteins have high affinity for non-target DNA and spend most of their time associated with DNA. As a consequence, these proteins find their target site on DNA essentially by unidimensional diffusion and therefore, their

Table 3. Reaction Constants for Binding of Photolyase to DNA[a]

Method	K_A (M^{-1})	K_N (M^{-1})	k_1 (M^{-1}s^{-1})	k_2 (s^{-1})
Flash photolysis	4.7×10^7	—	$1.4-4 \times 10^6$	3×10^{-2} (fast) 6×10^{-4} (slow)
Filter binding	6×10^7	—	ND	ND
Gel retardation	2.6×10^8	4×10^3	ND	4.4×10^{-2} (fast) 3.55×10^{-4} (slow)
Kinetic (k_1/k_2)	9.4×10^7	—	NA	NA
In vivo (flash)	1×10^8	$\leq 10^3$	1.1×10^6	1.3×10^{-2} (fast) 6×10^{-4} (slow)

[a] After Husain and Sancar;[78] K_A = specific binding constant; K_N = non-specific binding constant; ND, not determined; NA, not applicable.

rate of association with the specific site on DNA is much more rapid than would be predicted from Smoluchovski equation for a diffusion controlled bimolecular reaction. This has indeed been found to be the case for the *lac* repressor.[71] In contrast, the association rate constant for *E. coli* photolyase (1.4×10^6 M^{-1}s^{-1}) is well within the limit of 3-D diffusion and consistent with the fact that this enzyme makes only two ionic bonds with the DNA substrate.[74] Similar values have been found for *S. griseus, S. cerevisine,* and *M. Thermoautotrophicum* photolyases (see. Ref. 77) and it is safe to assume that photolyases make no use in reduced dimentionality to find their target. Notwithstanding claims to the contrary, it is highly questionable that target location on DNA by diffusion in reduced dimensionality has any evolutionary significance. The two modes of target location most likely represent two convergent ways of accomplishing the same goal, that of achieving optimal specificity and nothing more.

The dissociation rate constants for photolyases have two interesting features. First, they range from 5×10^{-1} for *S. griseus*[55] to 5×10^{-2} for *E. coli*[74] to 2.5 $\times 10^{-4}$ for *M. thermoautotrophicum*[31] and since the association rate constants are quite similar, the dissociation rates largely determines the differences between the equilibrium constants of all photolyases. Thus, *M. thermoautotrophicum* has the highest binding constant of all photolyases, reported to date, $K_A \sim$ 10^{10} M^{-1}. Second, in all cases investigated the dissociation rate constant is biphasic, a fast component (the values listed above) for the 75-85% of the complexes and a slow component for the remaining fraction. Originally, this biphasic kinetics was attributed to the heterogeneous nature of the substrate, heterogeneity stemming from the facts that UV-irradiated DNA contains cyclobutane dimers of TT, TC, CT, and CC dipyrimidines in various sequence contexts.[62,74] However, the same type of k_2 heterogeneity and to the same extent was also observed with a uniform substrate, a 43-mer DNA duplex containing a centrally located T<>T.[78] With this substrate it was found that 85% of the enzyme-substrate complexes dissociated rapidly with a half-life of 30 seconds while the rest dissociated with a half-life of 30 minutes. Thus it appears that two apparently homogeneous components (photolyase and the 43-mer with T<>T) make at least two different classes of complexes or that the two components make a homogeneous complex that dissociates by at least two separate pathways. Factors which may contribute to heterogeneity in the enzyme such as different amounts of folate chromophore or different redox states of the flavin cofactor were eliminated as possible explanations and it was concluded that the heterogeneity resulted from other factors such as "partially unfolded enzyme" or partially non B-form DNA.[78]

Effect of Primary and Secondary Structures

In vivo studies in *E. coli* revealed that T<>T is repaired twice as fast as T<>C (C<>T) which is repaired twice as fast as C<>C.[79] It was not clear from these studies, however, whether this hierarchy was due to differential binding or differential photolyasis or both. Myles et al.[80] found that both factors contributed to the poor repairability of cytosine containing dimers and by analyzing the repair of individual Pyr<>Pyr in a DNA fragment of a defined sequence concluded that certain C<>C especially in GC rich (rigid) regions of DNA fragment of a defined sequence were poorly bound and poorly photolyzed. In contrast to such a drastic effect of the type of dimer on binding, there was no significant effect of the neighboring sequences on binding to a *c,s*-,T<>T.[81] Perhaps more significantly, *E. coli* photolyase bound to Pyr<>Pyr in double and single-stranded DNA with the same affinity.[74] This unique property of photolyase among all known specific DNA binding proteins, implies that all the important binding determinants of the substrate are on the dimer-containing strand. This has indeed been found to be the case by molecular probes of the enzyme-substrate interaction (see below).

Effect of Chromophores on Binding

E. coli photolyase can be prepared in various forms;[82] apoenzyme, holoenzyme (E-FADH$_2$-MTHF), or enzyme containing one or the other of the two chromophores. In addition, the MTHF may contain glu residues ranging from one to six, and the flavin cofactor may be fully oxidized (FAD), flavosemiquinone (FADH °) of fully]educed (FADH$_2$). Considering the high]efficiency of energy and electron transfer mediated by these chromophore-cofactors it is reasonable to assume that the cofactors may be in intimate contact with the substrate and therefore have profound effect on binding. This is indeed the case for the flavin cofactor as neither apoenzyme nor E-MTHF bind substrate[50] suggesting that FAD helps in forming the substrate binding pocket perhaps by direct contact with Pyr<>Pyr in the form of van der Waals interaction and

H-bonding. Interestingly, 5-deazaFAD which is photochemically inert in *E. coli* photolyase restores its binding affinity fully. This clearly indicates that the N5 position of the isoallozine ring (which is replaced by a carbon in 5-deazaflavin) is not involved in binding, specifically in making H-bonds with substrate.[82] Regarding the effect of redox status of flavin on binding, only a minor difference was found between the affinities of E-FADH° and E-FAD$_{ox}$ forms of the enzyme[74,82] which is more likely due to the fact that "yellow enzyme" preparations invariably contain a fraction of inactive enzyme. The binding of E-FADH$_2$ form of *E. coli* photolyase has not been studied in detail. However, the yeast photolyase which contains FADH$_2$ binds with the same affinity as the E-FADH° form.

In contrast, to these drastic effects of flavin on binding, the folate chromophore apparently has no effect. Enzyme containing the monoglutamate form of MTHF but no flavin does not bind substrate[82] and MTHF either in mono- or polyglutamate forms does not seem to affect the affinity of E-FADH° for substrate.[78]

Interaction with Other Repair Enzymes

Certain *E. coli* strains deficient in photolyase are more UV sensitive compared to wild type even when the cells are kept in dark following UV irradiation.[83] This could be taken as evidence for a dark repair function of photolyase. However, Yamomoto et al.[84] observed that this effect could be observed only in *recA*$^-$ cells and not at all in *uvrA*$^-$ cells indicating that the effect must have been an indirect mechanism. Sancar et al.[85] examined the effect of photolyase on *E. coli* (A) BC excinuclease directly using purified enzymes. (A)BC excinuclease is an ATP-dependent DNA repair enzyme that repairs, among many other DNA lesions, Pyr<>Pyr by incising the eighth phosphodiester bond 5′ and the fifth phosphodiester bond 3′ to the Pyr<>Pyr.[86] The A and B subunits of the enzyme recognize the damage and make a stable enzyme-substrate complex (B-DNA) which does not lead to incision until the C subunit is added. To investigate the effect of (A)BC excinuclease on photolyase the Pyr<>Pyr containing DNA was incubated with the A and B subunits, then photolyase was added and rate of photoreactivation was measured. It was found that the A and B subunits of the excision nuclease had no effect on the repair rate.

When the complementary experiment was conducted by incubating DNA with excess photolyase to bind all Pyr<>Pyr and then (A)BC excinuclease added and the excision kinetics followed under non-photoreactivating conditions (yellow light) a paradoxical result was obtained: photolyase, instead of binding to Pyr<>Pyr and blocking its access to (A)BC excinculease and thus inhibiting the nucleotide excision enzyme it actually stimulated both the rate and the extent of Pyr<>Pyr removal by the (A)BC excinuclease.[85] The reason for this stimulation appears to be that photolyase binds to the thymine dimer on the face of DNA opposite to that where the A and B subunits of (A)BC excinuclease bind and by doing so increases the deformity in DNA, making it a better substrate for the excision nuclease which does not recognize specific chemical structures in DNA but rather overall structural deformities. The stimulatory effect of *E. coli* photolyase is species specific as under the same experimental conditions yeast photolyase which is functional in *E. coli*[87] inhibits (A)BC excinuclease both in vitro and in vivo[88] but stimulates yeast excision nuclease, and *S. griseus* and *Halobacterium halobium* photolyases inhibit *E. coli* nucleotide excision when expressed in an *E. coli* cell.[89] It thus appears that in organisms with both repair enzymes the two repair systems have evolved to function coordinately and that some possibly minor differences in shape and/or interactions of photolyases with DNA determines whether they will stimulate or inhibit an excision nuclease. Only two photolyases have been tested in a human nucleotide excision repair system, the *E. coli* and the yeast enzymes, and both were found to inhibit the human excision nuclease.[90]

In addition to the photolyase and excision nuclease there is a third enzyme which acts on Pyr<>Pyr, the pyrimidine dimer DNA glycosylase. This enzyme cleaves the glycosylic bond of the 5′ pyridmidine of the dimer and then the intradimer phosphodiester bond.[3,4] The enzyme has been found in two sources only: *Micrococcus luteus* and T4 phage infected *E. coli*. *M. luteus* does not have a photolyase. However, *M. luteus* Pyr<>Pyr glycosylase inhibits *E. coli* and yeast photolyases and in turn is inhibited by these enzymes.[85,91] The T4 phage Pyr<>Pyr glycosylase also has the same effect[85] and therefore in an *E. coli* infected with T4 phage the two enzymes are likely to compete for the same substrate. However, the level of Pyr<>Pyr glycosylase in infected cells is so high compared to photolyase that the inhibition of T4 Pyr<>Pyr glycosylase by the indigenous cellular photolyase is insignificant.

An interesting observation regarding interaction of photolyase with other enzyme systems is the finding of increased activity in *E. coli* cells deprived for adenine.[59,92,93] It appears that this effect is due to a postranslational modification of pre-existing photolyase molecules by a protein encoded by a gene lying 1.3 to 4.2 kb upstream of *phr*, the photolyase gene.[93]

In Vivo Studies

The flash photolysis method was adapted to study of photolyase by Rupert and colleagues in an ingeneous set of experiments.[57-68,94] The basic experimental principle is to expose photolyase-substrate mixtures to an intense light flash of ~ 1 ms duration (camera flash) and sufficient intensity to repair all substrate complexed with the enzyme instantaneously, but which is of too short duration to allow a second round of binding and repair. Using this simple approach Harm, Harm and Rupert (see Ref. 94) obtained very accurate values for the various rate constants for the yeast enzyme in vitro and for the *E. coli* photolyase in vivo. The following is an elegant example of the utilization of the flash photolysis method to determine the reaction rate constants in vivo.[64]

To measure k_2 (the off rate for formation of the E.S. complex) *E. coli* is infected with UV-irradiated T1 phage and the cells are incubated in dark long enough (as determined by flash photolysis) for formation of the photolyase-Pyr<>Pyr complexes with phage DNA, then the cells are irradiated with 254 nm over a few second period with a UV (254 nm) dose which introduces a vast excess of Pyr<>Pyr into the host DNA over those present in the phage DNA without introducing additional Pyr<>Pyr into the phage DNA because of its much smaller size (8×10^6 nucleotides for *E. coli* versus 5×10^4 nucleotides for T1 phage). At time intervals after the UV exposure the infected bacteria are exposed to single camera flashes and the fraction of Pyr<>Pyr repaired in phage DNA is estimated from the increase in number of plaques formed by the infecting phage upon plating. With time, essentially all photolyase molecules dissociate from phage DNA and bind to the much more abundant cellular DNA and the light flashes fail to increase the number of plaques formed by the UV-irradiated phage. A first order plot of fraction of phage DNA repaired as a function of time after introducing Pyr<>Pyr into cellular yields the off rate coefficient for the photolyase-Pyr<>Pyr complexes. The kinetics obtained by this method also show a biphasic behavior and the K_{eq} binding equilibrium constant, the k_1 second order association constant as well as k_2 obtained in vivo by the flash photolysis method are, in general, in excellent agreement with the values obtained in vitro with the purified *E. coli* photolyase. In Table 3 the in vivo rate constants for the dark reaction are included for comparison with the in vitro values.

Molecular Aspects

The interactions of two folate class photolyases (*E. coli* and *S. cerevisiae*) and one deazaflavin class enzyme (*M. thermoautotrophicum*) with a T<>T in DNA have been probed by enzymatic and chemical means to identify the contact sites on DNA at atomic resolution.[31,69,95] Surprisingly, these three enzymes representing the three biological kingdoms and differing in their affinity to substrate by a factor of ~ 100 make basically the same contacts with DNA.

All three enzymes contact the phosphodiester bond immediately 5' and the 3 phosphodiester bonds immediately 3' to the dimer (but not the intradimer phosphate) on the damaged strand and the phosphate opposite the dimer across the minor groove on the complementary strand (Figure 11). Thus, the enzymes appear to bind on one face of DNA over half-a-turn of the duplex. Probing sugar contacts by hydroxyl radical footprinting[96] revealed that approximately 5 deoxyribose moieties centered around the dimer were "contacted" on both strands although the contract on the damaged strand was more intimate. Methylation protection and interference experiments reveal "contacts" in the major groove 3' to the dimer over 5 nucleotides and in the minor groove 5' to the dimer over a 2-nucleotide distance. From the effects of methylation of major groove nitrogens on binding it was concluded that the *M. thermoautotrophicum* photolyase is buried deeper into the major groove 3' to the dimer and thus displaces 3-4 water

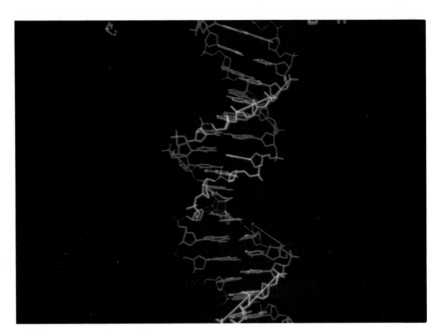

Figure 11. Contact sites of photolyase on DNA. The duplex is unwound by 14° and bent into the major groove by 30°. The enzyme contacts the phosphate immediately 5′ and the three phosphates immediately 3′ to the Thy<>Thy on the damaged strand, and the phosphate opposite the dimer across the minor groove on the undamaged strand. The intradimer phosphate is not contacted. The phosphates contacted by photolyase as well as the cyclobutane ring protruding into the major groove are highlighted in red. The same phosphate contacts have been found for *E. coli, S. cerevisiae,* and *M. thermoautotrophicum* photolyases, although some differences are observed in groove contacts between enzymes from the three sources.

molecules from the major groove during binding. It is conceivable that the entropy contribution of this displacement is responsible for the higher binding affinity of the methanogen enzyme compared to all other photolyases investigated to date. It must be emphasized, however, that there is no evidence for formation of H-bonds by any of the photolyases with H-bond donors or acceptors in the major or minor groove. This is to be expected from the fact that binding of photolyases to T<>T is little influenced by the neighboring sequences which present their unique spatial patterns of H-bond donors and acceptors in the grooves.[97]

The molecular model that emerges from these results is as follows. Photolyases recognize the unique configuration of the phosphodiester bond around the photodimer and make specific contacts with 4 phosphates on the damaged strand and one phosphate on the complementary strand. Considering the fact that ionic bonds have no directionality and therefore cannot contribute to specificity we suspect that only two of the phosphate contacts are in the form of salt bridges as predicted from the effect of ionic strength on binding affinity[74] and that the other phosphate contacts are in the form of H-bonds which confer specificity. Additional specificity is probably achieved by van der Waals interactions with the Pyr<>Pyr and perhaps H-bonding to C4 = 0 of T<>T and U<>U which might explain the higher affinity of these Pyr<>Pyr for photolyase compared to C<>C. Aromatic residues especially trp are also involved in specific binding and it is reasonable to assume that these residues contribute to binding affinity by either van der Waals or stacking interaction with the bases adjacent to those making the Pyr<>Pyr.[41] This model is also entirely consistent with the fact that photolyases have nearly equal affinity for a T<>T in single or double-stranded DNA[98,99] as molecular dynamics calculations[18,100] indicate that the torsion angles of the damaged strand in the region of T<>T are remarkably similar in double- and single-stranded DNA. Since the damaged strand carries all of the important specificity determinants and molecular contacts it is of no surprise that photolyase binds to it with similar affinities regardless as to whether the strand is in single or double stranded context.

4.2. Photodimer Recognition

Photolyase is specific for Pyr<>Pyr; it does not recognize other UV lesions such as (6-4) photoproducts[101] or pyrimidine hydrates or glycolys. The chemical footprinting experiments would indicate that a substrate of the structure $_pT<>T_pN_pN_p$ would be the essential minimal substrate for photolyase. Indeed, this substrate binds to *E. coli* photolyase with nearly the same affinity as a T<>T in B-DNA.[99] However, subsequent studies have shown that the enzyme binds to and repairs T<>T in shorter oligonuleotides. Liuzzi et al.[102] showed that *E. coli* photolyase repairs T<>T in T<>T_pT about 2-times faster than in T_pT<>T confirming the importance of the phosphate(s) 3′ to T<>T in binding and repair. Similarly Weinfield et al.[103-105] found that cleavage of the intradimer phosphodiester bond in these substrate did not inhibit photolyase, in agreement with the chemical footprinting experiments which indicated that the intradimer phosphate is not contacted by the enzyme. Furthermore, more recent results have shown that a uridine- or thymidine dinucleotide dimer[106] and even a thymine base dimer, T<>T[107] can be repaired by the *E. coli* photolyase, albeit with low efficiency. Thus, two saturated pyrimidine joined by a cyclobutane ring in *cis-syn* conformation appear to be the minimal essential substrate, other structural features increase the affinity of the enzyme but are not essential for binding or photolysis. Does the enzyme bind to and repair other cyclobutane pyrimidine adducts? Of the four steroisomers of Pyr<>Pyr only the *cis,syn* form is repaired[108] and presumably only this form binds to photolyase. Thymine-psoralen furan side monoadduct[85] and psoralen interstrand crosslink have been tested and failed to be repaired by photolyase but it is conceivable that other 5,6-cyclobutane adducts of pyrimidines with less bulky side chain will be recognized and repaired by the enzyme.

Caffeine has long been known to inhibit photoreactivation;[64] it has recently been shown that this inhibition is due to interference of the intercalated drug with binding of photolyase to substrate.[109]

5. CATALYSIS (PHOTOLYSIS)

Photolyase converts light energy into chemical energy. The reaction catalyzed is basically a light-initiated (2 + 2) cycloreversion of the cyclobutane ring joining two pyrimidines. However, the photolyase-mediated reaction is not a simple symmetry-allowed photocycloreversion because the light utilized most efficiently by all known photolyases, 300-500 nm, is of insufficient energy to populate excited states (singlet or triplet) of Pyr<>Pyr. Therefore, catalysis must involve other mechanisms of converting light energy into chemical energy. The mechanism of photolysis has been investigated in model systems and more recently with photolyases and simple substrates.

5.1. Model Systems

While the ultimate understanding of the reaction mechanism(s) of photolyases will come from studies on the enzymes, extensive work has been done on model systems for splitting photodimers. Although these studies have some limitations they have been quite useful in providing a theoretical framework for the enzymatic reaction and therefore will be reviewed briefly.

Direct Photoreversal

Formation of Pyr<>Pyr via cycloaddition of the 5,6 double bonds of the bases results in loss of aromaticity and loss of the absorption peak at 250-270 nm typical of DNA bases (Figure 4). However, absorption of Pyr<>Pyr at these wavelengths is not negligible and as a consequence irradiation of DNA with the germicidal wavelength of 254 nm results in a photo-steady state such that 30% of Ts are in T<>T form and 70% are monomers. In fact, when DNA containing preformed T<>Ts was irradiated with 240 nm where T<>T absorbs significantly nearly quantitative conversion to monomers accompanied with the restoration of biological activity was accomplished.[110] This is possible because while T<>T is formed with a quantum yield of 0.02, it is photoreversed with a quantum yield of near unity.[111,112]

The photochemical and photophysical properties of T<>T have been addressed by Lamola[111] at some length, whose findings may be summarized as follows: First, all T<>Ts undergo photoscission very efficiently such that in 1 : 1

ethylene glycol: water at 80K and with 248 nm the quantum yields for splitting were 1.03 for $c,s,$-T<>T, 0.95 for $t,s,$-T<>T, and 0.95 for the c,a-T<>T isomer. Second, T<>Ts show only end absorption in aqueous solutions at $\lambda >$ 185 nm (which becomes a peak with $\varepsilon \sim 10^4$ at 220 nm in the 1,3-dimethyl-T<>T derivative) and the threshold of the absorption spectra of the methylated T<>T are at $\lambda \sim 290$ nm which is taken to be the S_1 state (99 kcal) and a T_1 of 75-85 kcal was estimated.

An interesting aspect of direct reversal is its dependence on wavelength such that the quantum yield for splitting at 290 nm was about half the value of that at 240 nm,[2,112] which led to the suggestion that deactivation by rapid internal conversion would lead to a ground state with a 90 kcal/mole of vibrational energy, sufficient to overcome the "forbiddenness" of ground state cyclorever-sion and lead to dimer splitting. As an alternative the author suggested that the splitting reaction may occur from triplet states. Whatever the mechanism may be, the important fact is that direct photoreversal is extremely efficient and may share some features with the equally efficient photoenzymatic reversal which uses light of much lower energy.

Photosensitized Reversal

The photoinitiated cycloreversion of Pyr<>Pyr can be affected by many compounds by several different mechanisms such as energy transfer, redox photosensitized systems, and charge transfer to or from the photodimer (see Table 4 and below). In addition to these, Lamola[111] considered a "chemical pathway" for photosensitized cleavage whereby the photosensitizer, upon exci-tation, makes a covalent bond with Pyr<>Pyr which results in bond rearrange-ment and splitting of the cyclobutane ring. This pathway has been dismissed as a model for photolyase because it is not possible to draw a realistic "chemical scheme" equally applicable to T<>T, T<>T, and C<>C, all of which are known to be repaired by photolyases.[111]

Energy Transfer

The first sensitized photoscission of a Pyr<>Pyr was accomplished by Wacker et al.[113] who showed that in presence of uranyl acetate, c,s-T<>T could be monomerized with wavelengths which were absorbed by uranyl but not the dimer. This was followed by demonstration by Lamola[114] that 2,6-naphthalene-disulfonate photosensitized splitting of T<>T by 300 nm. Ben-Hur and Rosen-thal[115] found that several quinones including chloranil, benzoquinone, naphtho-quinones, and anthroquinones were very efficient in sensitization of T<>T photocylcloreversion, and Hélène and Charlier[116] demonstrated that indole deriv-atives as well could photoreverse T<>T at $\lambda > 280$ nm.

In considering the mechanisms of photosensitized cleavage by the organic dyes singlet-singlet energy transfer was eliminated as a possible mechanism because Pyr<>Pyr have no absorbance at the photosensitizing wavelengths. Furthermore singlet-triplet energy transfer was also eliminated because T<>T did not quench the fluorescence of any of the dyes tested and in addition the 2,6-naphthalenedisulfonate-sensitized cleavage of T<>T was totally inhibited by a triplet quencher, isoprene.[114] Although no phosphorescence could be detected at 77 K, 5,6-dihydrothymine which could reasonably be considered to be equivalent of one half of T<>T was found to be phosphorescent at 77 K and a T_1 energy of 73.5 kcal/mole was calculated from the phosphorescence spectrum. However, even if one assumes that a T<>T has a triplet of ~ 74 kcal it is still not possible to achieve efficient energy transfer by the classical mechanism (Förster) from photosensitizers with triplet energies of 65-70 kcal/mole. Therefore Lamola[114] proposed non-vertical energy transfer as a possible mechanism.

In non-vertical energy transfer the nuclear geometry of the acceptor changes during the process and as a result the acceptor possesses a non-spectroscopic electronic state which makes this seemingly endothermic energy transfer possible. Such a mechanism could easily explain the photosensitization reaction by organic dyes and, it was suggested, might be even applicable to photolyases whose triplet states were significantly lower than those of the photosensitizing dyes. However, not all of the organic dyes with appropriate levels of triplet energies acted as photosensitizers. In fact, the two dyes with the highest triplet energies, acetophenone (73 kcal) and 3-benzophenone sulfonate (71 kcal/mole) were inert. Lamola[111,114] suggested that this lack of activity might be attributed to the short life-times of the triplets of the latter two compared to the photochemically competent photosensitizers. Thus, non-vertical energy transfer as the mechanism of photosensitization for organic dyes and even photolyases cannot be rejected on theoretical grounds. However, no experimental evidence exists for this mechanism in either model or biological systems. In fact, in their attempt to demonstrate photocycloreversion of T<>T by non-vertical energy transfer from 2-anthroquinone-sulfonate Roth and Lamola[127] obtained the first evidence for dimer splitting by charge transfer, electron abstraction by the dye from the photodimer.

An additional mechanism for accomplishing a seemingly endothermic energy transfer from a sensitizer to substrate is the formation of a complex between the two, either in the ground state (charge-transfer complex, CT) or in the excited state (exciplex). There is no experimental evidence for either mechanism in model systems. However, it was reported[117] that a charge-transfer band ($\lambda = 350$ nm) was formed between an *E. coli* photolyase which did not absorb at $\lambda > 300$ nm and a Pyr<>Pyr-containing substrate. It has since been shown that these results were an experimental artifact as, among other things, there is no *E. coli* photolyase which does not have near-UV absorption.[118-123] In summary, at present, there is no evidence for cycloreversion of Pyr<>Pyr by electronic energy transfer of any form (Förster, non-vertical, in charge-transfer complex) either in model systems or in photolyases.

Redox Photosensitized Systems.   Pac et al.[124] discovered a novel mechanism of photosensitization which they christened redox photosensitization. The system consists of a photosensitizer which in its excited singlet state ($^1s*$) abstracts an electron from an aromatic hydrocarbon, the resulting cation radical reacts with substrate and initiates a chemical reaction. In one particular case *p*-dicyanobenzene was the photosensitizer and phenanthrene the redox catalyst aromatic hydrocarbon. Using this couple and N_1N_1-dimethylthymine cyclobutane dimers as substrate the authors demonstrated that with 313 nm irradiation a redox catalytic chain reaction could be initiated whereby the phenanthrene cation radical generated by electron abstraction by$^1s*$ of *p*-dicyanobenzene would react with Pyr<>Pyr to initiate splitting of the cyclobutane ring and emerge from the reaction as a cation radical again, capable of entering new rounds of cycloreversion such that quantum yields of "photocycloreversion" of up to 3.0 could be achieved.

Mechanistically, the authors eliminated a "hole transfer" from phenanthrene cation radical to T<>T as a possibility because based on the redox potential of the couple such a mechanism is endergonic ($\Delta G° = + 65$ kcal/mole) and is incompatible with the high-efficiency of the cycloreversion. The authors proposed that phenanthrene cation radical made a "Π complex" with the photodimer. Furthermore, they found that oxygen greatly increased the quantum yield of photocycloreversion reaction. In an effort to explain this unexpected oxygen effect they obtained high-resolution absorption spectra of *c,s*-T<>T in the presence and absence of oxygen. They reported that oxygen caused a small but significant bathochromic shift of the end absorption of T<>T and concluded that *c,s*-T<>T formed a charge-transfer complex with oxygen where O_2 is the electron acceptor in this complex. The cycloreversion reaction in presence of oxygen then involves the formation of a Π complex between the phenanthrene cation radical and the $O_2 - c,s$-T<>T charge-transfer complex.

When the "quantum efficiency" of cyloreversion of *c,s*-T<>T, *c,s*-U<>U, and *t,s*-T<>T were compared it was found that *c,s*-T<>T was repaired at least an order of magnitude more efficiently than *t,s,*-T<>T even though the latter has a lower oxidation potential. It was suggested that *c,s*-T<>T was the most reactive because as the C(6) -C(6)′ bond elongated in the Π complex as a result of development of a partial positive charge on this bond, there is a concomitant increase of interactions between the C(5)-C(5)′ and C(6)-C(6)′ bonds resulting in a near-concerted splitting. As a consequence *c,s,*-T<>T which has the maximal steric repulsion and is the most likely to allow through-bond interactions is split the most efficiently. As this order of repair holds true for photolyases it was suggested that a complete electron transfer resulting in a discrete Pyr<>Pyr$^{+\cdot}$ (which would result in a reverse order of repair efficiency) was an unlikely mechanism for photolyases. As it turns out, photolyses probably catalyze Pyr<>Pyr splitting by electron donation.

Charge Transfer   All known photosensitizers which catalyze the splitting of Pyr<>Pyr by a conventional photoreaction do so either by abstracting an electron from the photodimer or donating an electron. Aside from certain heavy metal compounds such as uranylacetate (which abstracts an electron) the best characterized photosensitizers are quinones whose excited state triplets abstract an electron from Pyr<>Pyr, and indoles whose excited state singlets donates an electron to Pyr<>Pyr. Molecular orbital calculations predict that both Pyr<>Pyr$^{+\cdot}$ [125] and Pyr<>Pyr$^{-\cdot}$ [126] are prone to collapse by ring splitting to constituent monomers.

Quinones as Photosensitizers

Chloranil, benzoquinone, naphthoquinone, and anthroquinone are effective photosensitizers.[115] The photosensitization reactions by 2-anthraquinonesulfonate (AQS) and chloranil (CHL) have been investigated in some detail.

From a Stern-Volmer plot for quenching of photosensitized reaction by a triplet quencher it was concluded that photosensitization occurred from the triplet state of AQS.[111] The photosensitization reaction is extremely efficient and a sensitization plot of ϕ^{-1} vs $[T<>T]^{-1}$ extrapolates to 1.0 suggesting that the quantum yield for photocycloreversion is unity. The first unambiguous evidence for the mechanism of photosensitization came from photo-CIDNP experiments. Roth and Lamola[127] observed an emission signal at the position of the methyl proton during irradiation of AQS plus (1,3-me)-T<>T with $\lambda > 340$ nm which was ascribed to (1,3-me)-T$^{+\cdot}$. Kemmick et al.[128] conducted time-resolved photo-CIDNP with the same system and obtained similar results. At the earliest time resolution that could be achieved (0.2 μs) no other species, that is (1,3-me)-T<>T$^{+\cdot}$ which is expected to be a precursor, were detected. Thus, it was concluded that the dimer radical cation is split in less than 200 ns. Indeed the lack of photodimer CIDNP signal in these experiments could have been interpreted to mean that there was no actual charge transfer but that bond breaking and electron transfer were simultaneous. To resolve this issue Young et al.[129] conducted photo-CIDNP experiments with a system consisting of 3,3'-dimethyl 1,1'-trimethylenebis (thymine)-cyclobutane dimer and AQS. In this system the authors were able to detect an emission from cyclobutyl hydrogens (Figure 12) in the light minus dark spectrum and enhanced absorption by C(6)-H and emission from the C(5)-CH$_3$ of the product. The authors concluded that this pattern was not only indicative of T$^{+\cdot}$ production by charge transfer to ^{3}AQS* but that it also provided strong evidence for the presence of a T<>T$^{+\cdot}$ as a precursor for the monomeric cation radical. It appears that utilization of a "tethered" dimer in these experiments was the key for detection of the dimer cation radical which had eluded the other investigators in the earlier attempts. The following scheme was proposed for the overall reaction.

$$T<>T + {}^3AQS \longrightarrow {}^3[T<>T^{+\cdot} + AQS^{-\cdot}] \qquad (2)$$

$$^3[T<>T^{+\cdot} + AQS^{-\cdot}] \longrightarrow {}^3[T^{+\cdot} + AQS^{-\cdot}] \qquad (3) \text{ or}$$

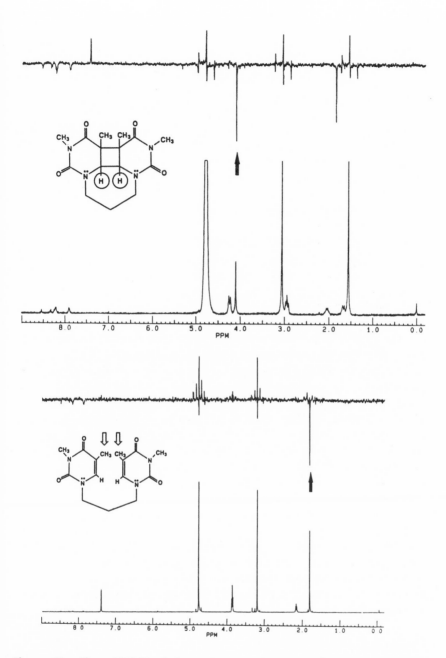

Figure 12. Photo-CIDNP of Pyr<>Pyr. (**A**) *Upper:* Anthraquinonesolfonate-sensitized photo-CIDNP difference spectrum (light-minus dark) of the photodimer shown; the arrow indicates emission from cyclobutyl hydrogens (circled). *Lower:* dark spectrum of the photodimer. (**B**) Photo-CIDNP of 3,3'-dimethyl-1,1'-trimethylenebis(thymine). *Upper,* anthraquinone-sulfonate sensitized difference spectrum (light-minus dark). *Lower,* dark spectrum of the bis-thymine. From Young et al.[129]

$$^3[T<>T^{+\cdot} + AQS^-] \longrightarrow T^{+\cdot} + AQS^{-\cdot} \qquad (4)$$

Interestingly, when in this system 1,1'-trimethylene-bis (thymine)-cyclobutane dimer ("tethered" thymine dimer) was used as the substrate an emission signal for the cyclobutyl hydrogens was obtained indicative of thymine dimer radical cation but no emission from C(5) methyl groups (thymine radical cation) was seen suggesting that in this system charge recombination with $AQS^{-\cdot}$ predominates. This could be taken as evidence that a thymine radical cation in DNA (where the two thymines are held together by the phosphodiester bond) may not be prone to splitting and therefore photolyases may not be able to split dimers by electron abstraction.

Photosensitized splitting of Pyr<>Pyr by another quinone, chloranil has also been investigated in some detail.[130] Steady-state experiments and time-resolved absorption spectroscopy showed that the chloranil triplet abstracts an electron from Pyr<>Pyr and initiates a monomerization reaction which yields quantum yields of 0.34 for $c,s(1,3$-me)-T<>T, 0.39 for the t,s-isomer and $<<10^{-2}$ for the $cis,anti$ dimer. Interestingly, it was found that $^3(CHL)^*$ abstracts an electron from the c,a-Pyr<>Pyr nearly as efficiently as from the other isomers and the poor quantum yield of splitting was ascribed to a lack of through bond coupling of the diagonal orbitals separated by the two C-C sigma orbitals of the cyclobutane ring.

The rate of electron transfer in this system was calculated from Stern-Volmer plot for quenching of CHL-photosensitized monomerization of T<>T and it was estimated to be $8.1 \times 10^8 \ M^{-1}S^{-1}$ for c,s and $12.6 \times 10^8 \ M^{-1}S^{-1}$ for the $t,s,$-T<>T. From these values as well as from the relative yields of photosplitting of the cytoclobutane ring it was concluded that the rate of ring cleavage was $\geq 10^9 S^{-1}$. In addition, in this system is was found that Mg^{2+} forms a complex with either $^3CHL^*$ or $CHL^{-\cdot}$ and by doing so retards geminate charge recombination and increases the quantum yield of dimer splitting to 0.49 for c,s-T<>T and 0.59 for t,s-T<>T. The extremely rapid rate of ring cleavage in Pyr<>Pyr$^{+\cdot}$ found in this system along with the theoretical work of Pabon and Bauld[125] would indicate a concerted mechanism of cleavage of Pyr<>Pyr radical cation. However, this must be reconciled with the fact that a 5,5'-linked (bis)pyrimidine was isolated in quinone-sensitized splitting of 1,3-dimentyluracil dimer[131] which may be taken as evidence for a stepwise mechanism.[129]

Indoles as Photosensitizers

Indoles, free in solution, "tethered" to a Pyr<>Pyr, or in proteins (DNA binding proteins, anti-Pyr<>Pyr antibodies) photosensitize the splitting of pyrimidine dimers upon irradiation with 290-300 nm. Hélène and Charlier[116] and Lamola[111] reported that Pyr<>Pyr quenches the fluorescence of tryptophan and in the process pyrimidine monomers are produced. It appears that in this system photocycloreversion occurs by two mechanisms: electron transfer by the tryptophan singlet to Pyr<>Pyr, and photoionization of tryptophan to yield aquated electrons which attach to the dimers. The end results of both reactions is the same: generation of Pyr<>Pyr$^{-\cdot}$ which then splits to individual pyrimidines. The contribution of the two reactions results in an overall quantum of 0.007. Although it is known that excited trp singlet is a good electron donor[111] and that Pyr<>Pyr are good electron scavengers and are split by aquated electrons[132] there is no direct evidence proving that trp photosensitized splitting of Pyr<>Pyr involves electron transfer in this system. Regardless, this is the most likely mechanism and it appears that the photosensitizer is not consumed in the reaction which makes the following a likely scheme for the overall reaction.[116]

$$^1Trp^* + T<>T \longrightarrow [Trp^{+\cdot} - T<>^{-\cdot}] \qquad (5)$$

$$[Trp^{+\cdot} - T<>T^{-\cdot}] \longrightarrow Trp^{+\cdot} + T^{-\cdot} + T \qquad (6)$$

$$Trp^{+\cdot} + T^{-\cdot} + T \longrightarrow Trp + 2T \qquad (7)$$

Photosensitized splitting by covalently bound indoles has been accomplished by Rose and colleagues.[129,133-137] By linking the Pyr<>Pyr to an indole via an ester bridge or a two-carbon linker (Figure 13) these workers reduced the electron transfer reaction to an intramolecular process so as to better mimic the reaction catalyzed by photolyases. While the photolyase reaction in reality involves an intermolecular electron transfer, the enzyme-substrate complex in a

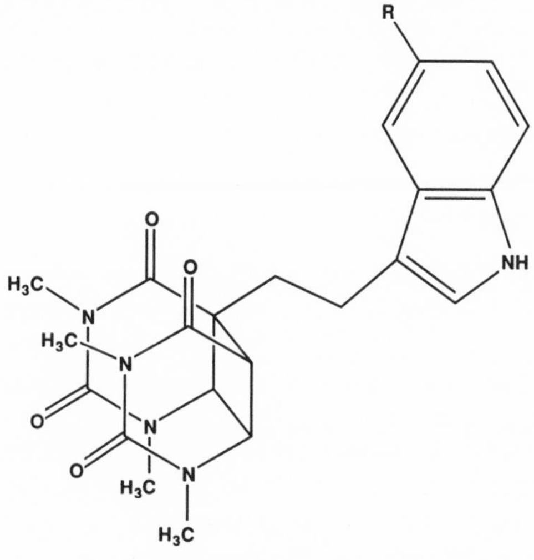

1: R = OCH$_3$
2: R = H

Figure 13. Structures of covalently linked indole-Thy<>Ura systems used for studying intramolecular electron transfer. From Kim et al.[137]

standard reaction condition is formed prior to absorption of a photon, thus positioning the chromophore and the photodimer in close proximity, so that for all intensive purposes the electron transfer may be treated as intramolecular. With the indole tethered Pyr<>Pyr system Van Camp et al.[133] found > 95% quenching of indole fluorescence upon excitation with 287 nm and a quantum yield of 0.05 in excellent agreement with efficiency Pyr<>Pyr splitting in aqueous solutions by uptake of e^-(aq) produced by pulse radiolysis. However, the photosplitting with the tethered indole was a truly intramolecular event and did not involve e^-(aq) as evidenced by the fact that the yield was concentration independent and was not affected by the e^-(aq) scavenger N_2O.

Further insight into the photophysics of the indole-sensitized photosplitting of Pyr<>Pyr was gained from time-resolved absorption and fluorescence spectroscopy conducted by Young et al.[134] This study showed that the fluorescence lifetime of indole attached to Pyr<>Pyr was 0.85 ns compared to the 9.7 ns lifetime for tryptophol. For the electron-rich methoxyindole tethered to a Pyr<>Pyr the fluorescence lifetime was 0.53 ns compared to 4.6 ns for free tryptophol. The quantum yields for splitting Pyr<>Pyr were 0.04 for the unsubstituted indole and 0.08 for methoxyindole. As there was no evidence of deactivation of indole singlet in the tethered system by intersystem crossing (no increase in phosphorescence) it was concluded that the deactivation was mostly if not exclusively by electron transfer to Pyr<>Pyr. Based on this assumption electron transfer rates of $1.7 \times 10^9 s^{-1}$ and $1.1 \times 10^9 s^{-1}$ were calculated for the two systems. Furthermore, the fact that the fluorescence lifetime was reduced by the same factor for both the indole and the methoxyindole moieties indicated that the different efficiencies of e^- transfer was not the cause of the quantum yield difference by a factor of 2. Instead, it was argued[137] that the efficiency was essentially determined by the back reaction (charge recombination) and that this reaction was energetically more favorable in the indole system compared to methoxyindole.

Transient absorption spectroscopy of free tryptophol (Trp) yielded an absorption spectrum (at 0.7 μs) with peaks at 340 nm and 580 nm attributed to $Trp^{+\cdot}$, a minor peak at 430 nm attributed to ^{3}tryptophol*, and a broad peak at 700 nm typical of solvated electrons. In the Pyr<>Pyr-tethered to indole there was an overall quenching of all of these at 0.7 μs. Significantly, there was no 700 nm peak indicating that there was no ejection of free electrons from the indole in this system, suggesting that all quenching by Pyr<>Pyr in the tethered molecule was via electron transfer to the dimer. However no sign of Pyr<>Pyr$^{-\cdot}$ absorption with an expected $\lambda_{max} = 440$ nm [132] or of $Trp^{+\cdot}$ with $\lambda_{max} = 340$ nm was seen by transient absorption spectroscopy. This was attributed to charge annihilation by very rapid back reaction.

Perhaps the most significant results to come so far from the covalently linked dimer-indole system is the finding that the quantum yield for photocycloreversion has been found to be dramatically dependent on the dielectric constant of the solvent, approaching the efficiency of photolyases in the least polar solvents.[137] Finally, Kim and Rose[135,136] by using the covalently linked dimer-indole system have shown that the photocycloreversion reaction but not the electron transfer step is completely inhibited at 77 K and concluded that splitting of the cyclo-butane ring of the dimer radical anion involves a chemical step whose activation barrier cannot be surmounted at 77 K. They suggested that photolyases may play two roles in dimer splitting after the initial electron transfer step, stabilization of charge-separated species, and stabilization of a transition state in the thermal step so as to favor the forward reaction.

The indole photosensitized splitting of Pyr<>Pyr by indoles in peptides and proteins was conducted by Hélène and Charlier.[116] These studies showed that T<>T in single-stranded DNA were bound by the Lys-Trp-Lys tripeptide or the 32 kDa single-stranded specific gene 32 protein of T4 phage and repaired relatively efficiently with light of 254-400 nm. Evidence was presented suggest-ing that the Lys residues in the tripeptide, and Lys as well as other positively charged residues in the protein made ionic bonds with the phosophodiester backbone facilitating the binding by stacking interactions of the Trp residues. Trp fluorescence was quenched in both systems and the free electron scavenger N_2O had no effect on the photocycloreversion of Pyr<>Pyr indicating that, in contrast to photosensitized splitting with free Trp and other indoles, in these systems solvated electrons produced by photosensitization of Trp played no role in dimer splitting. Similar results have been obtained for repair of photodimers by anti-Pyr<>Pyr antibodies in a preliminary report.[138]

Flavins as Photosensitizers

Following identification of flavins as cofactors in photolyases,[24-26] attempts were made to photosensitize dimer splitting with various flavins. Lamola[111] failed to photosensitize dimer splitting with lumichrome and lumiflavin at pH 7 while Eker et al.[30] achieved a low level of dimer splitting with 7,8-didemethyl-8-hydroxy-5-deazaflavin.

An extensive study of flavin photosensitized Pyr<>Pyr cycloreversion was conducted by Rokita and Walsh.[139] These authors failed to achieve photosen-sitized dimer cleavage with 8-hyroxy-5-deazaflavin or other flavins with high electron density such as 8-hydroxyriboflavin, and 8-(alklamino)riboflavin but were able to photosensitize Pyr<>Pyr splitting with flavins with relatively low electron density. The other main findings of this work may be summarized as follows: (1) 8-methoxy-7,8-didemethyl-N^{10}-ethyl-5-deazaflavin, 5-deazaflavin, and lumiflavin acted as efficient photosensitizers; (2) the action spectra were, in general, in agreement with the photosensitizers absorption spectra indicating a simple photosensitization reaction; (3) the photosensitizers acted catalytically and therefore were not consumed in the reaction; (4) photosensitization occurred only at pH 10-12 and was negligible at neutral pH (it was not clear whether the pH effect was exerted by causing ionization of the substrate, the sensitizer, or both); (5) the photosensitization required strict anaerobiosis and the reaction was completely inhibited by the flavin triplet quenchers, Dabco and oxygen; and (6) although an accurate quantum yield could not be obtained, it was estimated to be 10^{-2}-10^{-3} for all active flavins. Based on these results the authors suggested that an excited flavin triplet abstracts an electron from T<>T to yield a dimer radical cation and flavin semiquinone and eventual collapse of the $T<>T^{+\cdot}$ to yield two thymines.

It was difficult to reconcile this model with the finding that the active form of E. coli photolyase contained fully reduced flavin (electron rich) instead of flavin radical.[24,45,74] Therefore, Jorns[140] attempted to affect T<>T photosplitting with reduced flavins. The effect seen with $FADH_2$ was only marginal; however, photosplitting with dihydro-1-deazaflavin at a quantum yield of 10^{-2} was achieved. As the photochemistry of this species has not been studied in any detail it was impossible to tell whether photosplitting occurred by an electron abstraction or donating mechanism. Finally, Walsh[141] has reported that by tethering 8-hydroxy-5-deazaflavin to a T<>T it was possible to photosensitize T<>T cleavage by the 8-hydroxy-5-deazaflavin with a quantum yield of 6×10^{-4}.

General Conclusions from Model Systems

While direct photocycloreversion of Pyr<>Pyr is very efficient ($\phi \sim 0.8$-1.0) all of the model systems investigated failed to yield any evidence for energy transfer to a low-lying (non-spectroscopic) excited state of Pyr<>Pyr to affect the cycloreversion reaction. Instead, it appears that all photosensitizers tested promote cycloreversion by charge transfer. Therefore, these studies raised the possibility of electron transfer as the most likely mechanism for photolyases. However, model systems failed to give a clear indication as to whether photolyases initiated dimer fragmentation by electron abstraction or electron donation.

In general, model studies tended to favor electron abstraction as the possible mechanism for photolyase. This was because of the extremely high efficiency of cyclobutane ring splitting achieved with photosensitizers which cause population of a positive charge on the dimer (or on cyclobutanes in simpler systems) as a result of partial or complete removal of an electron, in contrast to low efficiency splitting achieved by electron donors[142] as seen in Table 4. In addition, molecular orbital calculations predicted that cyclobutane cation radical splits by a concerted mechanism (Pabon and Bauld, 1984) and it was determined experimentally that $T<>T^{+\cdot}$ monomerized in $\leq 10^{-9}$s. In contrast, MO calculations suggested that the anion radical of Pyr<>Pyr could split by a stepwise or non-concerted mechanism.[126] However, certain other observations raised serious questions about $Pyr<>Pyr^{+\cdot}$ being an intermediate in photolyase catalyzed cycloreversion. First, all known photolyases contain $FADH_2$ which alone, in the absence of the second chromophore, can function as a photocatalyst with high quantum yield.[45,50] $FADH_2$ is known to be an excellent electron donor both in the ground state and in

Table 4. Photorepair of Pyrimidine Dimers by Four Mechanisms

Mechanism	Quantum Yield	Reference
(1) Energy Transfer (220-280 nm)	0.8	Patrick and Rahn [112]
(2) Redox Photosensitization	3.0	Pac et al. [124]
(3) Electron Transfer by Donation to Pyr<>Pyr		
a-Tryptophan (free)	0.007	Hélène and Charlier [116]
b-Indole (tethered)	0.043	Van Camp et al. [133]
c-Indole (tethered)/apolar solvent	0.41	Kim et al. [137]
d-"Solvated electron"	0.060	Santus et al. [132]
e-Reduced 1-deazaflavin	0.010	Jorns [140]
(4) Electron Transfer by Abstraction from Pyr<>Pyr		
a-Chloranil	0.6	Pac et al. [130]
b-Anthraquinone sulfonate	1.0	Lamola [111]
c-5-deazariboflavin	0.001	Rokita and Walsh [139]
d-5-deazariboflavin (tethered)	0.0006	Walsh and Begley [141]

Table 5. Quantum Yields of Splitting of 1 and 2
in Various Solvents,[a,b]

Solvent[c]	$\phi(1)$	$\phi(2)$
H_2O	0.06	0.05
DMSO	0.15	0.09
Acctonitrile	0.19	0.14
Methanol	0.23	0.17
Ethanol	0.24	0.19
1-Propanol	0.25	0.19
2-Propanol	0.25	0.20
1-Butanol	0.26	0.20
1-Pentanol	0.27	0.22
1-Hexanol·	0.30	0.23
Diethyl ether	0.37	0.29
Benzene	0.39	0.30
1,4-Dioxane	0.40	0.31
Ether-isopentane (10:90)	0.41	—
Dioxane-isopentane (5:95)	0.41	—

[a] From Kim et al. [137] [b] Irradiation at 290 nm. [c] Solvents are arranged from top to bottom in decreasing order of dielectric constant, except for solvent mixtures, whose positions are qualitatively assigned.

excited state and it appears to be thermodynamically incapable of oxidizing Pyr<>Pyr in either state. Second, AQS which is very efficient in splitting tetramethyl-T<>T is incapable of doing so when the two thymines are covalently linked[134] suggesting that in DNA where the two Pyr halves of the photodimer are covalently linked the pyrimidine cation radical may be more prone to back reaction resulting in inefficient splitting of the cyclobutane ring. In addition, a 5,5'-linked (bis)pyrimidine has been isolated in quinone-sensitized splitting of $1,3-(CH_3)_2-U<>U$ indicating that, contrary to the theoretical predictions, splitting of $Pyr<>Pyr^{+\cdot}$ is stepwise and may not be that efficient. Most significantly, however, it has recently been shown[137] that the pyrmidine dimer radical anion is split very efficiently in solvents of low polarity (Table 5), clearly indicating that $Pyr<>Pyr^{-\cdot}$ is not intrinsically resistant to splitting. As photolyases appear to have hydrophobic active sites,[41,50,55,75] it is quite possible that photolyases split dimer through an anion radical intermediate.

5.2. Photolysis with Photolyase

Photosplitting of $Pyr<>Pyr$ by photolyases occur with relatively high quantum efficiency. Following the discovery of flavin and deazaflavin in photolyases[24,25,30] it appeared that these chromophores would function as simple photosensitizers, splitting photodimers by either energy or electron transfer. However, it was soon realized that the *E. coli* photolyase contained a second chromophore[28] which was later identified as 5,10-methenyltetrahydrofolate.[29] Similarly, it was found that the deazaflavin class photolyases contained another chromophore as well, flavin adenine dinucleatide, apparently in $FADH_2$ form.[26] Taking into account the central role played by $FADH_2$ in catalysis in both classes of photolyase, it was proposed that the folate and the 5-deazaflavin be termed as "second chromophores."[3,143] It does indeed appear that the second chromophores in both classes function as photoantennas, transferring energy to the flavin at the reaction center, in analogy with the antenna and electron donating chlorophylls in photosynthetic systems.

Roles of the Chromophores

The first unambiguous evidence of the central role of the flavin in the folate class photolyase came from the observation that *E. coli* photolyase containing flavin in one and two-electron oxidized forms had reduced or no activity.[75,76] The definitive experiment demonstrating that the folate cofactor was not required for catalysis was the finding that photolyase depleted of folate by photodecomposition was fully active catalyzing $Pyr<>Pyr$ splitting with a quantum yield of about 0.5.[45] This has been confirmed by reconstituting photolyase from apoenzyme plus FAD followed by conversion of FAD to $FADH_2$ by a photosensitized reaction; the enzyme thus reconstituted was fully functional without any need for the folate chromophore.[50,144] The same is also true for the deazaflavin class enzymes. Takao et al.[145] expressed the *A. nidulans* photolyase, and Kobayashi et al.[89] expressed the *S. griseus* and *H. halobium* photolyases in *E. coli*. These enzymes were functional in the heterologous system even though *E. coli* does not synthesize the 8-HDF cofactor. Thus, it is clear that these photolyases are also fully functional in the absence of 8-HDF. Although the in vivo action spectrum of the *A. nidulans* enzyme expressed in *E. coli* suggested that it may contain the folate chromophore as well,[145] this does not detract from the main conclusion that the flavin is necessary and sufficient for catalysis in both classes of photolyase.

Since $FADH_2$ is the catalytic cofactor it was natural to assume that the second chromophores functioned as photoantennas.[76] However, initial experiments did not eliminate the possibility of electron transfer by the second chromophore independent of $FADH_2$. It was also suggested that the second chromophore may participate in catalysis by preventing charge recombination between the radical ion pair thought to be an intermediate in flavin-initiated catalysis.[76] Subsequent experiments have demonstrated that the folate chromophore in *E. coli* photolyase does not participate in independent electron transfer[146] nor does it affect the back electron transfer in the flavin initiated charge separation.[50]

Li and Sancar[146] by site-specific mutagenesis, substituted a Phe or Tyr for Trp at position 306 of *E. coli* photolyase. These mutant proteins were no longer photoreducible and thus this study identified Trp 306 as the primary (intrinsic) electron donor in photoreduction of photolyase FADH° chromophore to $FADH_2$. Equally important, these studies provided unambiguous evidence that the folate cofactor was incapable of initiating electron transfer and repair on its own. The mutant proteins in their E-FADH° -MTHF forms had spectroscopic properties identical to wild type, and bound to substrate with identical affinities providing evidence that they had not undergone any gross conformational change as a result of the mutations. Thus, any change in catalytic activity could be ascribed to the lack of photoreducibility of FADH°. When these mutants were tested for repair of Pyr<>Pyr no activity was detectable at a level of 0.01% of wild type photolyase. Although it could be argued that MTHF could transfer electron only when associated with $FADH_2$, the most likely explanation of these results is that MTHF does not act as electron donor/acceptor in photorepair. This premise could not be tested directly in E-MTHF form of the enzyme as this form does not bind substrate.[82]

As to the role of the second chromophore in the deazaflavin class enzymes, its function has not been probed directly. However, the following experiment suggests that 5-deazaflavin is also incapable of initiating photoinduced charge separation and DNA repair by photolyase. The flavin cofactor of *E. coli* photolyase was replaced with 5-deaza-FAD, and the analog-substituted enzyme was tested for activity.[82] Although 5-dFAD restored specific affinity of the enzyme for substrate, it failed to restore its catalytic function leading to the conclusion that 8-hydroxy-5-deazaflavin in deazaflavin class enzymes must function as a photoantenna.[82] It must be pointed out however, that the analog used in this experiment was 5-dFAD and not 8-OH-5-deazaflavin and that the analog was made to bind in the FAD pocket, naturally occupied by $FADH_2$ in both classes of enzyme. In fact, a study with *A. nidulans* enzyme has directly implicated 8-OH-5-deazaflavin, in photorepair by charge separation.[27] The flavin cofactor of this enzyme, like that of the *E. coli* photolyase, becomes oxidized to the flavosemiquinone during purification and can be photoreduced in the presence of reducing agents. However, in contrast to *E. coli* photolyase whose photolytic cross-section increases by a factor of 10-15 upon photoreduction, it was reported that photoreduction had no detectable effect on photoreactivating activity, leading to the conclusion that absorption of light by 8-HDF resulted in photorepair directly through 8-HDF.

However, these experiments were not designed to measure quantum yields and therefore the results were equally compatible with photoreduction of FADH° by 8-HDF* followed by repair by $FADH_2$.[27] Under enzyme turnover conditions where the ''dark reactions'' (mainly the off rate) are rate limiting the effects of different quantum yields might be difficult to measure. In fact, even if 8-HDF were capable of direct repair the photo-reactivating activity of E-8HDF-FADH° would be expected to be lower than E-8HDF-$FADH_2$ as there would be two competing deactivating pathways in the radical form, energy transfer to FADH° to cause photoreduction, and photorepair presumably by charge transfer. In conclusion, there is no experimental evidence indicating that 8-HDF can catalyze photorepair in either class of photolyase, in contrast to the overwhelming evidence that the second chromophores transfer energy to $FADH_2$ (FADH°) in both classes of enzyme.

The roles of MTHF and 8-HDF appear to function as photoantennas. The first experimental evidence for energy transfer from the second chromophore to the flavin cofactor came from photoreduction studies with *E. coli* photolyase. Heelis et al[147] found both by steady state and time-resolved absorption spectroscopy that irradiation of *E. coli* photolyase with either 353 nm (where both chromophores absorb) or 535 nm (where only FADH° absorbs) led to photoreduction with essentially the same quantum yield. As photoreduction occurred even in the absence of MTHF, folate was excluded as the electron donor in photoreduction; it was concluded that folate transferred energy to FADH° with nearly 100% efficiency. Picosecond flash photolysis of the E-FADH°-MTHF form of the enzyme gave evidence for rapid energy transfer between the two chromophores[147] which eventually generates an FADH° quartet.[148] These results have been confirmed by fluorescence quenching measurements. Steady state[144,149] and time resolved[49] fluorescence measurements with E-FADH°-MTHF and E-MTHF forms of the enzyme have revealed energy transfer from MTHF and FADH° at > 90% efficiency. The experimental evidence for energy transfer from 8-HDF to FADH° (FADH) in deazaflavin class photolyses is not as extensive but no less compelling. The FADH° cofactor of the *A. nidulans* enzyme was photoreduced with either 437 nm (where ~ 80% of absorption is due to 8-HDF) and >500 nm (only FADH° absorption) with the same efficiency.[27]

To summarize, all experimental evidence available to date is consistent with the second chromophores (MTHF and 8-HDF) functioning as photoantennas transferring energy to $FADH_2$ at the catalytic center which splits Pyr<>Pyr by charge separation.

Action Spectra

The overall reaction catalyzed by DNA photolyase can be written as follows:[10]

$$E + S \xrightleftharpoons[k_2]{k_1} ES \xrightarrow[hv]{k_3} E + P \tag{8}$$

The binding step is light-independent. The action spectra of various forms of photolyases are therefore expected to yield useful information regarding the functions of individual chromophores in overall photolysis. Rupert[10,62] developed a simple approach for a quantitative treatment of action spectra data in complex systems which has been used extensively in photolyase research.

Rupert Equation.   Under enzyme excess condition the reaction (8) becomes pseudo-first order

$$d[ES]/dt = k_3 [ES] \tag{9}$$

and the integrated form

$$[ES]_t/[ES]_o = e^{-k_3 t} \tag{10}$$

The first order rate constant k_3 may be written

$$k_3 = I. \phi. s. \tag{11}$$

where I = light intensity, ϕ = quantum yield of repair, and s = molecular absorbance cross section [p(probability that a photon passing through a molecule will be absorbed) X a (cross section of the molecule)]. Defining $k_p = \phi.s$, then

$$[ES]_t/[ES]_o = e^{-k_p I t} \tag{12}$$

From the equivalency of theoretical and experimental definitions of transmission

$$T = I/I_o = e^{-nsl} = 10^{-\epsilon cl} \tag{13}$$

where n = [absorbing units], s = absorbance cross section, and l = pathlength of light passing through sample. From this equation it can be shown (by applying appropriate conversion factors)

$$s \; (mm^2/molec) = 3.83 \times 10^{-10} \; \epsilon(M^{-1}cm^{-1}) \tag{14}$$

Therefore,

$$k_p \; (mm^2/photon) = 3.83 \times 10^{-19} \; \epsilon(M^{-1}cm^{-1}) \times \phi \tag{15}$$

Using the energy equivalence of a photon

$$E_{(hv)} = 19.8 \times 10^{-10} \; erg/\lambda(nm) \tag{16}$$

Substituting into (15) and rearranging

$$\epsilon \; (M^{-1}cm^{-1}) \times \phi = 5.2 \times 10^9 \; \frac{k_p \; (mm^2/erg)}{\lambda \; (nm)} \tag{17}$$

Therefore, by plotting fraction of dimers remaining unrepaired as a function of light dose from the integrated form of Rupert Equation (12)

$$\ln [ES]_t/[ES]_o = -k_pL \qquad (18)$$

where $L = I.t$ one obtains k_p from the slope of this first-order rate equation and substituting into (17) the photolytic cross section ($\epsilon\phi$) is obtained. The advantage of this form of absolute action spectra analysis is twofold: (1), it enables one to measure the photolytic cross-section in a complex system such as a cell where the light absorbing species of interest contributes only a small- and unknown-fraction of total absorption; and (2) even in well-defined systems such as purified photolyase plus DNA mixture where photolyase is the only light absorbing species at the photoreactivating wavelength, the photolytic cross-section can be obtained at enzyme-substrate concentrations typically used in biochemical experiments (nanomolar to micromolar), where the fraction of light absorbed by the system is so low (typically $<0.1\%$) as to be practically immeasurable by currently available technology. Finally, since fractions of Pyr<>Pyr remaining unrepaired in a photoreactivated cell can be easily calculated from cellular survival this analytical approach can be applied to in vivo and in vitro systems with equal theoretical rigorousness and thus allows one to obtain values in the two systems which can be directly compared.

Preillumination Effect. The first absolute action spectrum of a pure photo-lyase was obtained with the *E. coli* enzyme.[76] This spectrum, shown in Figure 14A revealed some unexpected features. First, the photolytic cross-section ($\epsilon\phi$) even at its highest was approximately an order of magnitude lower than the $\epsilon\phi$

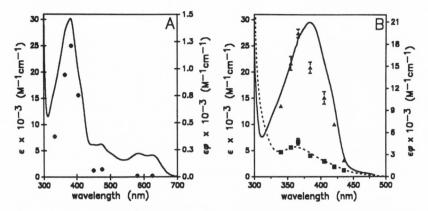

Figure 14. Absorbance and absolute action spectra of radical and reduced forms of *E. coli* photolyase. (**A**) Radical: E-FADH°-MTHF; (**B**) Reduced: E-FADH$_2$-MTHF form (triangles), and E-FADH$_2$ form (squares). Note the difference in $\epsilon\phi$ scale of (**A**) and (**B**) and also the drastic divergence between ϵ and $\epsilon\phi$ of E-FADH°MTHF at $\lambda > 400$ nm.

values measured in vivo.[64] Second, the action spectrum did not match the absorption spectrum, a rare occurrence in bimolecular photochemical reactions suggesting either a biphotonic reaction or photochemistry from higher excited states. However, the reaction was monophotonic as determined by the time-fluence rate reciprocity relationship. Third, even though the enzyme had a relatively high extinction coefficient at the 450-650 nm interval ($\varepsilon \sim$ 4000-5000), photoreactivation at these wavelengths was negligible. This latter finding was consistent with the vast literature on in vivo photoreactivation, indicating an absence of activity at $\lambda > 500$ nm, hence the common practice of conducting the "dark reactions" of photolyase under yellow light.

The cause of these unexpected findings became apparent when it was realized that the E-FADH° form of the enzyme was a purification artifact[45,76] and that the FADH° was being photoreduced during the photoreactivation reaction. Thus, it became possible to explain all three unusual features of the in vitro action spectrum. The photolytic cross-section was low because in reality it was the photolytic cross section of photoreduction of FADH° to $FADH_2$[44] and not of photosplitting of Pyr<>Pyr. The action spectrum did not match the absorption spectrum because the active cofactor in repair is $FADH_2$ and not FADH° which dominates the absorption spectrum of purified enzyme at $\lambda > 450$ nm. The sequence of events turned out to be the photoreduction of FADH° followed by repair by $FADH_2$ which absorbs a second photon. However, the reaction is not biphotonic because once FADH° is photoreduced to $FADH_2$ the latter could participate in several rounds of repair before becoming reoxidized. Finally, the 450-650 nm region was not active in photorepair because absorption in this region is due to the catalytically inert FADH° which does not exist in vivo as evidenced by the lack of an EPR signal in photolyase overproducing cell.[45] When the action spectrum of $E-FADH_2$-MTHF form (the in vivo form) was obtained the in vitro spectrum was more consistent with in vivo results (Figure 14B and Figure 15).

Incidentally, these findings explained a curious phenomenon which was puzzling during the early stages of characterization of photoenzymatic repair. In 1962, Rupert, while defining the basic reaction mechanism of photolyase using cell-free yeast extract, demonstrated that photorepair occurred only when the enzyme-substrate mixture was irradiated and that there was no repair if the two components were separately exposed to light and then mixed.[10] However, the preilluminated enzyme showed higher activity upon mixing with substrate and re-exposing to photoreactivating light. This phenomenon, called the "preillumination effect" was investigated in some detail.[62,67,68] Harm and Rupert[67] obtained an "action spectrum" for the preillumination effect and noted that while this, in general, resembled the action spectrum for photoreactivation there was significant preillumination effect with $\lambda = 546$ nm, where no photoreactivation could be detected. Harm[68] identified a $\lambda_{max} = 577$ nm for the preillumination effect and found that under non-turnover conditions photoreactivation with non-preilluminated enzyme was bi-photonic provided that the second photon was delivered

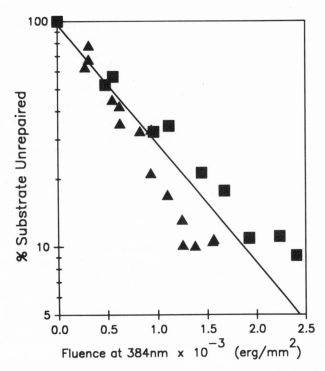

Figure 15. Rupert plot for repair in vivo and in vitro by *E. coli* photolyase. The fraction of T<>T (*in vitro*) or photorepairable lesions (in vivo) remaining as a function of light dose at 384 nm. Squares, purified photolyase; triangles, in vivo photoreactivation. From Payne and Sancar.[50]

within 1 msec of the first. As this was not a bi-photonic reaction in the generally accepted sense it was termed "two-photon photolysis." If the enzyme was preilluminated the reaction was a typical one-photon photolysis. In light of the studies with the E-FADH° form of *E.coli* photolyase and the findings of E-FADH° form in yeast photolyase[43] it appears that the preillumination effect is simply the result of the photoreduction of FADH°. This has indeed now been demonstrated with pure *E. coli* photolyase.[45] It is worth noting though, that while photoreduced *E. coli* photolyase reoxidizes rapidly to the FADH° form, the yeast photolyase is more resistant to air oxidation and therefore the "preillumination effect" has a half-life of about six hours at 5 °C.[67]

Photophysics of Photolyase (Energy and Electron Transfer)

All available evidence indicates that the second chromophore (MTHF or 8-HDF) transfers energy to $FADH_2$ which repairs Pyr<>Pyr by a charge transfer mechanism. Experimental data for this model have come from three different approaches.

Absolute Action Spectrum. Absolute action spectra are now available for the *E. coli* and *S. cerevisiae* enzymes in vivo[94] and for *E. coli*[50,76] and *S. cerevisiae*[150] with purified enzymes. An absolute action spectrum for *M. thermoautotrophicum* photolyase[31] and relative action spectra for *S. griseus*[55] and *A. nidulans*[27] have also been published. The most extensively investigated is the *E. coli* DNA photolyase which will be discussed in detail.

The absolute action spectra of *E. coli* photolyase emphasizing the contributions of the two known ($FADH_2$ and MTHF) and one suspected (aromatic amino acids) chromophores are shown in Figure 16A, B, and C, respectively. To clearly define the role of $FADH_2$ in photolysis the enzyme was defolated by photodecomposition and the flavin was photoreduced, and then the absolute action spectrum of the E-$FADH_2$ form was obtained under anaerobic conditions (Figure 16A). The results shown in Figure 16A reveal a close correspondence between the absorption and action spectra. From this data it appears that the quantum yield for repair $\phi_R = 0.69$ and that $FADH_2$ transfers an electron at a quantum yield of $\phi_{ET} > \phi_R = 0.69$. Figure 16B shows the absolute action spectrum of the holoenzyme (E-$FADH_2$-MTHF). Perhaps the most striking feature of this spectrum is the much higher values of $\varepsilon\phi$ at every wavelength compared to the E-$FADH_2$ form. As an example at 366 nm, which is the most efficient wavelength for both forms, $\varepsilon\phi$ of the holoenzyme is 4-fold higher than $\varepsilon\phi$ of the $FADH_2$ form. Thus, it is clear from these figures that even though $FADH_2$ appears to be the catalytic cofactor, three out of every four photons used for photorepair is absorbed by the antenna molecule, MTHF. Assuming that MTHF's sole function is energy transfer the quantum yield of energy transfer at every wavelength can be calculated from[50]

$$\varepsilon\phi \text{ (E-}FADH_2\text{-MTHF)} = \varepsilon(FADH_2) \times \phi_{ET}(FADH_2) + \varepsilon(MTHF) \times \phi_{eT}(MTHF) \times \phi_{ET}(FADH_2)$$

Although the efficiency of energy transfer shows some variability with wavelengths it is relatively constant over the whole spectrum with an average value of $\phi_{eT}(MTHF) = 0.8$. The relatively small but reproducible discrepancy between the absorption spectrum of holoenzyme and its action spectrum probably reflects the unusual mechanism of energy transfer from MTHF to $FADH_2$ which is not completely understood at present.

In Figure 16C the action spectrum was extended into far-UV to find out whether aromatic residues (Trp, Cys, Tyr) in the apoenzyme contributed to repair either by energy transfer to the catalytic cofactor $FADH_2$ or by direct charge transfer. It appears that they do not contribute significantly by either mechanism. The very efficient photorepair achieved at far-UV can be totally accounted for by the absorption of the two near UV chromophores (MTMF and $FADH_2$) in this region of the spectrum. More recent work has shown that Trp227 repairs T<>T by direct electron transfer.[155]

To find out whether the primary and secondary structures affect the photochemical step the repair of various substrates shown in Figure 17 were investi-

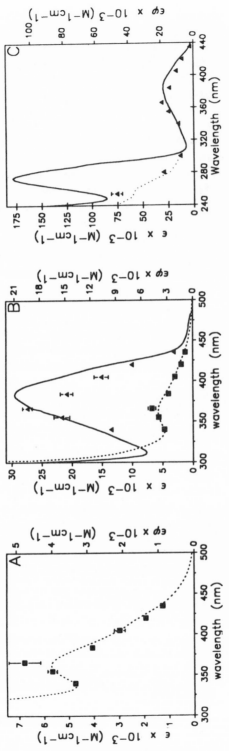

Figure 16. Absorbance and absolute action spectrum of *E. coli* photolyase. (**A**) E-FADH₂ in the near-UV-visible range; (**B**) Holoenzyme (E-FADH₂-MTHF) and E-FADH₂ in the near-UV-visible range; (**C**) Holoenzyme in the far-UV-visible range. The data points for εφ were obtained from Rupert plots. *Solid lines* represent experimentally measured absorption spectrum; *Broken line* is the calculated absorption of FADH₂ + MTHF in the far-UV, based on the absorption spectra of free chromophores. From Payne and Sancar.[50]

Substrate	Length	Φ_{384}
5'-...GCAGGCAAGT<>TGGAGGAATT... 3'-...CGTCCGTTCA--ACCTCCTTAA...	48 bp	0.503 ± 0.026
5'-GCAGCTGACGAAT<>TTAGCTC 3'-GACTGGTTA--AATCGAGCTCG	20 bp (A)	0.489 ± 0.041
5'-GCTCGAGCTCAAT<>TAGTCAG 3'-CTCGAGTTA--ATCAGTCCTCG	20 bp (B)	0.478 ± 0.079
5'-GCAGCTGACTAAT<>TGAGCTC 3'-GACTGATTA--ACTCGAGCTCG	20 bp (C)	0.504 ± 0.061
5'-GCTCGAGCTAT<>TAACGTCAG 3'-CTCGATA--ATTGCAGTCGACG	20 bp (D)	0.449 ± 0.022
5'...GCAGGCAAGT<>TGGAGGAATT...	48 bases	0.429 ± 0.030

Figure 17. Effect of primary and secondary structures on the photochemical step of *E.coli* photolyase holoenzyme. The first five substrates were tested in double-stranded form. The 48 mer was also denatured and used in a photorepair experiment to investigate the effect of a strandedness on photorepair. From Payne and Sancar.[50]

gated. It appears from that the strandedness of DNA and the neighboring sequences do not affect the photochemistry of repair by *E. coli* photolyase.[50]

Time Resolved Absorbance. Picosecond flash photolysis studies have been conducted on various forms of *E. coli* photolyase.[147,148,151] When the E-FADH° form is irradiated with 353 nm a flavin doublet ($\tau = 10^{-10}$s) is identified which becomes a flavin quartet ($\tau = 10^{-6}$s) on its way to photoreduction or non-radiative decay. If the E-FADH°-MTHF is irradiated the first species observed at 40 ps was originally assigned to an encounter complex between *MTHF and FADH°[147] but it now appears to be pure MTHF* singlet which decays within 500 ps but it is quenched very rapidly to yield the FADH° quartet.[149] This was the first direct evidence for energy transfer with high yield from MTHF to FADH°. A similar situation with the E-FADH$_2$-MTHF form of the enzyme has been observed. Transient spectrum of E-MTHF reveals a MTHF singlet with a lifetime $\tau \simeq 400$ ps. In the E-FADH$_2$-MTHF form the earliest recorded species (40 ps) shows a peak at ~480 nm (MTHF* singlet) which is nearly completely quenched by 100 ps. There is no obvious sign for an encounter complex between the two chromophores in the transient spectra. In the presence of FADH$_2$, the MTHF singlet lifetime goes down from ~400 ps to 130 ps indicating energy transfer with >62% efficiency.

Picosecond flash photolysis with the enzyme plus substrate system have been equally informative.[151] Most of these experiments have been conducted with the E-FADH$_2$ (folate free)-form of the enzyme so as to observe the electron transfer reaction independent of energy transfer processes. Figure 18 shows the transient spectra of E-FADH$_2$ + U<>U and E-FADH$_2$ + U-U systems after a 353 nm

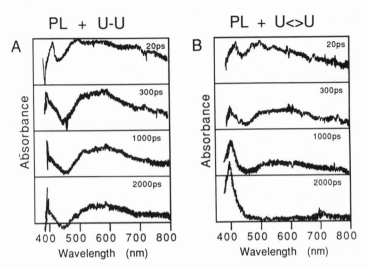

Figure 18. Picosecond flash photolysis of photolyase-substrate complex. Transient absorption spectra of E-FADH$_2$ form of *E. coli* photolyase in presence of: (**A**) Up U dinucleotide; or (**B**), U<>U dinucleotide photodimer. The mixtures were exposed to a 12 ps 340 nm pulse and spectra were recorded after the indicated delay times. The transient spectra of E-FADH$_2$ alone is identical to that shown in **A** at all time points. After Okamura et al.[151]

laser pulse of 12 ps duration. As is apparent from the figure, in the absence of substrate an FADH$_2$ singlet is generated by the pulse which decays with a lifetime of $\tau = 1.7$ ns. In the presence of substrate, the singlet is quenched efficiently ($\tau = 0.2$ ns) and a new species ($\lambda_{max} = 400$ nm) appears at $\tau = 300$ ps and continues to accumulate up to 2 ns. This is assigned to a radical (presumably substrate) intermediate of the splitting reaction. From the lifetimes of the flavin singlet in presence and absence of substrate and assuming electron transfer as the sole deactivating reaction the quantum yield of electron transfer is calculated to be $\phi_{ET} = 0.88$.

Steady-State and Time-Resolved Fluorescence. Steady-state fluorescence measurements by Jorns et al.[144] and Kim et al.[149] revealed that folate fluorescence was efficiently quenched by FADH° and FADH$_2$ (by measuring MTHF fluorescence in E-MTHF, E-FADH°-MTHF and E-FADH$_2$-MTHF forms of the enzyme) and that substrate quenched the flavin fluorescence in the E-FADH$_2$ + T<>T system. The folate fluorescence intensity was reduced to 3.5% by FADH° and to 8% by FADH$_2$.[149] More accurate values for energy transfer were obtained from the folate fluorescence times of various forms of the enzyme:[149] E-MTHF ($\tau = 354$ ps), E-MTHF-FADH$_2$ ($\tau = 134$ ps) and E-FADH°-MTHF

($\tau < 30$ ps). From these, energy transfer efficiencies were calculated to be $>92\%$ for MTHF $\rightarrow$ FADH°, and 62% for MTHF $\rightarrow$ FADH$_2$.

To measure rate and efficiency of electron transfer the fluorescence lifetime of E-FADH$_2$ was measured in the presence and absence of substrate:

$$\tau_F(\text{E-FADH}_2) \ = \ 1.3 \text{ ns and } \tau_F(\text{E-FADH}_2 + \text{U}<>\text{U}) \ = \ 0.16 \text{ ns.}$$

From these values the quantum yield of electron transfer $\phi_{ET} = 0.88$ is calculated which is in excellent agreement with the result obtained by transient absorption spectroscopy.

In conclusion, the steady-state Pyr<>Pyr photolysis experiments, and studies by time resolved absorption, and time-resolved fluorescence are in good agreement regarding the rates and efficiencies of energy and electron transfer processes involved in photolyase mediated photorepair: MTHF transfers energy by dipole-dipole interaction or electron exchange mechanism to FADH$_2$ with a quantum yield of $\phi_{eT} = 0.63\text{-}0.8$ which then transfers electron to substrate with a quantum yield $\phi_{ET} = 0.88$. The resulting Pyr<>Pyr radical splits with $\phi_{Spl} = 0.69$ for an overall quantum yield of repair $\phi_R = 0.5\text{-}0.59$.

Photochemistry of Repair

All available evidence indicate that photolyases repair Pyr<>Pyr by a charge transfer mechanism. Furthermore, the fact that the catalytic cofactor is FADH$_2$ in both the folate and flavin class photolyases makes it very likely that the initial reaction involves charge transfer from FADH$_2$ to substrate, as this cofactor is an excellent electron donor in ground state ($E° = 0.2$ V) and expected to be so in excited state as well. However, direct experimental proof of the predicted radical intermediates is lacking. In general three methods have been employed for detecting radical intermediates in chemical reactions:[152] direct observation of the radical species by time-resolved absorption or EPR spectroscopy; use of substrate analogs whose products carry a signature of a radical precursor or influence the reaction rate in certain ways, and finally the transformation of the transient radicals into stable paramagnetic species with "spin traps." Two of these methods have been employed to provide experimental evidence for a radical intermediate in photolyase reaction and to determine the direction of electron transfer in the initial stages of photolysis.

Witmer et al.[106] attempted to determine the direction of electron transfer by measuring the secondary deuterium isotope effects (V/K) on the cleavage of 5,5′-dideuterio, 6,6′-dideuterio, and tetradeuterio-U<>Us. Photodimer splitting by reduction is predicted to lead to cleavage of C5-C5′ bond followed by C6-C6′ while splitting by oxidation may proceed by fragmentation of C6-C6′ followed by cleavage of C5-C5′ bond (Figure 19) provided that the splitting is not concerted in these reactions. Assuming that the cleavage of the first C-C bond is the rate limiting step than a V/K effect is predicted for the 5,5′-dideuterio form in the dimer reduction pathway, and for the 6,6′-dideuterio form in the

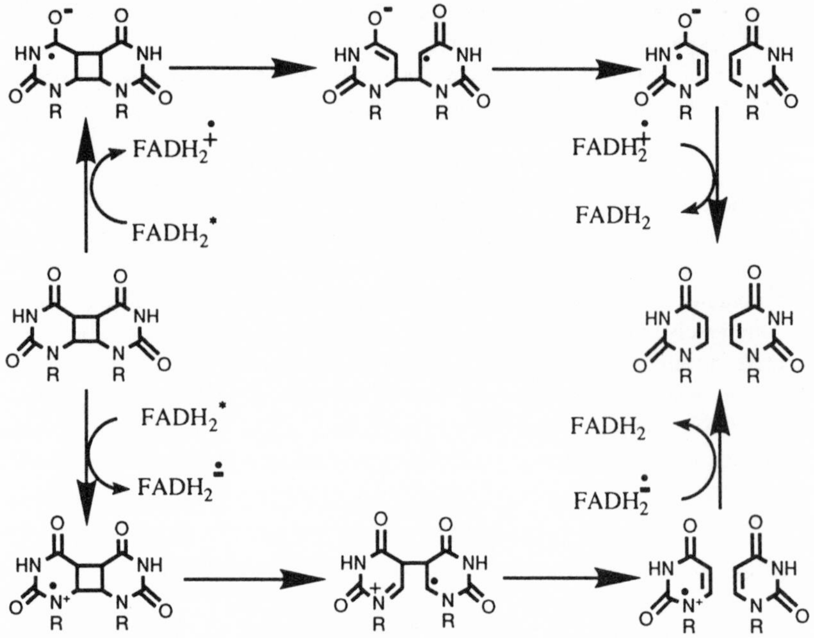

Figure 19. Two potential mechanisms for photolyase. In the reductive pathway (*top*) photoexcited flavin ($FADH_2$) donates an electron to generate dimerization intermediate while in the oxidative pathway (*bottom*) $FADH_2$ oxidizes the dimer to generate dimer radical cation. Although in this scheme the subsequent bond rearrangements are shown sequentially the secondary isotope effect on photolyase mediated cleavage indicates concerted- and perhaps synchronous- cleavage of C5-C5' and C6-C6' bonds. From Witmer et al.[106]

dimer oxidation pathway. The secondary deuterium isotope effects of these three forms of U<>U are summarized in Table 6.[106] The two dideuterio forms have virtually the same V/K effect and the effect of the tetradeuterio-U<>U is equal to the product of the V/K effects of the two dideuterio photodimers. The most likely explanation for these results is that photolyase mediated Pyr<>Pyr splitting occurs by a concerted mechanism. Although concerted cleavage for cyclobutane cation radical has been proposed[153–154] which would favor a photodimer cation mechanism for photolyase, there is no experimental evidence for sequential cleavage of the two C-C bond in cyclobutane anion radical and therefore, these results do not rule out a Pyr<>Pyr anion intermediate in repair. In fact, a 5,5'-linked bis (pyrimidine) intermediate was observed in anthroquinone sensitized splitting of 1,3-dimethyluracil photodimer.[131] As this splitting occurs by dimer cation radical intermediate[129] the concerted splitting observed by Witmer et

Table 6. V/K Isotope Effect on *E. coli* Photolyase[a]

Substrate	D(V/K)[b]
$H_4 - (U<>U) + 6, 6',5,5' - D_4 - (U<>U)$	1.15
$H_4 - (U<>U) + 5,5' - D_2 - (U<>U)$	1.08
$H_4 - (U<>U) + 6,6' - D_2 - (U<>U)$	1.07

[a] From Witmer et al. [106]. [b] All isotope effects were corrected to 100% deuteration.

al.[106] with *E. coli* photolyase could be taken as evidence for Pyr<>Pyr splitting via photodimer anion mechanism (top pathway in Figure 19).

Okamura et al[151] used transient absorption spectroscopy in an effort to discover and identify the radical intermediates in photolysis. The results of one such experiment is shown in Figure 18. In the absence of Pyr<>Pyr, excitation with a 12 ps pulse generates a broad band in the 500-900 nm region which decays with a lifetime of 1.7 ns. This species, which is attributed to $FADH_2$ singlet is strongly quenched by U<>U and after about 0.5 ns delay a new species absorbing around 400 nm appears. It is not possible to assign this transient to any of the radical species shown in Figure 19. However, it is quite significant that quenching of flavin singlet did not produce and absorption band attributable to $FADH_2^{+\cdot}$ with its maximum at ~500 nm ($\varepsilon \sim 10^4$), as would be expected for a Pyr<>Pyr anion radical mechanism. However, electron abstraction by $FADH_2$ from U<>U can be rejected on thermodynamic grounds. One likely explanation for the transient spectra is the following. It is possible that the two-electron reduced flavin of photolyase is in the $FADH^-$ form and not $FADH_2$. Indeed, neutral reduced flavins have a $\lambda_{max} \sim 390$ nm with a relatively low extinction coefficient ($\varepsilon = 2,000-3,000$) whereas the $FADH^-$ form has a λ_{max} at 340-370 nm with a relatively high extinction coefficient. Then, an electron loss from $FADH^-$ to Pyr<>Pyr would generate $FADH^\circ$ which has a broad absorption band in the 500-700 nm region which would be obscured by the absorption of the flavin singlet. That no absorption is observed at $\lambda>450$ nm after 2 ns implies that $FADH^-$ is reformed by back electron transfer leaving behind a Pyr + Pyr$^{-\cdot}$, within this time scale. It is interesting that there is no complementarity between the level of flavin singlet quenching and the magnitude of the 400 nm species. It is quite possible that the cyclobutane ring of the Pyr<>Pyr anion radical is split by a concerted mechanism in <2 ns such that the Pyr<>Pyr radical anion (top pathway in Figure 19) which exists during this period may not be observable because of low absorbance at $\lambda>400$ nm and that the 400 nm species is actually a uracil biradical or a uracil radical anion.

To summarize, the picosecond flash photolysis studies provide evidence for a radical intermediate in Pyr<>Pyr splitting and are consistent with a Pyr<>Pyr radical ion intermediate.

SPECTROSCOPIC PROPERTIES OF REACTION INTERMEDIATES (10^{-11} – 10^{0} s) OF *E. COLI* DNA PHOTOLYASE

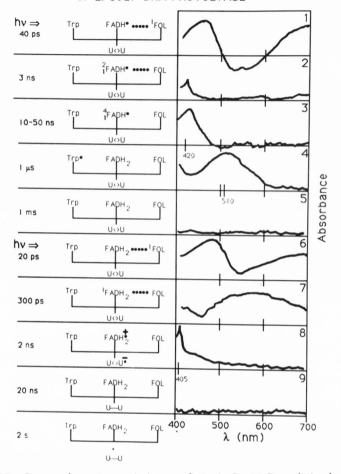

Figure 20. Proposed spectroscopic intermediates in Pyr<>Pyr splitting by *E. coli* photolyase. This scheme is for repair initiating with the radical form of the enzyme, i.e., steps **1–4** reflect the events and spectra of enzyme in which FADH° is photo-reduced to $FADH_2$. Steps **5-9** occur with the activated form of the enzyme. The spectra shown are actually difference spectra drawn as absolute absorbance to emphasize the absorbance of the excited or intermediate states. The composite drawing shown here includes data from picosecond, nanosecond, and millisecond flash photolysis as well as steady state illumination. The assignment of the intermediates is as follows: **1**, folate excited state singlet; **2**, flavin excited state doublet; **3**, flavin radical quartet (λ_{max} = 420 nm); **4**, Trp neutral radical (formed by H abstraction by $^4FADH°$ from Trp 306); **5**,E-$FADH_2$-MTHF ground state (λ_{max} = 384 nm is not shown in difference spectra; **6**, folate excited state singlet; **7**, $FADH_2$ excited state singlet formed by direct absorption or energy transfer from folate; **8**, Radical reaction intermediate (λ_{max} = 400 nm), possibly of substrate; **9**, ground state enzyme following repair (difference spectrum).

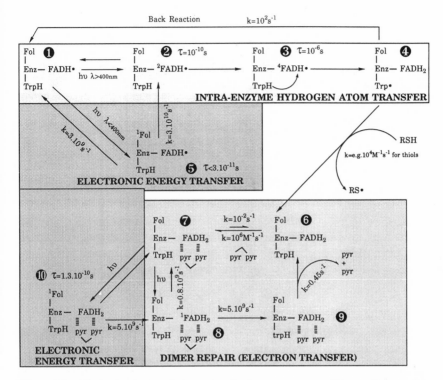

Figure 21. Photophysical and photochemical rate constants of Pyr<>Pyr repair by photolyase. The process, in vitro, involves energy, electron, and hydrogen atom transfer. This is an updated version of the scheme published by Heelis et al.[147]

Thermal Effects

The rate of photoreactivation, like all enzyme catalyzed reactions, is temperature dependent in the range of $+ 37\,^{\circ}C$ to $+ 3\,^{\circ}C$.[62] However, this is a simple consequence of the effect of temperature on the rate of formation of enzyme-substrate complex. The photolytic step itself, as expected for a photochemical reaction, is temperature independent over this range. In contrast a drastic drop in the quantum yield of repair was observed below $-2\,^{\circ}C$ both with the yeast enzyme[59] and live *E. coli* cells.[60] Furthermore, the rate of repair becomes dose-rate dependent at lower temperatures indicating a bi-photonic reaction. These studies have not been repeated with purified photolyases nor have they been subjected to a rigorous quantitative analysis. However, recently Kim and Rose[135,136] have investigated the effect of temperature on Pyr<>Pyr anion splitting by using the tethered indole-Pyr<>Pyr system. In this system too, a drastic temperature-dependence was seen. By comparing the fluorescence quenching (electron transfer) to splitting at various temperatures the authors were able to show that electron transfer occurred efficiently even at low temperatures where

Table 7. Dimer-indole Splitting in EPA and PMM[a]

Medium	Temperature	Splitting[b]	Fluorescence quenching (%)[c]
EPA	≅298 K	+	>90
EPA	77 K	−	50
PMM	≅298 K	+	65
PMM	77 K	−	>30[d]

[a] From Kim and Rose.[(135)] [b] A ' + ' indicates splitting was detectable; a ' − ' indicates splitting was not detectable under the conditions employed. [c] Quenching is reported relative to the fluorescence of 5-methoxytryptophol by the same method and at the same temperature, except as noted. [d] Relative to 5-methoxytryptophol in PMM at room temperature.

splitting was very inefficient and concluded that the activation energy barrier of Pyr<>Pyr anion was such (~ 1.3 kcal.mol^{-1}) that it favored charge recombination over charge separation at low temperatures (Table 7).

5.3. Conclusions

E. coli photolyase, and perhaps all other photolyases, repair photodimers by transferring electronic energy from their second chromophores to $FADH_2$ at the reaction center which then donates an electron to the photodimer to initiate splitting of the cyclobutane ring by a concerted mechanism. Figure 20 shows an idealized picture of the spectroscopic species generated during these processes and Figure 21 summarizes the rate constants for the various reactions between the absorption of a photon and the repair and release of a pyrimidine dimer.

ACKNOWLEDGMENTS

I thank my colleagues T. Begley, P. F. Heelis, S. T. Kim, Y. F. Li, T. Okamura and G. Payne for providing me some of the figures used in this review and for helpful discussions. This work was supported by NIH Grant GM31082.

REFERENCES

1. Jagger, J. Solar UV-Actions on Living Cells, Praeger, N. Y. **1985.**
2. Wang, S. Y. *Photochem. Photobiol. of Nucleic Acids,* Vols. I, II, Academic Press, N. Y. **1976.**
3. Sancar, A.; Sancar, G. B. *Annu. Rev. Biochem.* **1988,** *57,* 29–67.
4. Myles, G.; Sancar, A. *Chem. Res. Tox.* **1989,** *2,* 197–226.
5. Kelner, A. Proc. Natl. Acad. Sci. USA **1949,** *35,* 73–79.
6. Rupert, C. S.; Goodgal, S. H.; Herriott, R. M. *J. Gen. Physiol.* **1958,** *41,* 451–471.
7. Beukers, R.; Berends, W. *Biochim. Biophys.* Acta **1960,** *41,* 550–551.
8. Wang, S. Y. *Nature* **1960,** *188,* 844–845.
9. Rupert, C. S. *J. Gen. Physiol.* **1962,** *45,* 703–724.

10. Rupert, C. S. *J. Gen. Physiol.* **1962**, *45*, 725–471.
11. Wulff, D. L.; Rupert, C. S. *Biochem. Biophys. Res. Comm.* **1962**, *7*, 237–240.
12. Setlow, J. K.; Setlow, R. B. *Nature* **1963**, *197*, 560–562.
13. Lamola, A. A.; Yamane, T. Proc. Natl. Acad. Sci. USA **1967**, *58*, 443–446.
14. Camerman, N.; Camerman, A. *J. Am. Chem. Soc.* **1970**, *92*, 2523–2527.
15. Cadet, J.; Voituriez, L.; Hruska, F. E.; Grand, A. *Biopolymers* **1985**, *24*, 897–903.
16. Hruska, F. E.; Voituriez, L.; Grand, A.; Cadet, J. *Biopolymers* **1986**, *25*, 1399–1417.
17. Rao, S. N.; Keepers, J. W.; Kollman, P. *Nucleic Acids Res.* **1984**, *12*, 4789–4807.
18. Pearlman, D. A.; Holbrook, S. R.; Pirkle, D. H.; Kim, S.-H. *Science* **1985**, *227*, 1304–1308.
19. Kemmink, J.; Boelens, R.; Koning, T.; van der Marel, G. A.; van Boom, J. H.; Kaptein, R. *Nucleic Acids Res.* **1987**, *15*, 4645–4653.
20. Taylor, J.-S.; Garrett, D. S.; Brockie, I. R.; Svoboda, D. L.; Telser, J. *Biochemistry* **1990**, *29*, 8858–8866.
21. Hayes, F. N.; Williams, D. L.; Ratliff, R. L.; Varghese, A. J.; Rupert, C. S. *J. Am. Chem. Soc.* **1971**, *93*, 4940–4942.
22. Ciarrocchi, G.; Pedrini, A. M. *J. Molec. Biol.* **1982**, *155*, 177–183.
23. Husain, I.; Griffith, J.; Sancar, A. *Proc. Natl. Acad. Sci. USA* **1988**, *85*, 2258–2562.
24. Sancar, A.; Sancar, G. B. *J. Molec. Biol.* **1984**, *172*, 223–227.
25. Iwatsuki, N.; Joe, C. O.; Werbin, H. *Biochemistry* **1980**, *19*, 1172–1176.
26. Eker, A. P. M.; Hessels, J. K. C.; van de Velde, J. *Biochemistry* **1988**, *27*, 1758–1765.
27. Eker, A. P. M.; Kooiman, P.; Hessels, J. K. C.; Yasui, A. *J. Biol. Chem.* **1990**, *265*, 8009–8015.
28. Jorns, M. S.; Sancar, G. B.; Sancar A. *Biochemistry* **1984**, *23*, 2673–2679.
29. Johnson, J. L.; Hamm-Alvarez, S.; Payne, G.; Sancar, G. B.; Rajagopalan, K. V.; Sancar, A. *Proc. Natl. Acad. Sci. USA* **1988**, *85*, 2046–2050.
30. Eker, A. P. M.; Dekker, R. H.; Berends, W. *Photochem. Photobiol.* **1981**, *33*, 65–72.
31. Kiener, A.; Husain, I.; Sancar, A.; Walsh, C. *J. Biol. Chem.* **1989**, *264*, 13880–13887.
32. Kiener, A.; Gall, R.; Rechsteiner, T.; Leisinger, T. *Arch. Microbiol.* **1985**, *143*, 147–150.
33. Sabourin, C. L. K.; Ray, R. D. *Photochem. Photobiol.* **1988**, *47*, 717–723.
34. Giacomoni, P. J. Photochem. Photobiol., *B:Biol.* **1989**, *4*, 268–269.
35. Sancar, G. B.; Smith, F. W.; Lorence, M. C.; Rupert, C. S.; Sancar, A. *J. Biol. Chem.* **1984**, *259*, 6033–6038.
36. Sancar, G. B. *Nucleic Acids Res.* **1985**, *13*, 8231–8246.
37. Yasui, A.; Langeveld, S. A. *Gene* **1985**, *36*, 349–355.
38. Yasui, A.; Takao, M.; Oikawa, A.; Kiener, A.; Walsh, C. T.; Eker, A. P. M. *Nucleic Acids Res.* **1988**, *16*, 4447–4463.
39. Kobayashi, T.; Takao, M.; Oikawa, A.; Yasui, A. *Nucleic Acid. Res.* **1989**, *17*, 4731–4744.
40. Takao, M.; Kobayashi, T.; Oikawa, A.; Yasui, A. *J. Bacteriology* **1989**, *171*, 6323–6329.
41. Li, Y. F.; Sancar, A. *Biochemistry* **1990**, *29*, 5698–5706.
42. Malhotra, K.; Baer, M.; Li, Y. F.; Sancar, G. B.; Sancar, A. *J. Biol. Chem.* **1992**, *267*, in press.
43. Sancar, G. B.; Smith, F. W.; Heelis, P. F. *J. Biol. Chem.* **1987**, *262*, 15437–15445.
44. Heelis, P. F.; Sancar, A. *Biochemistry* **1986**, *25*, 8163–8166.
45. Payne, G.; Heelis, P. F.; Rohrs, B. R.; Sancar, A. *Biochemistry*, **1987**, *26*, 7121–7127.
46. Hamm-Alvarez, S.; Sancar, A.; Rajagopalan, K. V. *J. Biol. Chem.* **1989**, *264*, 9449–9656.
47. Heelis, P. F.; Payne, G. P.; Sancar, A. *Biochemistry* **1987**, *26*, 4634–4640.
48. Jordan, S. P.; Jorns, M. S. *Biochemistry* **1988**, *27*, 8915–8923.
49. Hamm-Alvarez, S. F.; Sancar, A.; Rajagopalan, K. V. *J. Biol. Chem.* **1990**, *265*, 18656–19662.
50. Payne, G.; Sancar, A. *Biochemistry* **1990**, *29*, 7715–7727.
51. Visser, A. J. W. G.; Ghisla, S.; Massey, V.; Miller, F.; Veeger, C. *Eur. J. Biochem.* **1979**, *101*, 13–21.
52. Kim, S.-T.; Babcock, G.; Sancar, A. Unpublished observation.

53. Spencer, R.; Fischer, J.; Walsh, C. *Biochemistry* **1976**, *15*, 1043–1053.
54. Eirich, L. D.; Vogels, G. D.; Wolfe, R. S. *Biochemistry*, **1978**, *17*, 4583–4593.
55. Eker, A. P. M.; Hessels, J. K. C.; Dekker, R. H. *Photochem. Photobiol.* **1986**, *44*, 197–205.
56. Mayerl, F.; Piret, J.; Kiener, A.; Walsh, C. T.; Yasui, A. *J. Bacteriol.* **1990**, *172*, 6061–6065.
57. Harm, H.; Rupert, C. S. *Mutation Res.* **1968**, *6*, 355–370.
58. Harm, W.; Harm, H.; Rupert, C. S. *Mutation Res.* **1968**, *6*, 371–385.
59. Harm, H. *Mutation Res.* **1969**, *7*, 261–271.
60. Harm, W. *Mutation Res.* **1969**, *8*, 411–415.
61. Harm, W. *Mutation Res.* **1970**, *10*, 277–290.
62. Harm, H.; Rupert, C. S. *Mutation Res.* **1970**, *10*, 291–306.
63. Harm, H.; Rupert, C. S. *Mutation Res.* **1970**, *10*, 307–318.
64. Harm, W. *Mutation Res.* **1970**, *10*, 319–333.
65. Nishioka, H.; Harm, W. *Mutation Res.* **1972**, *16*, 121–131.
66. Harm, W. *Mutation Res.* **1976**, *34*, 69–74.
67. Harm, H.; Rupert, C. S. *Mutation Res.* **1976**, *34*, 75–92.
68. Harm, W. *Mutation Res.* **1979**, *60*, 121–133.
69. Husain, I.; Sancar, G. B.; Holbrook, S. R.; Sancar, A. *J. Biol. Chem.* **1987**, *262*, 13188–13197.
70. Sancar, A. Ph. D. Dissertation, 1977, University of Texas at Dallas.
71. von Hippel, P. H.; Berg, O. G. *J. Biol. Chem.* **1989**, *264*, 675–678.
72. Record, T. M. Jr.; Lohman, T. M.; deHaseth, P. *J. Molec. Biol.* **1976**, *107*, 145–158.
73. Lohman, T. M.; deHaseth, P. L.; Record, T. M. Jr. *J. Molec. Biol.* **1980**, *14*, 3522–3530.
74. Sancar, G. B.; Smith, F. W.; Reid, R.; Payne, G.; Levy, M.; Sancar, A. *J. Biol. Chem.* **1987**, *262*, 478–485.
75. Jorns, M. S.; Baldwin, E. T.; Sancar, G. B.; Sancar, A. *J. Biol. Chem.* **1987**, *262*, 486–491.
76. Sancar, G. B.; Jorns, M. S.; Payne, G.; Fluke, D. J.; Rupert, C. S.; Sancar, A. *J. Biol. Chem.* **1987**, *262*, 492–498.
77. Sancar, G. *Mutation Res.* **1990**, *236*, 147–160.
78. Husain, I.; Sancar, A. *Nucleic Acids Res.* **1987**, *15*, 1109–1120.
79. Setlow, R. B.; Carrier, W. L. *J. Mol. Biol.* **1966**, *17*, 237–254.
80. Myles, G. M.; Van Houten, B.; Sancar, A. *Nucleic Acids Res.* **1987**, *15*, 1227–1243.
81. Svoboda, D. L.; Sancar, A.; Taylor, J.-S. Unpublished observation.
82. Payne, G.; Wills, M.; Walsh, C.; Sancar, A. *Biochemistry* **1990**, *29*, 5706–5711.
83. Harm, W.; Hillebrandt, B. *Photochem. Photobiol.* **1962**, *1*, 271–272.
84. Yamomoto, K.; Fujiwara, Y.; Shinagawa, H. *Mol. Gen. Genet.* **1983**, *192*, 282–284.
85. Sancar, A.; Franklin, K. A.; Sancar, G. B. *Proc. Natl. Acad. Sci. USA* **1984**, *81*, 7397–7401.
86. Sancar, A.; Rupp, W. D. *Cell* **1983**, *33*, 249–260.
87. Sancar, G. B. *J. Bacteriol.* **1985**, *161*, 769–771.
88. Sancar, G. B.; Smith, F. W. *Mol. Cell. Biol.* **1989**, *9*, 4767–4776.
89. Kobayaski, T.; Takao, M.; Oikawa, A.; Yasui, A. *Mutation Res.* **1990**, *236*, 27–34.
90. Sibghatullah; Sancar, A. *Biochemistry* **1990**, *29*, 5711–5718.
91. Patrick, M. H.; Harm, H. *Photochem. Photobiol.* **1973**, *18*, 371–386.
92. Sancar, A.; Rupert C. S. *Gene* **1978**, *4*, 294–308.
93. Alcorn, J. L.; Rupert C. S. *J. Bacteriol.* **1990**, *172*, 6885–6891.
94. Harm, H. In *Photochemistry and Photobiology of Nucleic Acids*, Wang, S. Y. Ed. Academic Press, New York, **1976**, *Vol. II*, pp. 219–263.
95. Baer, M.; Sancar, G. B. *Mol. Cell. Biol.* **1989**, *9*, 4777–4788.
96. Van Dyke, M. W.; Dervan, D. B. *Nucl. Acids Res.* **1983**, *11*, 5555–5567.
97. McClarin, J. A.; Frederick, C. W.; Wang, B. C.; Greene, P.; Boyer, H. W.; Grable, J.; Rosenberg, J. M *Science* **1986**, *234*, 1526–1541.
98. Sancar, G. B.; Smith, F. W.; Sancar, A. *Biolchemistry* **1985**, *14*, 1849–1855.

99. Jorns, M. S.; Sancar, G. B.; Sancar, A. *Biochemistry* **1985**, *14*, 1856–1861.
100. Broyde, S.; Stellman, S.; Hingerty, B. *Biopolymers* **1980**, *19*, 1695–1701.
101. Brash, D. E.; Franklin, W. A.; Sancar, G. B.; Sancar, A.; Haseltine, W. A. *J. Biol. Chem.* **1985**, *260*, 11438–11441.
102. Liuzzi, M.; Weinfield, M.; Paterson, M. *J. Biol. Chem.* **1989**, *264*, 6355–6363.
103. Weinfeld, M.; Gentner, N. E.; Johnson, L. D.; Paterson, M. C. *Biochemistry* **1986**, *25*, 2656–2664.
104. Weinfeld, M.; Paterson, M. C. *Nucleic Acids Res.* **1988**, *16*, 5693.
105. Weinfeld, M.; Liuzzi, M.; Paterson, M. C. *J. Biol. Chem.* **1989**, *264*, 6364–6370.
106. Witmer, M. R.; Altmann, E.; Youngm H.; Begley, T. P.; Sancar, A. *J. Am. Chem. Soc.* **1989**, *111*, 9264–9265.
107. Kim, S.-T.; Sancar, A. *Biochemistry* **1991**, *30*, 8623–8630.
108. Ben-Hur, E.; Ben-Ishai, R. *Biochim. Biophys. Acta* **1968**, *166*, 9–15.
109. Selby, C. P.; Sancar, A. *Proc. Natl. Acad. Sci. USA* **1990**, *87*, 3522–3525.
110. Setlow, R. B.; Setlow, J. K. *Proc. Natl. Acad. Sci. USA* **1962**, *48*, 1250–1257.
111. Lamola, A. A. *Mol. Photochem.* **1972**, *4*, 107–133.
112. Patrick, M. H.; Rahn, R. O. In *Photochemistry and Photobiology of Nucleic Acids*, Wang, S. Y. Ed. Academic Press, New York, **1976**, *Vol. II*, pp. 35–95; Lamola, A. A. *J. Am. Chem. Soc.* **1966**, *88*, 813–819.
113. Wacker, A.; Dellweg, H.; Traeger, A.; Kornhauser, A.; Lademann, E.; Tuerck, G.; Selzer, R.; Chandron, P.; Ishimoto, M. *Photochem. Photobiol.* **1964**, *3*, 369–376.
114. Lamola, A. A. *J. Am. Chem. Soc.* **1966**, *88*, 813–819.
115. Ben-Hur, E.; Rosenthal, I. *Photochem. Photobiol.* **1970**, *11*, 163–168.
116. Hélène, C.; Charlier, M. *Photochem. Photobiol.* **1977**, *25*, 429–434.
117. Sutherland, J. C. *Photochem. Photobiol.* **1977**, *25*, 435–440.
118. Sancar, A.; Rupert, C. S. *Mutation Res.* **1978**, *51*, 139–143.
119. Sancar, A.; Rupert, C. S. *J. Bacteriol* **1979**, *138*, 779–782.
120. Youngs, D. A.; Smith, K. C. *Mutation Res.* **1978**, *51*, 131–137.
121. Sancar, A.; Smith, F. W.; Sancar, G. B. *J. Biol. Chem.* **1984**, *259*, 6028–6032.
122. Husain, I.; Sancar, A. *J. Bacteriol.* **1987**, *169*, 2367–2372.
123. Husain, I.; Carrier, W. L.; Regan, J. D.; Sancar, A. *Photochem. Photobiol.* **1988**, *48*, 233–234.
124. Pac, C.; Kubo, J.: Majima, T.; Sakurai, H. *Photochem. Photobiol.* **1982**, *36*, 273–282.
125. Pabon, R. A.; Bauld, N. L. *J. Am. Chem. Soc.* **1984**, *106*, 1145–1146.
126. Hartman, R. F.; Van Camp, J. R.; Rose, S. D. *J. Org. Chem.* **1987**, *52*, 2684–2689.
127. Roth, H. D.; Lamola, A. A. *J. Am. Chem. Soc.* **1972**, *94*, 1013–1014.
128. Kemmink, J.; Eker, A. P. M.; Kaptein, R. *Photochem. Photobiol.* **1986**, *44*, 137–142.
129. Young, T.; Nieman, R.; Rose, S. D. *Photochem. Photobiol.* **1990**, *52*, 661–668.
130. Pac, C.; Miyamoto, I.; Masaki, Y.; Furusho, S.; Yanagida, S.; Ohno, T.; Yoshimura, A. *Photochem. Photobiol.* **1990**, *52*, 973–979.
131. Sasson, S.; Elad, D. *J. Org. Chem.* **1972**, *37*, 3164–3167.
132. Santus, R.; Hélène, C.; Ovadea, J.; Grossweiner, L. I. *Photochem. Photobiol.* **1972**, *16*, 65–67.
133. Van Camp, J. R.; Young, T.; Hartman, R. F.; Rose, S. D. *Photochem. Photobiol.* **1987**, *45*, 365–370.
134. Young, T.; Kim, S.-T.; Van Camp, J. R.; Hartman, R. F.; Rose, S. D. *Photochem. Photobiol.* **1988**, *48*, 635–641.
135. Kim, S.-T.; Rose, S. D. *Photochem. Photobiol.* **1988**, *47*, 725–729.
136. Kim, S.-T.; Rose, S. D. *J. Phys. Org. Chem.* **1990**, *3*, 581–586.
137. Kim, S.-T.; Hartman, R. F.; Rose, S. D. *Photochem. Photobiol.* **1990**, *52*, 789–794.
138. Cochran, A. G.; Sugasawara, R.; Schultz, P. G. *J. Am. Chem. Soc.* **1988**, *110*, 7888–7890.
139. Rokita, S. E.; Walsh, C. T. *J. Am. Chem. Soc.* **1984**, *106*, 4589–4595.
140. Jorns, M. S. *J. Am. Chem. Soc.* **1987**, *109*, 3133–3136.

141. Walsh, C. *Acc. Chem. Res.* **1986**, *19*, 216–221.
142. Pac, C.; Ishitani, O. *Photochem. Photobiol.* **1988**, *48*, 767–785.
143. Sancar, G. B.; Sancar, A. *Trends in Biochem. Sci. 1985, 12*, 259–261.
144. Jorns, M. S.; Wang, B.; Jordan, S. P.; Chanderkar, L. P. *Biochemistry* **1990**, *29*, 552–561.
145. Takao, M.; Oikawa, A.; Eker, A. P. M.; Yasui, A. *Photochem. Photobiol.* **1989**, *50*, 633–637.
146. Li, Y. F.; Heelis, P. F.; Sancar, A. Submitted for publication.
147. Heelis, P. F.; Okamura, T.; Sancar, A. *Biochemistry* **1990**, *29*, 5694–5698.
148. Okamura, T.; Sancar, A.; Heelis, P. Hirata, Y.; Mataga, N. *J. Am. Chem. Soc.* **1989**, *111*, 5967–5969.
149. Kim, S. T.; Heelis, P. F.; Okamura, T.; Hirata, Y.; Mataga, N.; Sancar, A. *Biochemistry* **1991**, *30*, 11262–11270.
150. Sancar, G. B.; Smith, F. W. Personal communication.
151. Okamura, T.; Sancar, A.; Heelis, P. F.; Begley, T.; Hirata, Y.; Mataga, N. *J. Am. Chem. Soc.* **1991**, *103*. In press.
152. Stubbe, J. *Biochemistry* **1988**, *27*, 3893–3900.
153. Bauld, N. L.; Bellville, D. J.; Pabon, R.; Chelsky, R.; Green, G. *J. Am. Chem. Soc.* **1983**, *105*, 2378–2382.
154. Lewis, F. D.; Kojima, M. *J. Am. Chem. Soc.* **1984**, *106*, 1145–1146.
155. Kim, S.-T.; Li, Y. F.; Sancar, A. *Proc. Natl. Acad. Sci. USA* **1992**, *89*, in press.

INDEX

Advances in
Electron Transfer Chemistry

Edited by **Patrick S. Mariano,** *Department of Chemistry and Biochemistry, University of Maryland, College Park*

Coverage in this series will focus on chemical and biochemical aspects of electron transfer chemistry. Recognition over the past decade that a wide variety of chemical processes operate by single electron transfer mechanisms has stimulated numerous efforts in this area. These range from (1) theoretical and experimental investigations of the rates of electron transfer in donor-acceptor systems, (2) studies of photo electron transfer reactions, (3) exploratory efforts probing electron transfer mechanisms for traditional nucleophilic substitution and addition processes, and (4) investigations of electron transfer mechanisms which operate in biochemical processes.

Advances in Electron Transfer Chemistry will cover topics in the recently developed and important areas. The coverage will span the broad areas of organic, physical, inorganic, and biological chemistry. Each of the contributions will be written on a level to make them understandable for graduate students and workers in the chemical and biochemical sciences, and will emphasize recent work of the contributing authors.

Volume 1, 1991, 197 pp. $78.50
ISBN 1-55938-167-1

CONTENTS: Introduction to Series: An Editor's Foreword, *Albert Padwa.* **Preface,** *Patrick S. Mariano.* **Photoinduced Electron Transfer on Irradiated Semiconductor Surfaces,** *Mary Anne Fox, University of Texas at Austin.* **Thermal and Photochemical Activation of Aromatic Donors by Electron Transfer,** *Christian Amatore, Ecole Normale Superieure and Jay K. Kochi, University of Houston.* **Distance and Angle Effects on Electron Transfer Rates in Chemistry and Biology,** *George L. McLendon and Anna Helms, University of Rochester.* **Electron Transfer Reactions Followed by Rapid Bond Cleavage: Intra-Ion Pair Electron Transfer Photoexcited Cyanine Borates and Chemically Initiated Electron-Exchange Luminescence,** *Gary B. Schuster, University of Illinois at Urbana-Champaign.*

**J
A
I

P
R
E
S
S**

JAI PRESS

Advances in Detailed Reaction Mechanisms

Edited by **James M. Coxon,** *University of Canterbury, Christchurch, New Zealand*

The questions why? and how? are synonymous with childhood. In the childhood of scientific knowledge these questions recur. This series is to be a record of this adventure and quest ...within the silica walled vessel; the solar environment; or the most intimate of laboratories, the human frame. The record of achievement testifies to the resourcefulness and imagination of people, the human spirit, and curiosity promising hope in the search for understanding.

The study of detailed reaction mechanisms, of how and why molecular change occurs, forms the basis of this series intended to highlight selected approaches which have led to advances. The first volume details reactions where radical and single electron transfer has been identified as important in the saga.

**Volume 1, Radical, Single Electron Transfers
and Concerted Reactions**
1991, 186 pp. $78.50
ISBN 1-55938-164-7

CONTENTS: Introduction to Series: An Editor's Foreword, *Albert Padwa.* **Preface.** *James M. Coxon.* **Radical Kinetics and Mechanicistic Probe Studies,** *Martin Newcomb, Texas A&M University.* **Free Radical Reactions: Fragmentation and Rearrangement in Aqueous Solutions,** *Michael J. Davis and Brice C. Gilbert, University of York.* **Carbon-Centered Radicals From Amino Acids and their Derivatives,** *Christopher J. Easton, University of Adelaide.* **Cycloadditions of Allenes Reactions of Unusual Mechanistic Perspicuity,** *William R. Dolbier, University of Florida*

JAI PRESS INC.

55 Old Post Road - No. 2
P.O. Box 1678
Greenwich, Connecticut 06836-1678
Tel: 203-661-7602

Advances in Cycloaddition

Edited by **Dennis P. Curran,** *Department of Chemistry, University of Pittsburgh*

"It is the intention of this volume to begin a serial coverage of the broad areas of cycloaddition chemistry. Cycloaddition reactions are among the most powerful reactions available to the organic chemist. The ability to simultaneously form and break several bonds, with a wide variety of atomic substitution patterns, and often with a high degree of stereocontrol, has made cycloaddition reactions the subject of intense study. The productive interplay between theory and experiment has resulted in sophisticated models which often allow one to predict reactivity, regioselectivity, and steroselectivity for given cycloaddition partners."
— *From the Preface to Volume 1*

REVIEW: "This volume is highly recommended to all those who want to stay abreast of developments in the mechanisms and synthetic applications of 1,3-dipolar cycloaddition reactions. The writers have realized a good balance between the summary of achievements and the reporting of gaps in understanding or remaining synthetic challenges. The articles are well written, they are amply illustrated with equations or schemes."

- Journal of the American Chemical Society

Volume 2, 1990, 220 pp. $78.50
ISBN 0-89232-951-3

CONTENTS: Introduction to the Series: An Editor's Foreword, *Albert Padwa.* **Preface,** *Dennis P. Curran.* **Intramolecular 1,3-Dipolar Cycloaddition Chemistry,** *Albert Padwa and Allen M. Schoffstall, Emory University.* **Stereochemical and Synthetic Studies of the Intramolecular Diel-Alder Reaction,** *William R. Roush, Indiana University, Bloomington.* **Thermal Reaction of Cyclopropenone Ketals, Key Mechanistic Features, Scope and Application of the Cycloaddition Reactions of Cyclopropenone Ketals and π -Delocalized Singlet Vinyl Carbenes; Three Carbon I,I-/1,3-Dipoles,** *Dale L. Boger, Purdue University, and Christine E. Brotherton-Pleiss, Syntex Research Institute of Bioinorganic Chemistry, Palo Alto.*

Also Available:
Volume 1 (1988) $78.50

**J
A
I

P
R
E
S
S**

Advances in Theoretically Interesting Molecules

Edited by **Randolph P. Thummel,** *Department of Chemistry, University of Houston*

This series presents review articles pertaining to molecular systems which are of interest due primarily to the presence of structural features or characteristics about which prior predictions can be made based on present knowledge of chemical theory. These molecules often test the outer limits of what can be prepared and studied with regard to theromodynamic stability and kinetic reactivity. Studies of such systems provide an excellent test for existing chemical theory and thus furnish perhaps the best opportunity for advancing the frontiers of chemical knowledge.

The articles contained in this series will discuss in detail the work originating from the author's laboratory. This work will be placed in the context of other similar work which has already been accomplished or is currently in progress. The format will be both explicit and pedagogical so that these articles should be of interest to novices as well as experts in the field. It is expected that a certain amount of historical background will be provided as well as speculation on possible new directions which the chemistry under discussion might follow.

Volume 1, 1989, 467 pp. $78.50
ISBN 0-89232-869-X

JAI PRESS INC.

55 Old Post Road - No. 2
P.O. Box 1678
Greenwich, Connecticut 06836-1678
Tel: 203-661-7602

Advances in Metal-Organic Chemistry

Edited by **Lanny S. Liebeskind,** *Department of Chemistry, Emory University*

REVIEW: *"Advances in Metal-Organic Chemistry* is an attractive volume that will be a worthwhile addition to private collections for active practitioners in germane areas. It should be found in all technical libraries as a useful reference book."

- Journal of Medicinal Chemistry

Volume 2, l991, 300 pp. $78.50
ISBN 0-89232-948-3

CONTENTS: Preface. Synthetic Applications of Chromium Tricarbonyl Stabilized Benzylic Carbanions, *Steven J. Coote, Stephen G. Davies, and Craig L. Goodfellow, The Dyson Perrins Laboratory, University of Oxford.* **Palladium-Mediated Arylation of Enol Ethers,** *G. Doyle Daves, Jr., Lehigh University.* **Transition-Metal Catalyzed Silymetallation of Acetylenes and Et3B Induced Radical Addition of Ph3SnH to Acetylenes-Selective Synthesis of Vinylsilanes and Vinlystannanes:,** *Koichioro Oshima, Kyoto University.* **Development of Carbene Complexes of Iron as New Reagents for Synthetic Organic Chemistry,** *Paul Helquist, University of Notre Dame.* **Tricarbonyl (½6-arene) Chromium Complexes in Organic Synthesis,** *Motokazu Uemura, Osaka City University.* **¹-Bond Hybridization in Transition Metal Complexes: A Stereoelectronic Model for Conformational Analysis,** *William E. Crowe and Stuart L. Schreiber, Sterling Chemistry Laboratory, Yale University.* **Palladium Mediated Methylenecyclopropane Ring Opening: Applications to Organic Synthesis,** *William A. Donaldson, Marquette University.*

Also Available:
Volume 1 (1989) $78.50

JAI PRESS INC.

55 Old Post Road - No. 2
P.O. Box 1678
Greenwich, Connecticut 06836-1678
Tel: 203-661-7602

Advances in
Classical Trajectory Methods

Edited by **William Hase,** *Department of Chemistry, Wayne State University*

Volume 1, 1991, 350 pp. $78.50
ISBN 1-55938-162-0

CONTENTS: Preface. **Classical Trajectory Studies of Intramolecular Dynamics: Local Mode Dynamics, Rotation-Vibration Interaction, and the Structure of Multidimensional Phase Space,** *Gregory S. Ezra, Cornell University.* **The Role of Mode-Mode Energy Transfer in Unimolecular Reactions,** *John S. Hutchinson, Rice University.* **Chemical Reactions as Problems in Nonlinear Dynamics: A Review of Statistical and Adiabatic Approximations from a Phase Space Perspective,** *Michael J. Davis, Argonne National Laboratory, and Rex T. Skodje, University of Colorado.* **Spectra and Eigenstates Associated with Periodic Orbits,** *Eric J. Heller, University of Washington.* **Signatures of Chaos in Quantum Dynamics and the Controllability of Evolution in a Quantum System,** *Stuart A. Rice, The University of Chicago, and Pierre Gaspard, Universite Libre de Bruxelles, and Katsuhiro Nakamura, Fukoka Institute of Technology, Japan.* **The Role of Potential Couplings and Isotopic Substitution on the Ultrafast Classical Relaxation of High Alkyl CH and CD Overtones,** *Csilla Duneczky, Kansas State University, and William P. Reinhardt, University of Pennsylvania.* **Dynamics of Overtone Induced Energy Flow and Fragmentation in Alkyl Hydroperoxides,** *Sally Chapman, Columbia University, and T. Uzer, Georgia Institute of Technology.*

JAI PRESS INC.

55 Old Post Road - No. 2
P.O. Box 1678
Greenwich, Connecticut 06836-1678
Tel: 203-661-7602